MEI
Innovators in Mathematics Education

Ben Sparks, Claire Baldwin

Series editors
Roger Porkess and Catherine Berry

A LEVEL

FURTHER MATHEMATICS

For Core Year 1 and AS

4th Edition

An OCR endorsed textbook

Hachette UK's policy is to use papers that are natural, renewable and recyclable products and made from wood grown in sustainable forests. The logging and manufacturing processes are expected to conform to the environmental regulations of the country of origin.

Orders: please contact Bookpoint Ltd, 130 Park Drive, Milton Park, Abingdon, Oxon OX14 4SE. Telephone: (44) 01235 827720. Fax: (44) 01235 400454. Email education@bookpoint.co.uk Lines are open from 9 a.m. to 5 p.m., Monday to Saturday, with a 24-hour message answering service. You can also order through our website: www.hoddereducation.co.uk

ISBN: 978 1471 852992

© Claire Baldwin, Catherine Berry, Roger Porkess, Ben Sparks, and MEI 2017

First published in 2017 by

Hodder Education,
An Hachette UK Company
Carmelite House
50 Victoria Embankment
London EC4Y 0DZ
www.hoddereducation.co.uk

Impression number   10 9   8   7   6   5
Year   2023 2022 2021 2020 2019

Cover photo © Adrianhancu/123RF.com

Typeset in Bembo Std, 11/13 pts. by Aptara, Inc.

Printed in Dubai

A catalogue record for this title is available from the British Library.

Contents

iii

Mathematics is not only a beautiful and exciting subject in its own right but also one that underpins many other branches of learning. It is consequently fundamental to our national wellbeing.

This book covers the compulsory core content of Year 1/AS Further Mathematics. The requirements of the compulsory core content for the second year are met in a second book, while the year one and year two optional applied content is covered in the Mechanics and Statistics books, and the remaining options in the Modelling with Algorithms, Numerical Methods, Further Pure Maths with Technology and Extra Pure Maths books.

Between 2014 and 2016 A Level Mathematics and Further Mathematics were very substantially revised, for first teaching in 2017. Major changes included increased emphasis on:

■ Problem solving

■ Mathematical proof

■ Use of ICT

■ Modelling.

This book embraces these ideas. A large number of exercise questions involve elements of problem solving. The ideas of **mathematical proof**, rigorous logical argument and mathematical modelling are also included in suitable exercise questions throughout the book.

The use of technology, including graphing software, spreadsheets and high specification calculators, is encouraged wherever possible, for example in the Activities used to introduce some of the topics. In particular, readers are expected to have access to a calculator which handles matrices up to order 3x3. Places where ICT can be used are highlighted by a ⓣ icon. Margin boxes highlight situations where the use of technology – such as graphical calculators or graphing software – can be used to further explore a particular topic.

Throughout the book the emphasis is on understanding and interpretation rather than mere routine calculations, but the various exercises do nonetheless provide plenty of scope for practising basic techniques. The exercise questions are split into three bands. Band 1 questions are designed to reinforce basic understanding; Band 2 questions are broadly typical of what might be expected in an examination; Band 3 questions explore around the topic and some of them are rather more demanding. In addition, extensive online support, including further questions, is available by subscription to MEI's Integral website, integralmaths.org.

In addition to the exercise questions, there are two sets of Practice questions, covering groups of chapters. These include identified questions requiring **problem solving** ⓟⓢ, **mathematical proof** ⓜⓟ, use of ICT ⓣ and **modelling** ⓜ.

This book is written on the assumption that readers are studying or have studied AS Mathematics. It can be studied alongside the Year 1/AS Mathematics book, or after studying AS or A Level Mathematics. There are places where the work depends on knowledge from earlier in the book or in the Year 1/AS Mathematics book and this is flagged up in the Prior knowledge boxes. This should be seen as an invitation to those who have problems with the particular topic to revisit it. At the end of each chapter there is a list of key points covered as well as a summary of the new knowledge (learning outcomes) that readers should have gained.

Although in general knowledge of A Level Mathematics beyond AS Level is not required, there are two small topics from year 2 of A Level Mathematics that are needed in the study of the material in this book. These are radians (needed in the work on the argument of a complex number) and the compound angle formulae, which are helpful in understanding the multiplication and division of complex numbers in modulus-argument form. These two topics are introduced briefly at the back of the book, for the benefit of readers who have not yet studied year 2 of A Level Mathematics.

Two common features of the book are Activities and Discussion points. These serve rather different purposes. The Activities are designed to help readers get into the thought processes of the new work that they are about to meet; having done an Activity, what follows will seem much easier. The Discussion points invite readers to talk about particular points with their fellow students and their teacher and so enhance their understanding. Another feature is a Caution icon ❗, highlighting points where it is easy to go wrong.

Answers to all exercise questions and practice questions are provided at the back of the book, and also online at www.hoddereducation.co.uk/MEIFurtherMathsYear1

This is a 4th edition MEI textbook so much of the material is well tried and tested. However, as a consequence of the changes to A Level requirements in Further mathematics, large parts of the book are either new material or have been very substantially rewritten.

Catherine Berry

Roger Porkess

Prior knowledge

This book is designed so that it can be studied alongside MEI A Level Mathematics Year 1 (AS). There are some links with work in MEI A Level Mathematics Year 2, but it is not necessary to have covered this work before studying this book. Some essential background work on radians and compound angle formulae is covered in An introduction to radians and The identities $\sin(\theta \pm \phi)$ and $\cos(\theta \pm \phi)$ as well as in MEI A Level Mathematics Year 2.

- **Chapter 1: Matrices and transformations** builds on GCSE work on transformations.

- **Chapter 2: Introduction to complex numbers** uses work on solving quadratic equations, covered in chapter 3 of MEI A Level Mathematics Year 1 (AS).

- **Chapter 3: Roots of polynomials** uses work on solving polynomial equations using the factor theorem, covered in chapter 7 of MEI A Level Mathematics Year 1 (AS).

- **Chapter 4: Sequences and series** builds on GCSE work on sequences. The notation and terminology used is also introduced in chapter 3 in MEI A Level Mathematics Year 2, but it is not necessary to have covered this work prior to this chapter.

- **Chapter 5: Complex numbers and geometry** develops the work in chapter 2. Knowledge of radians is assumed: this is covered in chapter 2 of MEI A Level Mathematics Year 2, but the required knowledge is also covered in An introduction to radians. It is also helpful to know the compound angle formulae which are introduced in chapter 8 of MEI A Level Mathematics Year 2; there is also a brief introduction in The identities $\sin(\theta \pm \phi)$ and $\cos(\theta \pm \phi)$.

- **Chapter 6: Matrices and their inverses** follows on from the work in chapter 1.

- **Chapter 7: Vectors and 3D space** builds on the vectors work covered in chapter 12 of MEI A Level Mathematics Year 1 (AS). Knowledge of 3D vectors is assumed, which are introduced in chapter 12 of MEI A Level Mathematics Year 2, but it is not necessary to have covered the Mathematics Year 2 chapter prior to this chapter. The work on the intersection of planes in 3D space, introduced in chapter 6, is also developed further in this chapter.

Acknowledgements

The Publishers would like to thank the following for permission to reproduce copyright material.

Practice questions have been provided by MEI (p. 95–96 and p. 167–168).

Photo credits

p.1 © ironstuff – iStock via Thinkstock/Getty Images; **p.39** © Markus Mainka/Fotolia; **p.42** © Wellcom Images via Wikipedia (https://creativecommons.org/licenses/by/4.0/); **p.52** © Dusso Janladde via Wikipedia Commons (https://en.wikipedia.org/wiki/GNU_Free_Documentation_License); **p.62** Public Domain; **p.71 (top)** © Charles Brutlag – 123RF; **p.71 (bottom)** © oriontrail – iStock via Thinkstock; **p.97 (top)** © Photodisc/Getty Images/ Business & Industry 1; **p.97 (bottom)** © Wolfgang Beyer (Wikipedia Commons, https://creativecommons.org/licenses/by-sa/3.0/deed.en); **p.124** © marcel/ Fotolia; **p.143** © lesley marlor/Fotolia.

Every effort has been made to trace all copyright holders, but if any have been inadvertently overlooked, the Publishers will be pleased to make the necessary arrangements at the first opportunity.

Although every effort has been made to ensure that website addresses are correct at time of going to press, Hodder Education cannot be held responsible for the content of any website mentioned in this book. It is sometimes possible to find a relocated web page by typing in the address of the home page for a website in the URL window of your browser.

1 Matrices and transformations

As for everything else, so for a mathematical theory – beauty can be perceived but not explained.

Arthur Cayley 1883

Figure 1.1 Illustration of some major roads and motorways joining some towns and cities in the north of England.

Discussion point

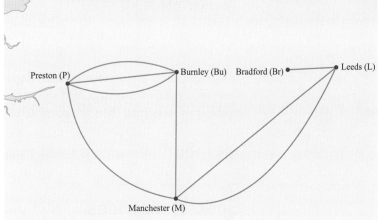

→ How many direct routes (without going through any other town) are there from Preston to Burnley? What about Manchester to Leeds? Preston to Manchester? Burnley to Leeds?

1 Matrices

You can represent the number of direct routes between each pair of towns (shown in Figure 1.1) in an array of numbers like this:

	Br	Bu	L	M	P
Br	0	0	1	0	0
Bu	0	0	0	1	3
L	1	0	0	2	0
M	0	1	2	0	1
P	0	3	0	1	0

This array is called a matrix (the plural is matrices) and is usually written inside curved brackets.

$$\begin{pmatrix} 0 & 0 & 1 & 0 & 0 \\ 0 & 0 & 0 & 1 & 3 \\ 1 & 0 & 0 & 2 & 0 \\ 0 & 1 & 2 & 0 & 1 \\ 0 & 3 & 0 & 1 & 0 \end{pmatrix}$$

It is usual to represent matrices by capital letters, often in bold print.

A matrix consists of rows and columns, and the entries in the various cells are known as **elements**.

The matrix $\mathbf{M} = \begin{pmatrix} 0 & 0 & 1 & 0 & 0 \\ 0 & 0 & 0 & 1 & 3 \\ 1 & 0 & 0 & 2 & 0 \\ 0 & 1 & 2 & 0 & 1 \\ 0 & 3 & 0 & 1 & 0 \end{pmatrix}$ representing the routes between the

towns and cities has 25 elements, arranged in five rows and five columns. $\mathbf{M}$ is described as a 5×5 matrix, and this is the **order** of the matrix. You state the number of rows first, then the number of columns. So, for example, the matrix

$\mathbf{A} = \begin{pmatrix} 3 & -1 & 4 \\ 2 & 0 & 5 \end{pmatrix}$ is a 2×3 matrix and $\mathbf{B} = \begin{pmatrix} 4 & -4 \\ 3 & 4 \\ 0 & -2 \end{pmatrix}$ is a 3×2 matrix.

Special matrices

Some matrices are described by special names which relate to the number of rows and columns or the nature of the elements.

Matrices such as $\begin{pmatrix} 4 & 2 \\ 1 & 0 \end{pmatrix}$ and $\begin{pmatrix} 3 & 5 & 1 \\ 2 & 0 & -4 \\ 1 & 7 & 3 \end{pmatrix}$ which have the same number of rows as columns are called **square matrices**.

The matrix $\begin{pmatrix} 1 & 0 \\ 0 & 1 \end{pmatrix}$ is called the 2×2 **identity matrix** or **unit matrix**, and

similarly $\begin{pmatrix} 1 & 0 & 0 \\ 0 & 1 & 0 \\ 0 & 0 & 1 \end{pmatrix}$ is called the 3×3 identity matrix. Identity matrices must

be square, and are usually denoted by I.

The matrix $\mathbf{O} = \begin{pmatrix} 0 & 0 \\ 0 & 0 \end{pmatrix}$ is called the 2×2 **zero matrix**. Zero matrices can be of any order.

Two matrices are said to be **equal** if and only if they have the same order and each element in one matrix is equal to the corresponding element in the other matrix. So, for example, the matrices **A** and **D** below are equal, but **B** and **C** are not equal to any of the other matrices.

$$\mathbf{A} = \begin{pmatrix} 1 & 3 \\ 2 & 4 \end{pmatrix} \quad \mathbf{B} = \begin{pmatrix} 1 & 2 \\ 3 & 4 \end{pmatrix} \quad \mathbf{C} = \begin{pmatrix} 1 & 3 & 0 \\ 2 & 4 & 0 \end{pmatrix} \quad \mathbf{D} = \begin{pmatrix} 1 & 3 \\ 2 & 4 \end{pmatrix}$$

Working with matrices

Matrices can be added or subtracted if they are of the same order.

$$\begin{pmatrix} 2 & 4 & 0 \\ -1 & 3 & 5 \end{pmatrix} + \begin{pmatrix} 1 & -1 & 4 \\ 2 & 0 & -5 \end{pmatrix} = \begin{pmatrix} 3 & 3 & 4 \\ 1 & 3 & 0 \end{pmatrix}$$

Add the elements in corresponding positions.

$$\begin{pmatrix} 2 & -3 \\ 4 & 1 \end{pmatrix} - \begin{pmatrix} 7 & -3 \\ -1 & 2 \end{pmatrix} = \begin{pmatrix} -5 & 0 \\ 5 & -1 \end{pmatrix}$$

Subtract the elements in corresponding positions.

But $\begin{pmatrix} 2 & 4 & 0 \\ -1 & 3 & 5 \end{pmatrix} + \begin{pmatrix} 2 & -3 \\ 4 & 1 \end{pmatrix}$ cannot be evaluated because the matrices are not of the same order. These matrices are **non-conformable** for addition.

You can also multiply a matrix by a **scalar** number:

$$2\begin{pmatrix} 3 & -4 \\ 0 & 6 \end{pmatrix} = \begin{pmatrix} 6 & -8 \\ 0 & 12 \end{pmatrix}$$

Multiply each of the elements by 2.

⌨ TECHNOLOGY

You can use a calculator to add and subtract matrices of the same order and to multiply a matrix by a number. For your calculator, find out:

- the method for inputting matrices
- how to add and subtract matrices
- how to multiply a matrix by a number for matrices of varying sizes.

Associativity and commutativity

When working with numbers the properties of **associativity** and **commutativity** are often used.

Associativity

Addition of numbers is **associative**.

$$(3 + 5) + 8 = 3 + (5 + 8)$$

> When you add numbers, it does not matter how the numbers are grouped, the answer will be the same.

Commutativity

Addition of numbers is **commutative**.

$$4 + 5 = 5 + 4$$

> When you add numbers, the order of the numbers can be reversed and the answer will still be the same.

Discussion points

→ Give examples to show that subtraction of numbers is not commutative or associative.

→ Are matrix addition and matrix subtraction associative and/or commutative?

Exercise 1.1

① Write down the order of these matrices.

(i) $\begin{pmatrix} 2 & 4 \\ 6 & 0 \\ -3 & 7 \end{pmatrix}$ (ii) $\begin{pmatrix} 0 & 8 & 4 \\ -2 & -3 & 1 \\ 5 & 3 & -2 \end{pmatrix}$ (iii) $\begin{pmatrix} 7 & -3 \end{pmatrix}$ (iv) $\begin{pmatrix} 1 \\ 2 \\ 3 \\ 4 \\ 5 \end{pmatrix}$

(v) $\begin{pmatrix} 2 & -6 & 4 & 9 \\ 5 & 10 & 11 & -4 \end{pmatrix}$ (vi) $\begin{pmatrix} 8 & 5 \\ -2 & 0 \\ 3 & -9 \end{pmatrix}$

② For the matrices

$$\mathbf{A} = \begin{pmatrix} 2 & -3 \\ 0 & 4 \end{pmatrix} \quad \mathbf{B} = \begin{pmatrix} 7 & -3 \\ 1 & 4 \end{pmatrix} \quad \mathbf{C} = \begin{pmatrix} 3 & 5 & -9 \\ 2 & 1 & 4 \end{pmatrix} \quad \mathbf{D} = \begin{pmatrix} 0 & -4 & 5 \\ 2 & 1 & 8 \end{pmatrix}$$

$$\mathbf{E} = \begin{pmatrix} -3 & 5 \\ -2 & 7 \end{pmatrix} \quad \mathbf{F} = \begin{pmatrix} 1 \\ 3 \\ 5 \end{pmatrix}$$

find, where possible

(i) $\mathbf{A} - \mathbf{E}$ (ii) $\mathbf{C} + \mathbf{D}$ (iii) $\mathbf{E} + \mathbf{A} - \mathbf{B}$ (iv) $\mathbf{F} + \mathbf{D}$ (v) $\mathbf{D} - \mathbf{C}$
(vi) $4\mathbf{F}$ (vii) $3\mathbf{C} + 2\mathbf{D}$ (viii) $\mathbf{B} + 2\mathbf{F}$ (ix) $\mathbf{E} - (2\mathbf{B} - \mathbf{A})$

③ The diagram in Figure 1.2 shows the number of direct flights on one day offered by an airline between cities P, Q, R and S.

The same information is also given in the partly-completed matrix **X**.

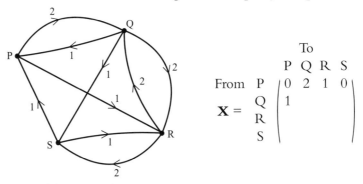

Figure 1.2

(i) Copy and complete the matrix **X**.

A second airline also offers flights between these four cities. The following matrix represents the total number of direct flights offered by the two airlines.

$$\begin{pmatrix} 0 & 2 & 3 & 2 \\ 2 & 0 & 2 & 1 \\ 2 & 2 & 0 & 3 \\ 1 & 0 & 3 & 0 \end{pmatrix}$$

(ii) Find the matrix **Y** representing the flights offered by the second airline.

(iii) Draw a diagram similar to the one in Figure 1.2, showing the flights offered by the second airline.

④ Find the values of w, x, y and z such that

$$\begin{pmatrix} 3 & w \\ -1 & 4 \end{pmatrix} + x \begin{pmatrix} 2 & -1 \\ y & z \end{pmatrix} = \begin{pmatrix} -9 & 8 \\ 11 & -8 \end{pmatrix}.$$

⑤ Find the possible values of p and q such that

$$\begin{pmatrix} p^2 & -3 \\ 2 & 9 \end{pmatrix} - \begin{pmatrix} 5p & -2 \\ -7 & q^2 \end{pmatrix} = \begin{pmatrix} 6 & -1 \\ 9 & 4 \end{pmatrix}.$$

⑥ Four local football teams took part in a competition in which they each played each other twice, once at home and once away. Figure 1.3 shows the results matrix after half of the games had been played.

	Win	Draw	Lose	Goals for	Goals against
City	2	1	0	6	3
Rangers	0	0	3	2	8
Town	2	0	1	4	3
United	1	1	1	5	3

Figure 1.3

(i) The results of the next three matches are as follows:

City   2   Rangers 0
Town 3   United   3
City   2   Town   4

Find the results matrix for these three matches and hence find the complete results matrix for all the matches so far.

(ii) Here is the complete results matrix for the whole competition.

$$\begin{pmatrix} 4 & 1 & 1 & 12 & 8 \\ 1 & 1 & 4 & 5 & 12 \\ 3 & 1 & 2 & 12 & 10 \\ 1 & 3 & 2 & 10 & 9 \end{pmatrix}$$

Find the results matrix for the last three matches (City vs United, Rangers vs Town and Rangers vs United) and deduce the result of each of these three matches.

⑦ A mail-order clothing company stocks a jacket in three different sizes and four different colours.

The matrix $\mathbf{P} = \begin{pmatrix} 17 & 8 & 10 & 15 \\ 6 & 12 & 19 & 3 \\ 24 & 10 & 11 & 6 \end{pmatrix}$ represents the number of jackets in

stock at the start of one week.

The matrix $\mathbf{Q} = \begin{pmatrix} 2 & 5 & 3 & 0 \\ 1 & 3 & 4 & 6 \\ 5 & 0 & 2 & 3 \end{pmatrix}$ represents the number of orders for

jackets received during the week.

(i) Find the matrix $\mathbf{P} - \mathbf{Q}$.

What does this matrix represent? What does the negative element in the matrix mean?

A delivery of jackets is received from the manufacturers during the week.

The matrix $\mathbf{R} = \begin{pmatrix} 5 & 10 & 10 & 5 \\ 10 & 10 & 5 & 15 \\ 0 & 0 & 5 & 5 \end{pmatrix}$ shows the number of jackets received.

(ii) Find the matrix which represents the number of jackets in stock at the end of the week after all the orders have been dispatched.

(iii) Assuming that this week is typical, find the matrix which represents sales of jackets over a six-week period. How realistic is this assumption?

2 Multiplication of matrices

When you multiply two matrices you do not just multiply corresponding terms. Instead you follow a slightly more complicated procedure. The following example will help you to understand the rationale for the way it is done.

There are four ways of scoring points in rugby: a try (five points), a conversion (two points), a penalty (three points) and a drop goal (three points). In a match Tonga scored three tries, one conversion, two penalties and one drop goal.

So their score was

$3 \times 5 + 1 \times 2 + 2 \times 3 + 1 \times 3 = 26$.

You can write this information using matrices. The tries, conversions, penalties and drop goals that Tonga scored are written as the 1×4 row matrix $(3 \ 1 \ 2 \ 1)$ and the points for the different methods of scoring as the 4×1 column

matrix $\begin{pmatrix} 5 \\ 2 \\ 3 \\ 3 \end{pmatrix}$.

These are combined to give the 1×1 matrix $(3 \times 5 + 1 \times 2 + 2 \times 3 + 1 \times 3) = (26)$.

Combining matrices in this way is called **matrix multiplication** and this

example is written as $(3 \ 1 \ 2 \ 1) \begin{pmatrix} 5 \\ 2 \\ 3 \\ 3 \end{pmatrix} = (26)$.

The use of matrices can be extended to include the points scored by the other team, Japan. They scored two tries, two conversions, four penalties and one drop goal. This information can be written together with Tonga's scores as a 2×4 matrix, with one row for Tonga and the other for Japan. The multiplication is then written as:

$$\begin{pmatrix} 3 & 1 & 2 & 1 \\ 2 & 2 & 4 & 1 \end{pmatrix} \begin{pmatrix} 5 \\ 2 \\ 3 \\ 3 \end{pmatrix} = \begin{pmatrix} 26 \\ 29 \end{pmatrix}.$$

So Japan scored 29 points and won the match.

This example shows you two important points about matrix multiplication. Look at the orders of the matrices involved.

The two 'middle' numbers, in this case 4, must be the same for it to be possible to multiply two matrices. If two matrices can be multiplied, they are conformable for multiplication.

$2 \times 4 \quad \times \quad 4 \times 1$

The two 'outside' numbers give you the order of the product matrix, in this case 2 x 1.

You can see from the previous example that multiplying matrices involves multiplying each element in a row of the left-hand matrix by each element in a column of the right-hand matrix and then adding these products.

Example 1.1

Find $\begin{pmatrix} 10 & 3 \\ -2 & 7 \end{pmatrix} \begin{pmatrix} 5 \\ 2 \end{pmatrix}$.

Solution

The product will have order 2×1.

Figure 1.4

Example 1.2

Find $\begin{pmatrix} 1 & 3 \\ -2 & 5 \end{pmatrix} \begin{pmatrix} 4 & 3 & 0 \\ -2 & -3 & 1 \end{pmatrix}$.

Solution

The order of this product is 2×3.

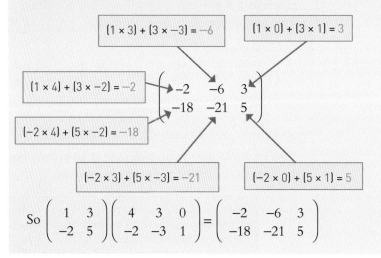

So $\begin{pmatrix} 1 & 3 \\ -2 & 5 \end{pmatrix} \begin{pmatrix} 4 & 3 & 0 \\ -2 & -3 & 1 \end{pmatrix} = \begin{pmatrix} -2 & -6 & 3 \\ -18 & -21 & 5 \end{pmatrix}$

Discussion point

➜ If $\mathbf{A} = \begin{pmatrix} 1 & 3 & 5 \\ -2 & 4 & 1 \\ 0 & 3 & 7 \end{pmatrix}$, $\mathbf{B} = \begin{pmatrix} 8 & -1 \\ -2 & 3 \\ 4 & 0 \end{pmatrix}$ and $\mathbf{C} = \begin{pmatrix} 5 & 0 \\ 3 & -4 \end{pmatrix}$

which of the products **AB**, **BA**, **AC**, **CA**, **BC** and **CB** exist?

Example 1.3

Find $\begin{pmatrix} 3 & 2 \\ -1 & 4 \end{pmatrix} \begin{pmatrix} 1 & 0 \\ 0 & 1 \end{pmatrix}$.

What do you notice?

Solution

The order of this product is 2×2.

$$\begin{pmatrix} 3 & 2 \\ -1 & 4 \end{pmatrix} \begin{pmatrix} 1 & 0 \\ 0 & 1 \end{pmatrix} = \begin{pmatrix} 3 & 2 \\ -1 & 4 \end{pmatrix}$$

$(3 \times 1) + (2 \times 0) = 3$

$(3 \times 0) + (2 \times 1) = 2$

$(-1 \times 0) + (4 \times 1) = 4$

$(-1 \times 1) + (4 \times 0) = -1$

Multiplying a matrix by the identity matrix has no effect.

Properties of matrix multiplication

In this section you will look at whether matrix multiplication is:

■ commutative

■ associative.

On page 4 you saw that for numbers, addition is both associative and commutative. Multiplication is also both associative and commutative. For example:

$$(3 \times 4) \times 5 = 3 \times (4 \times 5)$$

and

$$3 \times 4 = 4 \times 3$$

ACTIVITY 1.1

Using $\mathbf{A} = \begin{pmatrix} 2 & -1 \\ 3 & 4 \end{pmatrix}$ and $\mathbf{B} = \begin{pmatrix} -4 & 0 \\ -2 & 1 \end{pmatrix}$ find the products $\mathbf{AB}$ and $\mathbf{BA}$ and hence comment on whether or not matrix multiplication is commutative. Find a different pair of matrices, $\mathbf{C}$ and $\mathbf{D}$, such that $\mathbf{CD} = \mathbf{DC}$.

Multiplication of matrices

TECHNOLOGY

You could use the matrix function on your calculator.

ACTIVITY 1.2

Using $\mathbf{A} = \begin{pmatrix} 2 & -1 \\ 3 & 4 \end{pmatrix}$, $\mathbf{B} = \begin{pmatrix} -4 & 0 \\ -2 & 1 \end{pmatrix}$ and $\mathbf{C} = \begin{pmatrix} 1 & 2 \\ 2 & 3 \end{pmatrix}$, find the matrix products:

(i) $\mathbf{AB}$

(ii) $\mathbf{BC}$

(iii) $(\mathbf{AB})\mathbf{C}$

(iv) $\mathbf{A}(\mathbf{BC})$

Does your answer suggest that matrix multiplication is associative?

Is this true for all 2 × 2 matrices? How can you prove your answer?

Exercise 1.2

In this exercise, do not use a calculator unless asked to. A calculator can be used for checking answers.

① Write down the orders of these matrices.

(i)   (a) $\mathbf{A} = \begin{pmatrix} 3 & 4 & -1 \\ 0 & 2 & 3 \\ 1 & 5 & 0 \end{pmatrix}$ (b) $\mathbf{B} = \begin{pmatrix} 2 & 3 & 6 \end{pmatrix}$

   (c) $\mathbf{C} = \begin{pmatrix} 4 & 9 & 2 \\ 1 & -3 & 0 \end{pmatrix}$ (d) $\mathbf{D} = \begin{pmatrix} 0 & 2 & 4 & 2 \\ 0 & -3 & -8 & 1 \end{pmatrix}$

   (e) $\mathbf{E} = \begin{pmatrix} 3 \\ 6 \end{pmatrix}$ (f) $\mathbf{F} = \begin{pmatrix} 2 & 5 & 0 & -4 & 1 \\ -3 & 9 & -3 & 2 & 2 \\ 1 & 0 & 0 & 10 & 4 \end{pmatrix}$

(ii) Which of the following matrix products can be found? For those that can state the order of the matrix product.

   (a) $\mathbf{AE}$ (b) $\mathbf{AF}$ (c) $\mathbf{FA}$ (d) $\mathbf{CA}$ (e) $\mathbf{DC}$

② Calculate these products.

(i) $\begin{pmatrix} 3 & 0 \\ 5 & -1 \end{pmatrix}\begin{pmatrix} 7 & 2 \\ 4 & -3 \end{pmatrix}$

(ii) $\begin{pmatrix} 2 & -3 & 5 \end{pmatrix}\begin{pmatrix} 0 & 2 \\ 5 & 8 \\ -3 & 1 \end{pmatrix}$

(iii) $\begin{pmatrix} 2 & 5 & -1 & 0 \\ 3 & 6 & 4 & -3 \end{pmatrix}\begin{pmatrix} 1 \\ -9 \\ 11 \\ -2 \end{pmatrix}$

Check your answers using the matrix function on a calculator if possible.

③ Using the matrices $\mathbf{A} = \begin{pmatrix} 5 & 9 \\ -2 & 7 \end{pmatrix}$ and $\mathbf{B} = \begin{pmatrix} -3 & 5 \\ 2 & -9 \end{pmatrix}$, confirm that matrix multiplication is not commutative.

④ For the matrices

$$\mathbf{A} = \begin{pmatrix} 3 & 1 \\ 2 & 4 \end{pmatrix} \quad \mathbf{B} = \begin{pmatrix} -3 & 7 \\ 2 & 5 \end{pmatrix} \quad \mathbf{C} = \begin{pmatrix} 2 & 3 & 4 \\ 5 & 7 & 1 \end{pmatrix}$$

$$\mathbf{D} = \begin{pmatrix} 3 & 4 \\ 7 & 0 \\ 1 & -2 \end{pmatrix} \quad \mathbf{E} = \begin{pmatrix} 4 & 7 \\ 3 & -2 \\ 1 & 5 \end{pmatrix} \quad \mathbf{F} = \begin{pmatrix} 3 & 7 & -5 \\ 2 & 6 & 0 \\ -1 & 4 & 8 \end{pmatrix}$$

calculate, where possible, the following:

(i) **AB** (ii) **BA** (iii) **CD** (iv) **DC** (v) **EF** (vi) **FE**

⑤ Using the matrix function on a calculator, find $\mathbf{M}^4$ for the matrix

$$\mathbf{M} = \begin{pmatrix} 2 & 0 & -1 \\ 3 & 1 & 2 \\ -1 & 4 & 3 \end{pmatrix}.$$

> **Note**
> ----------------------------------
> $\mathbf{M}^4$ means $\mathbf{M} \times \mathbf{M} \times \mathbf{M} \times \mathbf{M}$

⑥ $\mathbf{A} = \begin{pmatrix} x & 3 \\ 0 & -1 \end{pmatrix} \quad \mathbf{B} = \begin{pmatrix} 2x & 0 \\ 4 & -3 \end{pmatrix}$:

(i) Find the matrix product **AB** in terms of x.

(ii) If $\mathbf{AB} = \begin{pmatrix} 10x & -9 \\ -4 & 3 \end{pmatrix}$, find the possible values of x.

(iii) Find the possible matrix products **BA**.

⑦ (i) For the matrix $\mathbf{A} = \begin{pmatrix} 2 & 1 \\ 0 & 1 \end{pmatrix}$, find

(a) $\mathbf{A}^2$

(b) $\mathbf{A}^3$

(c) $\mathbf{A}^4$

(ii) Suggest a general form for the matrix $\mathbf{A}^n$ in terms of n.

(iii) Verify your answer by finding $\mathbf{A}^{10}$ on your calculator and confirming it gives the same answer as (ii).

⑧ The map in Figure 1.5 below shows the bus routes in a holiday area. Lines represent routes that run each way between the resorts. Arrows indicated one-way scenic routes.

M is the partly completed 4 × 4 matrix which shows the number of direct routes between the various resorts.

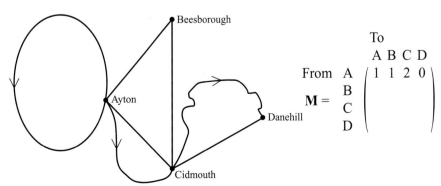

Figure 1.5

(i) Copy and complete the matrix **M**.

(ii) Calculate **M²** and explain what information it contains.

(iii) What information would **M³** contain?

⑨ $\mathbf{A} = \begin{pmatrix} 4 & x & 0 \\ 2 & -3 & 1 \end{pmatrix}$ $\mathbf{B} = \begin{pmatrix} 2 & -5 \\ 4 & x \\ x & 7 \end{pmatrix}$:

(i) Find the product **AB** in terms of x.

A symmetric matrix is one in which the entries are symmetrical about the

leading diagonal, for example $\begin{pmatrix} 2 & 5 \\ 5 & 0 \end{pmatrix}$ and $\begin{pmatrix} 3 & 4 & -6 \\ 4 & 2 & 5 \\ -6 & 5 & 1 \end{pmatrix}$.

(ii) Given that the matrix **AB** is symmetric, find the possible values of x.

(iii) Write down the possible matrices **AB**.

⑩ The matrix **A**, in Figure 1.6, shows the number of sales of five flavours of ice cream: Vanilla(V), Strawberry(S), Chocolate(C), Toffee(T) and Banana(B), from an ice cream shop on each of Wednesday(W), Thursday(Th), Friday(F) and Saturday(Sa) during one week.

$$\mathbf{A} = \begin{array}{c} \\ W \\ Th \\ F \\ Sa \end{array} \begin{array}{ccccc} V & S & C & T & B \\ \end{array} \\ \begin{pmatrix} 63 & 49 & 55 & 44 & 18 \\ 58 & 52 & 66 & 29 & 26 \\ 77 & 41 & 81 & 39 & 25 \\ 101 & 57 & 68 & 63 & 45 \end{pmatrix}$$

Figure 1.6

(i) Find a matrix **D** such that the product **DA** shows the total number of sales of each flavour of ice cream during the four-day period and find the product **DA**.

(ii) Find a matrix **F** such that the product **AF** gives the total number of ice cream sales each day during the four-day period and find the product **AF**.

The Vanilla and Banana ice creams are served with strawberry sauce; the other three ice creams are served with chocolate sprinkles.

(iii) Find two matrices, **S** and **C**, such that the product **DAS** gives the total number of servings of strawberry sauce needed and the product **DAC** gives the total number of servings of sprinkles needed during the four-day period. Find the matrices **DAS** and **DAC**.

The price of Vanilla and Strawberry ice creams is 95p, Chocolate ice creams cost £1.05 and Toffee and Banana ice creams cost £1.15 each.

(iv) Using only matrix multiplication, find a way of calculating the total cost of all of the ice creams sold during the four-day period.

⑪ Figure 1.7 shows the start of the plaiting process for producing a leather bracelet from three leather strands a, b and c.

The process has only two steps, repeated alternately:

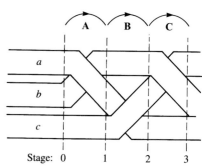

Figure 1.7

Step 1: cross the top strand over the middle strand

Step 2: cross the middle strand under the bottom strand.

At the start of the plaiting process, Stage 0, the order of the strands is given

by $\mathbf{S}_0 = \begin{pmatrix} a \\ b \\ c \end{pmatrix}$.

(i) Show that pre-multiplying $\mathbf{S}_0$ by the matrix $\mathbf{A} = \begin{pmatrix} 0 & 1 & 0 \\ 1 & 0 & 0 \\ 0 & 0 & 1 \end{pmatrix}$

gives $\mathbf{S}_1$, the matrix which represents the order of the strands at Stage 1.

(ii) Find the 3×3 matrix $\mathbf{B}$ which represents the transition from Stage 1 to Stage 2.

(iii) Find matrix $\mathbf{M} = \mathbf{BA}$ and show that $\mathbf{MS}_0$ gives $\mathbf{S}_2$, the matrix which represents the order of the strands at Stage 2.

(iv) Find $\mathbf{M}^2$ and hence find the order of the strands at Stage 4.

(v) Calculate $\mathbf{M}^3$. What does this tell you?

3 Transformations

You are already familiar with several different types of transformation, including reflections, rotations and enlargements.

- The original point, or shape, is called the **object**.
- The new point, or shape, after the transformation, is called the **image**.
- A transformation is a **mapping** of an object onto its image.

Some examples of transformations are illustrated in Figures 1.8 to 1.10 (note that

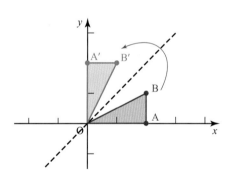

Figure 1.8 Reflection in the line $y = x$

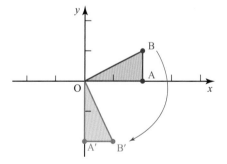

Figure 1.9 Rotation through 90° clockwise, centre O

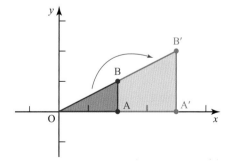

Figure 1.10 Enlargement centre O, scale factor 2

the vertices of the image are denoted by the same letters with a dash, e.g. A′, B′).

In this section, you will also meet the idea of

- a **stretch** parallel to the x-axis or y-axis
- a **shear**

and three-dimensional transformations where

- a shape is reflected in the planes $x = 0$, $y = 0$ or $z = 0$
- a shape is rotated about one of the three coordinate axes.

A transformation maps an object according to a rule and can be represented by a matrix (see next section). The effect of a transformation on an object can be found by looking at the effect it has on the **position vector** of the point $\begin{pmatrix} x \\ y \end{pmatrix}$,

i.e. the vector from the origin to the point (x, y). So, for example, to find the effect of a transformation on the point $(2, 3)$ you would look at the effect that the transformation matrix has on the position vector $\begin{pmatrix} 2 \\ 3 \end{pmatrix}$.

Vectors that have length or **magnitude** of 1 are called **unit vectors**.

In two dimensions, two unit vectors that are of particular interest are

$$\mathbf{i} = \begin{pmatrix} 1 \\ 0 \end{pmatrix} - \text{a unit vector in the direction of the } x\text{-axis}$$

$$\mathbf{j} = \begin{pmatrix} 0 \\ 1 \end{pmatrix} - \text{a unit vector in the direction of the } y\text{-axis.}$$

The equivalent unit vectors in three dimensions are

$$\mathbf{i} = \begin{pmatrix} 1 \\ 0 \\ 0 \end{pmatrix} - \text{a unit vector in the direction of the } x\text{-axis}$$

$$\mathbf{j} = \begin{pmatrix} 0 \\ 1 \\ 0 \end{pmatrix} - \text{a unit vector in the direction of the } y\text{-axis}$$

$$\mathbf{k} = \begin{pmatrix} 0 \\ 0 \\ 1 \end{pmatrix} - \text{a unit vector in the direction of the } z\text{-axis.}$$

Finding the transformation represented by a given matrix

Start by looking at the effect of multiplying the unit vectors $\mathbf{i} = \begin{pmatrix} 1 \\ 0 \end{pmatrix}$ and $\mathbf{j} = \begin{pmatrix} 0 \\ 1 \end{pmatrix}$ by the matrix $\begin{pmatrix} -1 & 0 \\ 0 & -1 \end{pmatrix}$.

The image of $\begin{pmatrix} 1 \\ 0 \end{pmatrix}$ under this transformation is given by

$$\begin{pmatrix} -1 & 0 \\ 0 & -1 \end{pmatrix}\begin{pmatrix} 1 \\ 0 \end{pmatrix} = \begin{pmatrix} -1 \\ 0 \end{pmatrix}.$$

> **Note**
> The letter I is often used for the point (1, 0).

Figure 1.11

The image of $\begin{pmatrix} 0 \\ 1 \end{pmatrix}$ under the transformation is given by

$$\begin{pmatrix} -1 & 0 \\ 0 & -1 \end{pmatrix}\begin{pmatrix} 0 \\ 1 \end{pmatrix} = \begin{pmatrix} 0 \\ -1 \end{pmatrix}.$$

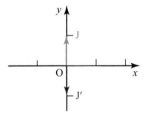

> **Note**
> The letter J is often used for the point (0, 1).

Figure 1.12

You can see from this that the matrix $\begin{pmatrix} -1 & 0 \\ 0 & -1 \end{pmatrix}$ represents a rotation, centre the origin, through 180°.

Example 1.4

Describe the transformations represented by the following matrices.

(i) $\begin{pmatrix} 0 & 1 \\ 1 & 0 \end{pmatrix}$ (ii) $\begin{pmatrix} 2 & 0 \\ 0 & 2 \end{pmatrix}$

Solution

(i) $\begin{pmatrix} 0 & 1 \\ 1 & 0 \end{pmatrix}\begin{pmatrix} 1 \\ 0 \end{pmatrix} = \begin{pmatrix} 0 \\ 1 \end{pmatrix}$ $\begin{pmatrix} 0 & 1 \\ 1 & 0 \end{pmatrix}\begin{pmatrix} 0 \\ 1 \end{pmatrix} = \begin{pmatrix} 1 \\ 0 \end{pmatrix}$

Figure 1.13   **Figure 1.14**

The matrix $\begin{pmatrix} 0 & 1 \\ 1 & 0 \end{pmatrix}$ represents a reflection in the line $y = x$.

(ii) $\begin{pmatrix} 2 & 0 \\ 0 & 2 \end{pmatrix} \begin{pmatrix} 1 \\ 0 \end{pmatrix} = \begin{pmatrix} 2 \\ 0 \end{pmatrix}$ $\begin{pmatrix} 2 & 0 \\ 0 & 2 \end{pmatrix} \begin{pmatrix} 0 \\ 1 \end{pmatrix} = \begin{pmatrix} 0 \\ 2 \end{pmatrix}$

Figure 1.15

Figure 1.16

The matrix $\begin{pmatrix} 2 & 0 \\ 0 & 2 \end{pmatrix}$ represents an enlargement, centre the origin, scale factor 2.

You can see that the images of $\mathbf{i} = \begin{pmatrix} 1 \\ 0 \end{pmatrix}$ and $\mathbf{j} = \begin{pmatrix} 0 \\ 1 \end{pmatrix}$ are the two columns of the transformation matrix.

Finding the matrix that represents a given transformation

The connection between the images of the unit vectors $\mathbf{i}$ and $\mathbf{j}$ and the matrix representing the transformation provides a quick method for finding the matrix representing a transformation.

It is common to use the unit square with coordinates O(0, 0), I(1, 0), P(1, 1) and J(0, 1).

You can think about the images of the points I and J, and from this you can write down the images of the unit vectors $\mathbf{i}$ and $\mathbf{j}$.

This is done in the next example.

> **Hint**
>
> You may find it easier to see what the transformation is when you use a shape, like the unit square, rather than points or lines.

Example 1.5

By drawing a diagram to show the image of the unit square, find the matrices which represent each of the following transformations:

(i)   a reflection in the x-axis

(ii) an enlargement of scale factor 3, centre the origin.

Solution

Figure 1.17

(i) You can see from Figure 1.17 that I (1, 0) is mapped to itself and J (0, 1) is mapped to J′ (0, −1).

So the image of **I** is $\begin{pmatrix} 1 \\ 0 \end{pmatrix}$

and the image of **J** is $\begin{pmatrix} 0 \\ -1 \end{pmatrix}$.

So the matrix which represents a reflection in the *x*-axis is $\begin{pmatrix} 1 & 0 \\ 0 & -1 \end{pmatrix}$.

(ii)

Figure 1.18

So the image of **I** is $\begin{pmatrix} 3 \\ 0 \end{pmatrix}$

You can see from Figure 1.18 that I (1, 0) is mapped to I′ (3, 0), and J (0, 1) is mapped to J′ (0, 3).

and the image of **J** is $\begin{pmatrix} 0 \\ 3 \end{pmatrix}$.

So the matrix which represents an enlargement, centre the origin, scale factor 3 is $\begin{pmatrix} 3 & 0 \\ 0 & 3 \end{pmatrix}$.

Discussion points

→ For a general transformation represented by the matrix $\begin{pmatrix} a & b \\ c & d \end{pmatrix}$, what are the images of the unit vectors $\begin{pmatrix} 1 \\ 0 \end{pmatrix}$ and $\begin{pmatrix} 0 \\ 1 \end{pmatrix}$?

→ What is the image of the origin (0,0)?

ACTIVITY 1.3

Using the image of the unit square, find the matrix which represents a rotation of 45° anticlockwise about the origin.
Use your answer to write down the matrices which represent the following transformations:
(i) a rotation of 45° clockwise about the origin
(ii) a rotation of 135° anticlockwise about the origin.

Example 1.6

(i) Find the matrix which represents a rotation through angle θ anticlockwise about the origin.

(ii) Use your answer to find the matrix which represents a rotation of 60° anticlockwise about the origin.

Solution

(i) Figure 1.19 shows a rotation of angle θ anticlockwise about the origin.

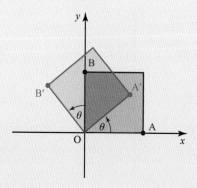

Figure 1.19

Call the coordinates of the point A′ (p, q). Since the lines OA and OB are perpendicular, the coordinates of B′ will be $(-q, p)$.

From the right-angled triangle with OA′ as the hypotenuse, $\cos\theta = \frac{p}{1}$ and so $p = \cos\theta$.

Similarly, from the right-angled triangle with OB′ as the hypotenuse, $\sin\theta = \frac{q}{1}$ so $q = \sin\theta$.

So, the image point A′ (p, q) has position vector $\begin{pmatrix} \cos\theta \\ \sin\theta \end{pmatrix}$ and the image point B′ $(-q, p)$ has position vector $\begin{pmatrix} -\sin\theta \\ \cos\theta \end{pmatrix}$.

Therefore, the matrix that represents a rotation of angle θ anticlockwise about the origin is $\begin{pmatrix} \cos\theta & -\sin\theta \\ \sin\theta & \cos\theta \end{pmatrix}$.

(ii) The matrix that represents an anticlockwise rotation of 60° about the origin is $\begin{pmatrix} \cos 60° & -\sin 60° \\ \sin 60° & \cos 60° \end{pmatrix} = \begin{pmatrix} \frac{1}{2} & -\frac{\sqrt{3}}{2} \\ \frac{\sqrt{3}}{2} & \frac{1}{2} \end{pmatrix}$.

Discussion point

➜ What matrix would represent a rotation through angle θ clockwise about the origin?

ACTIVITY 1.4

Investigate the effect of the matrices:

(i) $\begin{pmatrix} 2 & 0 \\ 0 & 1 \end{pmatrix}$ (ii) $\begin{pmatrix} 1 & 0 \\ 0 & 5 \end{pmatrix}$

Describe the general transformation represented by the

matrices $\begin{pmatrix} m & 0 \\ 0 & 1 \end{pmatrix}$ and $\begin{pmatrix} 1 & 0 \\ 0 & n \end{pmatrix}$.

Activity 1.4 illustrates two important general results.

- The matrix $\begin{pmatrix} m & 0 \\ 0 & 1 \end{pmatrix}$ represents a stretch of scale factor m parallel to the x-axis.

- The matrix $\begin{pmatrix} 1 & 0 \\ 0 & n \end{pmatrix}$ represents a stretch of scale factor n parallel to the y-axis.

Shears

Figure 1.20 shows the unit square and its image under the transformation

represented by the matrix $\begin{pmatrix} 1 & 3 \\ 0 & 1 \end{pmatrix}$ on the unit square. The matrix $\begin{pmatrix} 1 & 3 \\ 0 & 1 \end{pmatrix}$

transforms the unit vector $\mathbf{i} = \begin{pmatrix} 1 \\ 0 \end{pmatrix}$ to the vector $\begin{pmatrix} 1 \\ 0 \end{pmatrix}$ and transforms the

unit vector $\mathbf{j} = \begin{pmatrix} 0 \\ 1 \end{pmatrix}$ to the vector $\begin{pmatrix} 3 \\ 1 \end{pmatrix}$.

The point with position vector $\begin{pmatrix} 1 \\ 1 \end{pmatrix}$ is transformed to the point with

position vector $\begin{pmatrix} 4 \\ 1 \end{pmatrix}$.

As $\begin{pmatrix} 1 & 3 \\ 0 & 1 \end{pmatrix} \begin{pmatrix} 1 \\ 1 \end{pmatrix} = \begin{pmatrix} 4 \\ 1 \end{pmatrix}$.

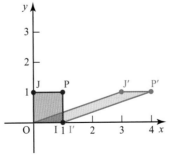

Figure 1.20

This transformation is called a **shear**. Notice that the points on the x-axis stay the same, and the points J and P move parallel to the x-axis to the right.

This shear can be described fully by saying that the x-axis is fixed, and giving the image of one point not on the x-axis, e.g. $(0, 1)$ is mapped to $(3, 1)$.

Generally, a shear with the x-axis fixed has the form $\begin{pmatrix} 1 & k \\ 0 & 1 \end{pmatrix}$ and a shear with the y-axis fixed has the form $\begin{pmatrix} 1 & 0 \\ k & 1 \end{pmatrix}$.

Example 1.7

Find the image of the rectangle with vertices A$(-1, 2)$, B$(1, 2)$, C$(1, -1)$ and D$(-1, -1)$ under the shear $\begin{pmatrix} 1 & 3 \\ 0 & 1 \end{pmatrix}$ and show the rectangle and its image on a diagram.

Solution

$$\begin{pmatrix} 1 & 3 \\ 0 & 1 \end{pmatrix} \begin{pmatrix} -1 & 1 & 1 & -1 \\ 2 & 2 & -1 & -1 \end{pmatrix} = \begin{pmatrix} 5 & 7 & -2 & -4 \\ 2 & 2 & -1 & -1 \end{pmatrix}$$

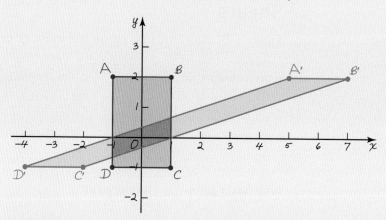

Figure 1.21

The effect of this shear is to transform the sides of the rectangle parallel to the y-axis into sloping lines. Notice that the gradient of the side A′D′ is $\frac{1}{3}$ which is the reciprocal of the top right-hand element of the matrix $\begin{pmatrix} 1 & 3 \\ 0 & 1 \end{pmatrix}$.

Note

Notice that under the shear transformation, points above the x-axis move to the right and points below the x-axis move to the left.

ACTIVITY 1.5

For each of the points A, B, C and D in Example 1.7, find

$$\frac{\text{distance between the point and its image}}{\text{distance of original point from } x\text{-axis}}.$$

What do you notice?

In the activity on the previous page, you should have found that dividing the distance between the point and its image by the distance of the original point from the x-axis (which is fixed), gives the answer 3 for all points, which is the number in the top right of the matrix. This is called the **shear factor** for the shear.

TECHNOLOGY

If you have access to geometrical software, investigate how shears are defined.

There are different conventions about the sign of a shear factor, and for this reason shear factors are not used to define a shear in this book. It is possible to show the effect of matrix transformations using some geometrical computer software packages. You might find that some packages use different approaches towards shears and define them in different ways.

Example 1.8

In a shear, S, the y-axis is fixed, and the image of the point $(1, 0)$ is the point $(1, 5)$.

(i) Draw a diagram showing the image of the unit square under the transformation S.

(ii) Find the matrix that represents the shear S.

Solution

(i)

Figure 1.22

(ii) Under S $\begin{pmatrix} 1 \\ 0 \end{pmatrix} \rightarrow \begin{pmatrix} 1 \\ 5 \end{pmatrix}$

and $\begin{pmatrix} 0 \\ 1 \end{pmatrix} \rightarrow \begin{pmatrix} 0 \\ 1 \end{pmatrix}$ ←—— Since the y-axis is fixed.

So the matrix representing S is $\begin{pmatrix} 1 & 0 \\ 5 & 1 \end{pmatrix}$.

Notice that this matrix is of the form $\begin{pmatrix} 1 & 0 \\ k & 1 \end{pmatrix}$ for shears with the y-axis fixed.

Summary of transformations in two dimensions

Reflection in the x-axis	$\begin{pmatrix} 1 & 0 \\ 0 & -1 \end{pmatrix}$	Reflection in the y-axis	$\begin{pmatrix} -1 & 0 \\ 0 & 1 \end{pmatrix}$
Reflection in the line $y = x$	$\begin{pmatrix} 0 & 1 \\ 1 & 0 \end{pmatrix}$	Reflection in the line $y = -x$	$\begin{pmatrix} 0 & -1 \\ -1 & 0 \end{pmatrix}$
Rotation anticlockwise about the origin through angle θ	$\begin{pmatrix} \cos\theta & -\sin\theta \\ \sin\theta & \cos\theta \end{pmatrix}$	Enlargement, centre the origin, scale factor k	$\begin{pmatrix} k & 0 \\ 0 & k \end{pmatrix}$
Stretch parallel to the x-axis, scale factor k	$\begin{pmatrix} k & 0 \\ 0 & 1 \end{pmatrix}$	Stretch parallel to the y-axis, scale factor k	$\begin{pmatrix} 1 & 0 \\ 0 & k \end{pmatrix}$
Shear, x-axis fixed, with $(0, 1)$ mapped to $(k, 1)$	$\begin{pmatrix} 1 & k \\ 0 & 1 \end{pmatrix}$	Shear, y-axis fixed, with $(1, 0)$ mapped to $(1, k)$	$\begin{pmatrix} 1 & 0 \\ k & 1 \end{pmatrix}$

Transformations in three dimensions

When working with matrices, it is sometimes necessary to refer to a **plane** – this is an infinite two-dimensional flat surface with no thickness. Figure 1.23 below illustrates some common planes in three dimensions – the XY plane, the XZ plane and YZ plane. These three planes will be referred to when using matrices to represent some transformations in three dimensions. The plane XY can also be referred to as $z = 0$, since the z-coordinate would be zero for all points in the XY plane. Similarly, the XZ plane is referred to as $y = 0$ and the YZ plane as $x = 0$.

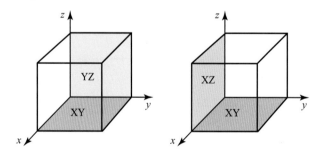

Figure 1.23

So far you have looked at transformations of sets of points from a plane (i.e. two dimensions) to the same plane. In a similar way, you can transform a set of points within three-dimensional space. You will look at reflections in the planes $x = 0$, $y = 0$ or $z = 0$, and rotations about one of the coordinate axes. Again, the matrix can be found algebraically or by considering the effect of the transformation on the three unit vectors

$$\mathbf{i} = \begin{pmatrix} 1 \\ 0 \\ 0 \end{pmatrix}, \mathbf{j} = \begin{pmatrix} 0 \\ 1 \\ 0 \end{pmatrix} \text{ and } \mathbf{k} = \begin{pmatrix} 0 \\ 0 \\ 1 \end{pmatrix}.$$

Think about reflecting an object in the plane $y = 0$. The plane $y = 0$ is the plane which contains the x- and z-axes. Figure 1.24 shows the effect of a reflection in the plane $y = 0$.

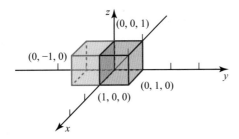

Figure 1.24

$$\mathbf{i} = \begin{pmatrix} 1 \\ 0 \\ 0 \end{pmatrix} \text{ maps to } \begin{pmatrix} 1 \\ 0 \\ 0 \end{pmatrix}, \mathbf{j} = \begin{pmatrix} 0 \\ 1 \\ 0 \end{pmatrix} \text{ maps to } \begin{pmatrix} 0 \\ -1 \\ 0 \end{pmatrix} \text{ and } \mathbf{k} = \begin{pmatrix} 0 \\ 0 \\ 1 \end{pmatrix} \text{ maps}$$

$$\text{to } \begin{pmatrix} 0 \\ 0 \\ 1 \end{pmatrix}.$$

The images of $\mathbf{i}$, $\mathbf{j}$ and $\mathbf{k}$ form the columns of the 3×3 transformation matrix.

$$\text{It is } \begin{pmatrix} 1 & 0 & 0 \\ 0 & -1 & 0 \\ 0 & 0 & 1 \end{pmatrix}.$$

Example 1.9

Find the matrix that represents a rotation of 90° anticlockwise about the x-axis.

Solution

A rotation of 90° anticlockwise about the x-axis is shown in Figure 1.25.

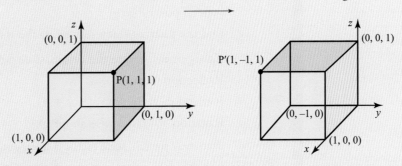

Figure 1.25

> **Note**
>
> Rotations are taken to be anticlockwise about the axis of rotation when looking along the axis from the positive end towards the origin.

Look at the effect of the transformation on the unit vectors $\mathbf{i}, \mathbf{j}$ and $\mathbf{k}$:

$$\mathbf{i} = \begin{pmatrix} 1 \\ 0 \\ 0 \end{pmatrix} \text{ maps to } \begin{pmatrix} 1 \\ 0 \\ 0 \end{pmatrix}, \mathbf{j} = \begin{pmatrix} 0 \\ 1 \\ 0 \end{pmatrix} \text{ maps to } \begin{pmatrix} 0 \\ 0 \\ 1 \end{pmatrix} \text{ and } \mathbf{k} = \begin{pmatrix} 0 \\ 0 \\ 1 \end{pmatrix}$$

$$\text{maps to } \begin{pmatrix} 0 \\ -1 \\ 0 \end{pmatrix}.$$

The images of $\mathbf{i}, \mathbf{j}$ and $\mathbf{k}$ form the columns of the 3×3 transformation matrix.

$$\text{The matrix is } \begin{pmatrix} 1 & 0 & 0 \\ 0 & 0 & -1 \\ 0 & 1 & 0 \end{pmatrix}.$$

Exercise 1.3

① Figure 1.26 shows a triangle with vertices at $O, A(1, 2)$ and $B(0, 2)$.

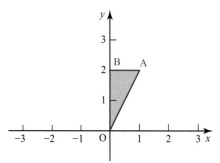

Figure 1.26

For each of the transformations below

(a) draw a diagram to show the effect of the transformation on triangle OAB

(b) give the coordinates of A' and B', the images of points A and B

(c) find expressions for x' and y', the coordinates of P', the image of a general point $P(x, y)$

(d) find the matrix which represents the transformation.

(i) Enlargement, centre the origin, scale factor 3

(ii) Reflection in the x-axis

(iii) Reflection in the line $x + y = 0$

(iv) Rotation 90° clockwise about O

(v) Two-way stretch, scale factor 3 horizontally and scale factor $\frac{1}{2}$ vertically.

② Describe the geometrical transformations represented by these matrices.

(i) $\begin{pmatrix} 1 & 0 \\ 0 & -1 \end{pmatrix}$ (ii) $\begin{pmatrix} 0 & -1 \\ -1 & 0 \end{pmatrix}$ (iii) $\begin{pmatrix} 2 & 0 \\ 0 & 3 \end{pmatrix}$

(iv) $\begin{pmatrix} 4 & 0 \\ 0 & 4 \end{pmatrix}$ (v) $\begin{pmatrix} 0 & 1 \\ -1 & 0 \end{pmatrix}$

③ Each of the following matrices represents a rotation about the origin. Find the angle and direction of rotation in each case.

(i) $\begin{pmatrix} \dfrac{1}{2} & -\dfrac{\sqrt{3}}{2} \\ \dfrac{\sqrt{3}}{2} & \dfrac{1}{2} \end{pmatrix}$

(ii) $\begin{pmatrix} 0.574 & -0.819 \\ 0.819 & 0.574 \end{pmatrix}$

(iii) $\begin{pmatrix} -\dfrac{1}{\sqrt{2}} & \dfrac{1}{\sqrt{2}} \\ -\dfrac{1}{\sqrt{2}} & -\dfrac{1}{\sqrt{2}} \end{pmatrix}$

(iv) $\begin{pmatrix} -\dfrac{\sqrt{3}}{2} & -\dfrac{1}{2} \\ \dfrac{1}{2} & -\dfrac{\sqrt{3}}{2} \end{pmatrix}$

④ Figure 1.27 shows a square with vertices at the points $A(1, 1), B(1, -1)$, $C(-1, -1)$ and $D(-1, 1)$.

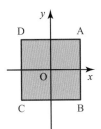

Figure 1.27

(i) Draw a diagram to show the image of this square under the transformation matrix $\mathbf{M} = \begin{pmatrix} 1 & 4 \\ 0 & 1 \end{pmatrix}$.

(ii) Describe fully the transformation represented by the matrix $\mathbf{M}$. State the fixed line and the image of the point A.

⑤ (i) Find the image of the unit square under the transformations represented by the matrices

(a) $\mathbf{A} = \begin{pmatrix} 1 & 0 \\ 5 & 1 \end{pmatrix}$ (b) $\mathbf{B} = \begin{pmatrix} 1 & 0.5 \\ 0 & 1 \end{pmatrix}$

(ii) Use your answers to part (i) to fully describe the transformations represented by each of the matrices $\mathbf{A}$ and $\mathbf{B}$.

⑥ Find the matrix that represents each of the following transformations in three dimensions.

(i) Rotation of 90° anticlockwise about the z-axis

(ii) Reflection in the plane $y = 0$

(iii) Rotation of 180° about the x-axis

(iv) Rotation of 270° anticlockwise about the y-axis

⑦ Figure 1.28 shows a shear that maps the rectangle ABCD to the parallelogram A'B'C'D'.

The angle A'DA is 60°.

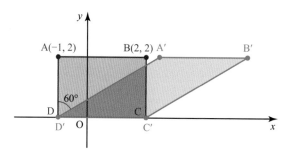

Figure 1.28

(i) Find the coordinates of A'.

(ii) Find the matrix that represents the shear.

⑧ The unit square OABC has its vertices at $(0, 0)$, $(1, 0)$, $(1, 1)$ and $(0, 1)$.

OABC is mapped to OA'B'C' by the transformation defined by the matrix $\begin{pmatrix} 4 & 3 \\ 5 & 4 \end{pmatrix}$.

Find the coordinates of A', B' and C' and show that the area of the shape has not been changed by the transformation.

⑨ The transformation represented by the matrix $\mathbf{M} = \begin{pmatrix} 1 & 2 \\ 0 & 1 \end{pmatrix}$ is applied to the triangle ABC with vertices $A(-1, 1)$, $B(1, -1)$ and $C(-1, -1)$.

(i) Draw a diagram showing the triangle ABC and its image A'B'C'.

(ii) Find the gradient of the line A'C' and explain how this relates to the matrix $\mathbf{M}$.

⑩ Describe the transformations represented by these matrices.

(i) $\begin{pmatrix} 1 & 0 & 0 \\ 0 & 0 & 1 \\ 0 & -1 & 0 \end{pmatrix}$ (ii) $\begin{pmatrix} 3 & 0 & 0 \\ 0 & 3 & 0 \\ 0 & 0 & 3 \end{pmatrix}$ (iii) $\begin{pmatrix} 1 & 0 & 0 \\ 0 & 1 & 0 \\ 0 & 0 & -1 \end{pmatrix}$ (iv) $\begin{pmatrix} 2 & 0 & 0 \\ 0 & 3 & 0 \\ 0 & 0 & \frac{1}{2} \end{pmatrix}$

⑪ Find the matrices that would represent

(i) a reflection in the plane $x = 0$

(ii) a rotation of 180° about the y-axis.

⑫ A transformation maps P to P' as follows:

■ Each point is mapped on to the line $y = x$.

■ The line joining a point to its image is parallel to the y-axis.

Find the coordinates of the image of the point (x, y) and hence show that this transformation can be represented by means of a matrix.

What is that matrix?

⑬ A square has corners with coordinates $A(1, 0)$, $B(1, 1)$, $C(0, 1)$ and $O(0, 0)$. It is to be transformed into another quadrilateral in the first quadrant of the coordinate grid.

Find a matrix which would transform the square into

(i) a rectangle with one vertex at the origin, the sides lie along the axes and one side of length is 5 units

(ii) a rhombus with one vertex at the origin, two angles of 45° and side lengths of $\sqrt{2}$ units; one of the sides lies along an axis

(iii) a parallelogram with one vertex at the origin and two angles of 30°; one of the longest sides lies along an axis and has length 7 units; the shortest sides have length 3 units.

Is there more than one possibility for any of these matrices? If so, write down alternative matrices that satisfy the same description.

4 Successive transformations

Figure 1.29 shows the effect of two successive transformations on a triangle. The transformation A represents a reflection in the x-axis. A maps the point P to the point A(P).

The transformation B represents a rotation of 90° anticlockwise about O. When you apply B to the image formed by A, the point A(P) is mapped to the point B(A(P)). This is abbreviated to BA(P).

Figure 1.29

 Note

Notice that a transformation written as BA means 'carry out A, then carry out B'. This process is sometimes called **composition of transformations**.

Discussion point

Look at Figure 1.29 and compare the original triangle with the final image after both transformations.

→ (i) Describe the single transformation represented by BA.
→ (ii) Write down the matrices which represent the transformations A and B. Calculate the matrix product **BA** and comment on your answer.

 Note

A transformation is often denoted by a capital letter. The matrix representing this transformation is usually denoted by the same letter, in bold.

In general, the matrix for a composite transformation is found by multiplying the matrices of the individual transformations in reverse order. So, for two transformations the matrix representing the first transformation is on the right and the matrix for the second transformation is on the left. For n transformations $T_1, T_2, \ldots, T_{n-1}, T_n$, the matrix product would be $T_n T_{n-1} \cdots T_2 T_1$.

You will prove this result for two transformations in Activity 1.6.

TECHNOLOGY

If you have access to geometrical software, you could investigate this using several different matrices for **T** and **S**.

ACTIVITY 1.6

The transformations T and S are represented by the matrices $\mathbf{T} = \begin{pmatrix} a & b \\ c & d \end{pmatrix}$ and $\mathbf{S} = \begin{pmatrix} p & q \\ r & s \end{pmatrix}$.

T is applied to the point P with position vector $\mathbf{p} = \begin{pmatrix} x \\ y \end{pmatrix}$. The image of P is P′.

S is then applied to the point P′. The image of P′ is P″. This is illustrated in Figure 1.30.

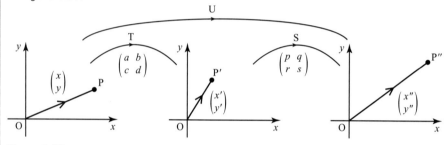

Figure 1.30

(i) Find the position vector $\begin{pmatrix} x' \\ y' \end{pmatrix}$ of P′ by calculating the matrix product $\mathbf{T} \begin{pmatrix} x \\ y \end{pmatrix}$.

(ii) Find the position vector $\begin{pmatrix} x'' \\ y'' \end{pmatrix}$ of P″ by calculating the matrix product $\mathbf{S} \begin{pmatrix} x' \\ y' \end{pmatrix}$.

(iii) Find the matrix product $\mathbf{U} = \mathbf{ST}$ and show that $\mathbf{U} \begin{pmatrix} x \\ y \end{pmatrix}$ is the same as $\begin{pmatrix} x'' \\ y'' \end{pmatrix}$.

Discussion point

→ How can you use the idea of successive transformations to explain the associativity of matrix multiplication $(\mathbf{AB})\mathbf{C} = \mathbf{A}(\mathbf{BC})$?

Proving results in trigonometry

If you carry out a rotation about the origin through angle θ, followed by a rotation about the origin through angle ϕ, then this is equivalent to a single rotation about the origin through angle $\theta + \phi$. Using matrices to represent these transformations allows you to prove the formulae for $\sin(\theta + \phi)$ and $\cos(\theta + \phi)$ given on page 172. This is done in Activity 1.7.

ACTIVITY 1.7
(i) Write down the matrix **A** representing a rotation about the origin through angle θ, and the matrix **B** representing a rotation about the origin through angle ϕ.
(ii) Find the matrix **BA**, representing a rotation about the origin through angle θ, followed by a rotation about the origin through angle ϕ.
(iii) Write down the matrix **C** representing a rotation about the origin through angle $\theta + \phi$.
(iv) By equating **C** to **BA**, write down expressions for $\sin(\theta + \phi)$ and $\cos(\theta + \phi)$.
(v) Explain why **BA = AB** in this case.

Example 1.10

(i) Write down the matrix **A** which represents an anticlockwise rotation of $135°$ about the origin.

(ii) Write down the matrices **B** and **C** which represent rotations of $45°$ and $90°$ respectively about the origin. Find the matrix **BC** and verify that $\mathbf{A} = \mathbf{BC}$.

(iii) Calculate the matrix $\mathbf{B}^3$ and comment on your answer.

Solution

(i) $\mathbf{A} = \begin{pmatrix} -\dfrac{1}{\sqrt{2}} & -\dfrac{1}{\sqrt{2}} \\ \dfrac{1}{\sqrt{2}} & -\dfrac{1}{\sqrt{2}} \end{pmatrix}$

(ii) $\mathbf{B} = \begin{pmatrix} \dfrac{1}{\sqrt{2}} & -\dfrac{1}{\sqrt{2}} \\ \dfrac{1}{\sqrt{2}} & \dfrac{1}{\sqrt{2}} \end{pmatrix}, \mathbf{C} = \begin{pmatrix} 0 & -1 \\ 1 & 0 \end{pmatrix}$

$\mathbf{BC} = \begin{pmatrix} \dfrac{1}{\sqrt{2}} & -\dfrac{1}{\sqrt{2}} \\ \dfrac{1}{\sqrt{2}} & \dfrac{1}{\sqrt{2}} \end{pmatrix} \begin{pmatrix} 0 & -1 \\ 1 & 0 \end{pmatrix} = \begin{pmatrix} -\dfrac{1}{\sqrt{2}} & -\dfrac{1}{\sqrt{2}} \\ \dfrac{1}{\sqrt{2}} & -\dfrac{1}{\sqrt{2}} \end{pmatrix} = \mathbf{A}$

(iii) $\mathbf{B}^3 = \begin{pmatrix} \dfrac{1}{\sqrt{2}} & -\dfrac{1}{\sqrt{2}} \\ \dfrac{1}{\sqrt{2}} & \dfrac{1}{\sqrt{2}} \end{pmatrix} \begin{pmatrix} \dfrac{1}{\sqrt{2}} & -\dfrac{1}{\sqrt{2}} \\ \dfrac{1}{\sqrt{2}} & \dfrac{1}{\sqrt{2}} \end{pmatrix} \begin{pmatrix} \dfrac{1}{\sqrt{2}} & -\dfrac{1}{\sqrt{2}} \\ \dfrac{1}{\sqrt{2}} & \dfrac{1}{\sqrt{2}} \end{pmatrix} = \begin{pmatrix} -\dfrac{1}{\sqrt{2}} & -\dfrac{1}{\sqrt{2}} \\ \dfrac{1}{\sqrt{2}} & -\dfrac{1}{\sqrt{2}} \end{pmatrix}.$

This verifies that three successive anticlockwise rotations of $45°$ about the origin is equivalent to a single anticlockwise rotation of $135°$ about the origin.

Exercise 1.4

① $\mathbf{A} = \begin{pmatrix} 3 & 0 \\ 0 & 3 \end{pmatrix}$, $\mathbf{B} = \begin{pmatrix} 0 & -1 \\ 1 & 0 \end{pmatrix}$, $\mathbf{C} = \begin{pmatrix} 1 & 0 \\ 0 & -1 \end{pmatrix}$ and $\mathbf{D} = \begin{pmatrix} 0 & 1 \\ 1 & 0 \end{pmatrix}$.

   (i)   Describe the transformations that are represented by matrices $\mathbf{A}, \mathbf{B}, \mathbf{C}$ and $\mathbf{D}$.

   (ii) Find the following matrix products and describe the single transformation represented in each case:

       (a) $\mathbf{BC}$ (b) $\mathbf{CB}$ (c) $\mathbf{DC}$ (d) $\mathbf{A}^2$ (e) $\mathbf{BCB}$ (f) $\mathbf{DC}^2\mathbf{D}$

   (iii) Write down two other matrix products, using the matrices $\mathbf{A}, \mathbf{B}, \mathbf{C}$ and $\mathbf{D}$, which would produce the same single transformation as $\mathbf{DC}^2\mathbf{D}$.

② The matrix $\mathbf{X}$ represents a reflection in the x-axis.

   The matrix $\mathbf{Y}$ represents a reflection in the y-axis.

   (i)   Write down the matrices $\mathbf{X}$ and $\mathbf{Y}$.

   (ii) Find the matrix $\mathbf{XY}$ and describe the transformation it represents.

   (iii) Find the matrix $\mathbf{YX}$.

   (iv) Explain geometrically why $\mathbf{XY} = \mathbf{YX}$ in this case.

③ The matrix $\mathbf{P}$ represents a rotation of $180°$ about the origin.

   The matrix $\mathbf{Q}$ represents a reflection in the line $y = x$.

   (i)   Write down the matrices $\mathbf{P}$ and $\mathbf{Q}$.

   (ii) Find the matrix $\mathbf{PQ}$ and describe the transformation it represents.

   (iii) Find the matrix $\mathbf{QP}$.

   (iv) Explain geometrically why $\mathbf{PQ} = \mathbf{QP}$ in this case.

④ In three dimensions, the four matrices $\mathbf{J}, \mathbf{K}, \mathbf{L}$ and $\mathbf{M}$ represent transformations as follows:

   $\mathbf{J}$ represents a reflection in the plane $z = 0$.

   $\mathbf{K}$ represents a rotation of $90°$ about the x-axis.

   $\mathbf{L}$ represents a reflection in the plane $x = 0$.

   $\mathbf{M}$ represents a rotation of $90°$ about the y-axis.

   (i)   Write down the matrices $\mathbf{J}, \mathbf{K}, \mathbf{L}$ and $\mathbf{M}$.

   (ii) Write down matrix products which would represent the single transformations obtained by each of the following combinations of transformations.

      (a) A reflection in the plane $z = 0$ followed by a reflection in the plane $x = 0$

      (b) A reflection in the plane $z = 0$ followed by a rotation of $90°$ about the y-axis

      (c) A rotation of $90°$ about the x-axis followed by a second rotation of $90°$ about the x-axis

      (d) A rotation of $90°$ about the x-axis followed by a reflection in the plane $x = 0$ followed by a reflection in the plane $z = 0$

⑤ The transformations R and S are represented by the matrices

    $\mathbf{R} = \begin{pmatrix} 2 & -1 \\ 1 & 3 \end{pmatrix}$ and $\mathbf{S} = \begin{pmatrix} 3 & 0 \\ -2 & 4 \end{pmatrix}$.

   (i)   Find the matrix which represents the transformation RS.

   (ii) Find the image of the point $(3, -2)$ under the transformation RS.

⑥ The transformation represented by $C = \begin{pmatrix} 0 & 3 \\ -1 & 0 \end{pmatrix}$ is equivalent to a single

transformation B followed by a single transformation A. Give geometrical descriptions of a pair of possible transformations B and A and state the matrices that represent them.

Comment on the order in which the transformations are performed.

⑦ Figure 1.31 shows the image of the unit square OABC under the combined transformation with matrix **PQ**.

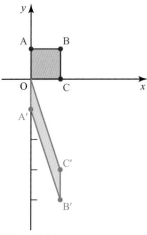

Figure 1.31

(i) Write down the matrix **PQ**.

Matrix **P** represents a reflection.

(ii) State the matrices **P** and **Q** and define fully the two transformations represented by these matrices. When describing matrix **Q** you should refer to the image of the point B.

⑧ Find the matrix **X** which represents a rotation of 135° about the origin followed by a reflection in the y-axis.

Explain why matrix **X** cannot represent a rotation about the origin.

⑨ Find the matrix **Y** which represents a reflection in the plane $y = 0$ followed by a rotation of 90° about the z-axis.

⑩ (i) Write down the matrix **P** which represents a stretch of scale factor 2 parallel to the y-axis.

(ii) The matrix $Q = \begin{pmatrix} 5 & 0 \\ 0 & -1 \end{pmatrix}$. Write down the two single

transformations which are represented by the matrix **Q**.

(iii) Find the matrix **PQ**. Write a list of the three transformations which are represented by the matrix **PQ**. In how many different orders could the three transformations occur?

(iv) Find the matrix **R** for which the matrix product **RPQ** would transform an object to its original position.

⑪ There are two basic types of four-terminal electrical networks, as shown in Figure 1.32.

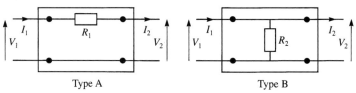

Type A   Type B

Figure 1.32

In Type A the output voltage V_2 and current I_2 are related to the input voltage V_1 and current I_1 by the simultaneous equations:

$$V_2 = V_1 - I_1 R_1$$
$$I_2 = I_1$$

The simultaneous equations can be written as $\begin{pmatrix} V_2 \\ I_2 \end{pmatrix} = \mathbf{A} \begin{pmatrix} V_1 \\ I_1 \end{pmatrix}$.

(i) Find the matrix $\mathbf{A}$.

In Type B the corresponding simultaneous equations are:

$$V_2 = V_1$$
$$I_2 = I_1 - \frac{V_1}{R_2}$$

(ii) Write down the matrix $\mathbf{B}$ which represents the effect of a Type B network.

(iii) Find the matrix which represents the effect of Type A followed by Type B.

(iv) Is the effect of Type B followed by Type A the same as the effect of Type A followed by Type B?

⑫ The matrix $\mathbf{B}$ represents a rotation of 45° anticlockwise about the origin.

$$\mathbf{B} = \begin{pmatrix} \dfrac{1}{\sqrt{2}} & -\dfrac{1}{\sqrt{2}} \\ \dfrac{1}{\sqrt{2}} & \dfrac{1}{\sqrt{2}} \end{pmatrix}, \mathbf{D} = \begin{pmatrix} a & -b \\ b & a \end{pmatrix}$$ where a and b are positive real numbers

Given that $\mathbf{D}^2 = \mathbf{B}$, find exact values for a and b. Write down the transformation represented by the matrix $\mathbf{D}$. What do the exact values a and b represent?

In questions 13 and 14 you will need to use the matrix which represents a reflection in the line $y = mx$. This can be written as $\dfrac{1}{1+m^2} \begin{pmatrix} 1-m^2 & 2m \\ 2m & m^2-1 \end{pmatrix}$.

⑬ (i) Find the matrix $\mathbf{P}$ which represents reflection in the line $y = \dfrac{1}{\sqrt{3}} x$, and the matrix $\mathbf{Q}$ which represents reflection in the line $y = \sqrt{3}x$.

(ii) Use matrix multiplication to find the single transformation equivalent to reflection in the line $y = \dfrac{1}{\sqrt{3}} x$ followed by reflection in the line $y = \sqrt{3}x$.
Describe this transformation fully.

(iii) Use matrix multiplication to find the single transformation equivalent to reflection in the line $y = \sqrt{3}x$ followed by reflection in the line $y = \dfrac{1}{\sqrt{3}} x$.
Describe this transformation fully.

⑭ The matrix $\mathbf{R}$ represents a reflection in the line $y = mx$.

Show that $\mathbf{R}^2 = \begin{pmatrix} 1 & 0 \\ 0 & 1 \end{pmatrix}$ and explain geometrically why this is the case.

5 Invariance

Invariant points

> **Discussion points**
> → In a reflection, are there any points which map to themselves?
> → In a rotation, are there any points which map to themselves?

Points which map to themselves under a transformation are called **invariant points**. The origin is always an invariant point under a transformation that can be represented by a matrix, as the following statement is always true:

$$\begin{pmatrix} a & b \\ c & d \end{pmatrix} \begin{pmatrix} 0 \\ 0 \end{pmatrix} = \begin{pmatrix} 0 \\ 0 \end{pmatrix}$$

More generally, a point (x, y) is invariant if it satisfies the matrix equation:

$$\begin{pmatrix} a & b \\ c & d \end{pmatrix} \begin{pmatrix} x \\ y \end{pmatrix} = \begin{pmatrix} x \\ y \end{pmatrix}$$

For example, the point $(-2, 2)$ is invariant under the transformation represented by the matrix $\begin{pmatrix} 6 & 5 \\ 2 & 3 \end{pmatrix}$: $\begin{pmatrix} 6 & 5 \\ 2 & 3 \end{pmatrix} \begin{pmatrix} -2 \\ 2 \end{pmatrix} = \begin{pmatrix} -2 \\ 2 \end{pmatrix}$

Example 1.11

M is the matrix $\begin{pmatrix} 2 & -1 \\ 1 & 0 \end{pmatrix}$.

(i) Show that $(5, 5)$ is an invariant point under the transformation represented by **M**.

(ii) What can you say about the invariant points under this transformation?

Solution

(i) $\begin{pmatrix} 2 & -1 \\ 1 & 0 \end{pmatrix} \begin{pmatrix} 5 \\ 5 \end{pmatrix} = \begin{pmatrix} 5 \\ 5 \end{pmatrix}$ so $(5, 5)$ is an invariant point under the transformation represented by **M**.

(ii) Suppose the point $\begin{pmatrix} x \\ y \end{pmatrix}$ maps to itself. Then

$$\begin{pmatrix} 2 & -1 \\ 1 & 0 \end{pmatrix} \begin{pmatrix} x \\ y \end{pmatrix} = \begin{pmatrix} x \\ y \end{pmatrix}$$

$$\begin{pmatrix} 2x - y \\ x \end{pmatrix} = \begin{pmatrix} x \\ y \end{pmatrix}$$

> Both equations simplify to $y = x$.

$\Leftrightarrow 2x - y = x$ and $x = y$.

So the invariant points of the transformation are all the points on the line $y = x$.

> These points all have the form (λ, λ). The point $(5,5)$ is just one of the points on this line.

The simultaneous equations in Example 1.11 were equivalent and so all the invariant points were on a straight line. Generally, any matrix equation set up to find the invariant points will lead to two equations of the form $ax + by = 0$, which can also be expressed in the form $y = -\dfrac{ax}{b}$. These equations may be equivalent, in which case this is a line of invariant points. If the two equations are not equivalent, the origin is the only point which satisfies both equations, and so this is the only invariant point.

Invariant lines

A line AB is known as an **invariant line** under a transformation if the image of every point on AB is also on AB. It is important to note that it is not necessary for each of the points to map to itself; it can map to itself or to some other point on the line AB.

Sometimes it is easy to spot which lines are invariant. For example, in Figure 1.33 the position of the points A–F and their images A′–F′ show that the transformation is a reflection in the line l. So every point on l maps onto itself and l is a **line of invariant points**.

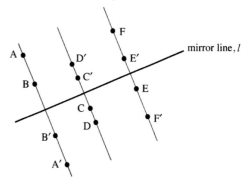

Look at the lines perpendicular to the mirror line in Figure 1.33, for example the line ABB′A′. Any point on one of these lines maps onto another point on the same line. Such a line is invariant but it is not a line of invariant points.

Figure 1.33

Example 1.12

Find the invariant lines of the transformation given by the matrix $\mathbf{M} = \begin{pmatrix} 5 & 1 \\ 2 & 4 \end{pmatrix}$.

Solution

> Let the original point be (x, y) and the image point be (x', y').

Suppose the invariant line has the form $y = mx + c$

$$\begin{pmatrix} x' \\ y' \end{pmatrix} = \begin{pmatrix} 5 & 1 \\ 2 & 4 \end{pmatrix}\begin{pmatrix} x \\ y \end{pmatrix} \Leftrightarrow x' = 5x + y \text{ and } y' = 2x + 4y$$

$$\Leftrightarrow \begin{cases} x' = 5x + mx + c = (5 + m)x + c \\ y' = 2x + 4(mx + c) = (2 + 4m)x + 4c \end{cases}$$

> Using $y = mx + c$.

As the line is invariant, (x', y') also lies on the line, so $y' = mx' + c$.

Therefore,

$$(2 + 4m)x + 4c = m[(5 + m)x + c] + c$$

$$\Leftrightarrow 0 = (m^2 + m - 2)x + (m - 3)c$$

For the left-hand side to equal zero, both $m^2 + m - 2 = 0$ and $(m - 3)c = 0$.

$$(m - 1)(m + 2) = 0 \Leftrightarrow m = 1 \text{ or } m = -2$$

and
$$(m - 3)c = 0 \Leftrightarrow m = 3 \text{ or } c = 0$$

> $m = 3$ is not a viable solution as $m^2 + m - 2 \neq 0$.

So, there are two possible solutions for the invariant line:
$$m = 1, c = 0 \Leftrightarrow y = x$$
or
$$m = -2, c = 0 \Leftrightarrow y = -2x$$

Figure 1.34 shows the effect of this transformation, together with its invariant lines.

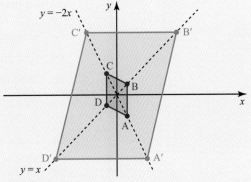

Figure 1.34

Exercise 1.5

① Find the invariant points under the transformations represented by the following matrices.

(i) $\begin{pmatrix} -1 & -1 \\ 2 & 2 \end{pmatrix}$ (ii) $\begin{pmatrix} 3 & 4 \\ 1 & 2 \end{pmatrix}$ (iii) $\begin{pmatrix} 4 & 1 \\ 6 & 3 \end{pmatrix}$ (iv) $\begin{pmatrix} 7 & -4 \\ 3 & -1 \end{pmatrix}$

② What lines, if any, are invariant under the following transformations?

(i) Enlargement, centre the origin

(ii) Rotation through 180° about the origin

(iii) Rotation through 90° about the origin

(iv) Reflection in the line $y = x$

(v) Reflection in the line $y = -x$

(vi) Shear, x-axis fixed

③ Figure 1.35 shows the effect on the unit square of a transformation represented by $\mathbf{A} = \begin{pmatrix} 0.6 & 0.8 \\ 0.8 & -0.6 \end{pmatrix}$.

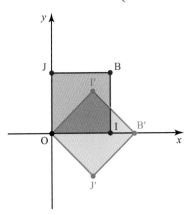

Figure 1.35

(i) Find three points which are invariant under this transformation.

(ii) Given that this transformation is a reflection, write down the equation of the mirror line.

(iii) Using your answer to part (ii), write down the equation of an invariant line, other than the mirror line, under this reflection.

(iv) Justify your answer to part (iii) algebraically.

④ For the matrix $\mathbf{M} = \begin{pmatrix} 4 & 11 \\ 11 & 4 \end{pmatrix}$

(i) show that the origin is the only invariant point

(ii) find the invariant lines of the transformation represented by $\mathbf{M}$.

⑤ (i) Find the invariant lines of the transformation given by the matrix

$\begin{pmatrix} 3 & 4 \\ 9 & -2 \end{pmatrix}$.

(ii) Draw a diagram to show the effect of the transformation on the unit square, and show the invariant lines on your diagram.

⑥ For the matrix $\mathbf{M} = \begin{pmatrix} 0 & 1 \\ -1 & 2 \end{pmatrix}$

(i) find the line of invariant points of the transformation given by $\mathbf{M}$

(ii) find the invariant lines of the transformation

(iii) draw a diagram to show the effect of the transformation on the unit square.

⑦ The matrix $\begin{pmatrix} \dfrac{1-m^2}{1+m^2} & \dfrac{2m}{1+m^2} \\ \dfrac{2m}{1+m^2} & \dfrac{m^2-1}{1+m^2} \end{pmatrix}$ represents a reflection in the line $y = mx$.

Prove that the line $y = mx$ is a line of invariant points.

⑧ The transformation T maps $\begin{pmatrix} x \\ y \end{pmatrix}$ to $\begin{pmatrix} a & b \\ c & d \end{pmatrix}\begin{pmatrix} x \\ y \end{pmatrix}$.

Show that invariant points other than the origin exist if $ad - bc = a + d - 1$.

⑨ T is a translation of the plane by the vector $\begin{pmatrix} a \\ b \end{pmatrix}$. The point (x, y) is mapped to the point (x', y').

(i) Write down equations for x' and y' in terms of x and y.

(ii) Verify that $\begin{pmatrix} x' \\ y' \\ z' \end{pmatrix} = \begin{pmatrix} 1 & 0 & a \\ 0 & 1 & b \\ 0 & 0 & 1 \end{pmatrix}\begin{pmatrix} x \\ y \\ 1 \end{pmatrix}$ produces the same equations as those obtained in part (i).

The point (X, Y) is the image of the point (x, y) under the combined transformation TM where

$\begin{pmatrix} X \\ Y \\ 1 \end{pmatrix} = \begin{pmatrix} -0.6 & 0.8 & a \\ 0.8 & 0.6 & b \\ 0 & 0 & 1 \end{pmatrix}\begin{pmatrix} x \\ y \\ 1 \end{pmatrix}$

(iii) (a) Show that if $a = -4$ and $b = 2$ then $(0, 5)$ is an invariant point of TM.

(b) Show that if $a = 2$ and $b = 1$ then TM has no invariant point.

(c) Find a relationship between a and b that must be satisfied if TM is to have any invariant points.

LEARNING OUTCOMES

When you have completed this chapter you should be able to:

➤ understand what is meant by the terms order of a matrix, square matrix, identity matrix, zero matrix and equal matrices

➤ add and subtract matrices of the same order

➤ multiply a matrix by a scalar

➤ know when two matrices are conformable for multiplication, and be able to multiply conformable matrices

➤ use a calculator to carry out matrix calculations

➤ know that matrix multiplication is associative but not commutative

➤ find the matrix associated with a linear transformation in two dimensions:

  ➤ reflections in the coordinate axes and the lines $y = \pm x$

  ➤ rotations about the origin

  ➤ enlargements centre the origin

  ➤ stretches parallel to the coordinate axes

  ➤ shears with the coordinate axes as fixed lines

➤ find the matrix associated with a linear transformation in three dimensions:

  ➤ reflection in $x = 0$, $y = 0$ or $z = 0$

  ➤ rotations through multiples of 90° about the x, y or z axes

➤ understand successive transformations in two dimensions and the connection with matrix multiplication

➤ find the invariant points for a linear transformation

➤ find the invariant lines for a linear transformation.

KEY POINTS

1 A matrix is a rectangular array of numbers or letters.

2 The shape of a matrix is described by its order. A matrix with r rows and c columns has order $r \times c$.

3 A matrix with the same number of rows and columns is called a square matrix.

4 The matrix $\mathbf{O} = \begin{pmatrix} 0 & 0 \\ 0 & 0 \end{pmatrix}$ is known as the 2×2 zero matrix. Zero matrices can be of any order.

5 A matrix of the form $\mathbf{I} = \begin{pmatrix} 1 & 0 \\ 0 & 1 \end{pmatrix}$ is known as an identity matrix. All identity matrices are square, with 1s on the leading diagonal and zeros elsewhere.

6 Matrices can be added or subtracted if they have the same order.

7 Two matrices $\mathbf{A}$ and $\mathbf{B}$ can be multiplied to give matrix $\mathbf{AB}$ if their orders are of the form $p \times q$ and $q \times r$ respectively. The resulting matrix will have the order $p \times r$.

Chapter 1 Matrices and transformations

1

8 Matrix multiplication

Row from left matrix with column from right matrix.

Figure 1.36

9 Matrix addition and multiplication are associative:
$$\mathbf{A} + (\mathbf{B} + \mathbf{C}) = (\mathbf{A} + \mathbf{B}) + \mathbf{C}$$
$$\mathbf{A}(\mathbf{BC}) = (\mathbf{AB})\mathbf{C}$$

10 Matrix addition is commutative but matrix multiplication is generally not commutative:
$$\mathbf{A} + \mathbf{B} = \mathbf{B} + \mathbf{A}$$
$$\mathbf{AB} \neq \mathbf{BA}$$

11 The matrix $\mathbf{M} = \begin{pmatrix} a & b \\ c & d \end{pmatrix}$ represents the transformation which maps the point with position vector $\begin{pmatrix} x \\ y \end{pmatrix}$ to the point with position vector $\begin{pmatrix} ax + by \\ cx + dy \end{pmatrix}$.

12 A list of the matrices representing common transformations, including rotations, reflections, enlargements, stretches and shears, is given on page 22.

13 Under the transformation represented by $\mathbf{M}$, the image of $\mathbf{i} = \begin{pmatrix} 1 \\ 0 \end{pmatrix}$ is the first column of $\mathbf{M}$ and the image of $\mathbf{j} = \begin{pmatrix} 0 \\ 1 \end{pmatrix}$ is the second column of $\mathbf{M}$.

Similarly, in three dimensions the images of the unit vectors $\mathbf{i} = \begin{pmatrix} 1 \\ 0 \\ 0 \end{pmatrix}$, $\mathbf{j} = \begin{pmatrix} 0 \\ 1 \\ 0 \end{pmatrix}$ and $\mathbf{k} = \begin{pmatrix} 0 \\ 0 \\ 1 \end{pmatrix}$ are the first, second and third columns of the transformation matrix.

14 The composite of the transformation represented by $\mathbf{M}$ followed by that represented by $\mathbf{N}$ is represented by the matrix product $\mathbf{NM}$.

15 If (x, y) is an invariant point under a transformation represented by the matrix $\mathbf{M}$, then $\mathbf{M} \begin{pmatrix} x \\ y \end{pmatrix} = \begin{pmatrix} x \\ y \end{pmatrix}$.

16 A line AB is known as an invariant line under a transformation if the image of every point on AB is also on AB.

FUTURE USES

■ Work on matrices is developed further in Chapter 6 'Matrices and their inverses'.

Introduction to complex numbers

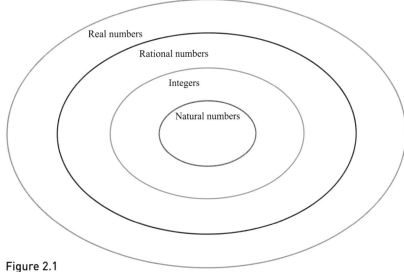

Figure 2.1

Discussion points

→ What is the meaning of each of the terms shown in Figure 2.1?

→ Suggest two numbers that could be placed in each part of the diagram.

1 Extending the number system

The number system we use today has taken thousands of years to develop. To classify the different types of numbers used in mathematics the following letter symbols are used:

Discussion point

→ Why is there no set shown on the diagram for irrational numbers?

$\mathbb{N}$	Natural numbers
$\mathbb{Z}$	Integers
$\mathbb{Q}$	Rational numbers
$\overline{\mathbb{Q}}$	Irrational numbers
$\mathbb{R}$	Real numbers

You may have noticed that some of these sets of numbers fit within the other sets. This can be seen in Figure 2.1.

ACTIVITY 2.1

On a copy of Figure 2.1 write the following numbers in the correct positions.

$7 \qquad \sqrt{5} \qquad -13 \qquad \dfrac{227}{109} \qquad -\sqrt{5} \qquad 3.1415 \qquad \pi \qquad 0.33 \qquad 0.\dot{3}$

What are complex numbers?

ACTIVITY 2.2

Solve each of these equations and decide which set of numbers the roots belong to in each case.

(i) $x + 7 = 9$ (ii) $7x = 9$ (iii) $x^2 = 9$

(iv) $x + 10 = 9$ (v) $x^2 + 7x = 0$

Now think about the equation $x^2 + 9 = 0$.

You could rewrite it as $x^2 = -9$. However, since the square of every real number is positive or zero, there is no real number with a square of -9. This is an example of a quadratic equation which, up to now, you would have classified as having 'no real roots'.

> Writing this quadratic equation as $x^2 + 0x + 9 = 0$ and calculating the discriminant for this quadratic gives $b^2 - 4ac = -36$ which is less than zero.

Prior knowledge

You should know how to solve quadratic equations using the quadratic formula.

The existence of such equations was recognised for hundreds of years, in the same way that Greek mathematicians had accepted that $x + 10 = 9$ had no solution; the concept of a negative number had yet to be developed. The number system has expanded as mathematicians increased the range of mathematical problems they wanted to tackle.

You can solve the equation $x^2 + 9 = 0$ by extending the number system to include a new number, i (sometimes written as j). This has the property that $i^2 = -1$ and it follows the usual laws of algebra. i is called an **imaginary** number.

The square root of any negative number can be expressed in terms of i. For example, the solution of the equation $x^2 = -9$ is $x = \pm\sqrt{-9}$. This can be written as $\pm\sqrt{9} \times \sqrt{-1}$ which simplifies to $\pm3i$.

Example 2.1

Use the quadratic formula to solve the quadratic equation $z^2 - 6z + 58 = 0$, simplifying your answer as far as possible.

TECHNOLOGY

If your calculator has an equation solver, find out if it will give you the complex roots of this quadratic equation.

Solution

$z^2 - 6z + 58 = 0$ ← Using the quadratic formula with $a = 1, b = -6$ and $c = 58$.

$z = \dfrac{6 \pm \sqrt{(-6)^2 - 4 \times 1 \times 58}}{2 \times 1}$

$= \dfrac{6 \pm \sqrt{-196}}{2}$

$= \dfrac{6 \pm 14i}{2}$ ← $\sqrt{-196} = \sqrt{196} \times \sqrt{-1} = 14i$.

$= 3 \pm 7i$

3 is called the real part of the complex number $3 + 7i$ and is denoted $\text{Re}(z)$.

You will have noticed that the roots $3 + 7i$ and $3 - 7i$ of the quadratic equation $z^2 - 6z + 58 = 0$ have both a **real part** and an **imaginary part**.

7 is called the imaginary part of the complex number and is denoted $\text{Im}(z)$.

Notation

Any number z of the form $x + yi$, where x and y are real, is called a **complex number**.

The letter z is commonly used for complex numbers, and w is also used. In this chapter a complex number z is often denoted by $x + yi$, but other letters are sometimes used, such as $a + bi$.

x is called the real part of the complex number, denoted by $\text{Re}(z)$ and y is called the imaginary part, denoted by $\text{Im}(z)$.

Working with complex numbers

The general methods for addition, subtraction and multiplication of complex numbers are straightforward.

TECHNOLOGY

Some calculators will allow you to calculate with complex numbers. Find out whether your calculator has this facility.

Addition: add the real parts and add the imaginary parts.

For example, $(3 + 4i) + (2 - 8i) = (3 + 2) + (4 - 8)i$
$$= 5 - 4i$$

Subtraction: subtract the real parts and subtract the imaginary parts.

For example, $(6 - 9i) - (1 + 6i) = 5 - 15i$

Multiplication: multiply out the brackets in the usual way and simplify.

For example,
$$(7 + 2i)(3 - 4i) = 21 - 28i + 6i - 8i^2$$
$$= 21 - 22i - 8(-1)$$
$$= 29 - 22i$$

When simplifying it is important to remember that $i^2 = -1$.

Division of complex numbers follows later in this chapter.

Historical note

Gerolamo Cardano (1501–1576) was an Italian mathematician and physicist who was the first known writer to explore calculations involving the square roots of negative quantities, in his 1545 publication *Ars magna* ('The Great Art'). He wanted to calculate:

$$\left(5 + \sqrt{-15}\right)\left(5 - \sqrt{-15}\right)?$$

Some years later, an Italian engineer named Rafael Bombelli introduced the words 'plus of minus' to indicate $\sqrt{-1}$ and 'minus of minus' to indicate $-\sqrt{-1}$.

However, the general mathematical community was slow to accept these 'fictional' numbers, with the French mathematician and philosopher René Descartes rather dismissively describing them as 'imaginary'. Similarly, Isaac Newton described the numbers as 'impossible' and the mystification of Gottfried Leibniz is evident in the quote at the beginning of the chapter! In the end it was Leonhard Euler who eventually began to use the symbol i, the first letter of 'imaginarius' (imaginary) instead of writing $\sqrt{-1}$.

Equality of complex numbers

Two complex numbers $z = x + yi$ and $w = u + vi$ are equal if both $x = u$ and $y = v$. If $x \neq u$ or $y \neq v$, or both, then z and w are not equal.

You may feel that this is obvious, but it is interesting to compare this situation with the equality of rational numbers.

For two complex numbers to be equal the real parts must be equal and the imaginary parts must be equal. Using this result is described as **equating real** and **imaginary parts**, as shown in the following example.

Example 2.2

The complex numbers z_1 and z_2 are given by
$$z_1 = (3 - a) + (2b - 4)i$$
and
$$z_2 = (7b - 4) + (3a - 2)i.$$

(i) Given that z_1 and z_2 are equal, find the values of a and b.

(ii) Check your answer by substituting your values for a and b into the expressions above.

Solution

(i) $(3 - a) + (2b - 4)i = (7b - 4) + (3a - 2)i$

Equating real and imaginary parts leads to two equations.

Equating real parts: $3 - a = 7b - 4$

Equating imaginary parts: $2b - 4 = 3a - 2$

$$\begin{cases} 7b + a = 7 \\ 2b - 3a = 2 \end{cases}$$

Simplifying the equations.

Solving simultaneously gives $b = 1$ and $a = 0$.

(ii) Substituting $a = 0$ and $b = 1$ gives $z_1 = 3 - 2i$ and $z_2 = 3 - 2i$ so z_1 and z_2 are indeed equal.

Exercise 2.1

Do not use a calculator in this exercise

① Write down the values of

(i) i^9 (ii) i^{14} (iii) i^{31} (iv) i^{100}

② Find the following:

(i) $(6 + 4i) + (3 - 5i)$ (ii) $(-6 + 4i) + (-3 + 5i)$

(iii) $(6 + 4i) - (3 - 5i)$ (iv) $(-6 + 4i) - (-3 + 5i)$

③ Find the following:

(i) $3(6 + 4i) + 2(3 - 5i)$ (ii) $3i(6 + 4i) + 2i(3 - 5i)$

(iii) $(6 + 4i)^2$ (iv) $(6 + 4i)(3 - 5i)$

④ (i) Find the following:

     (a) $(6 + 4i)(6 - 4i)$

     (b) $(3 - 5i)(3 + 5i)$

     (c) $(6 + 4i)(6 - 4i)(3 - 5i)(3 + 5i)$

(ii) What do you notice about the answers in part (i)?

⑤ Find the following:

(i) $(3 - 7i)(2 + 2i)(5 - i)$ (ii) $(3 - 7i)^3$

⑥ Solve each of the following equations.
In each case, check your solutions are correct by substituting the values back into the equation.

(i) $z^2 + 2z + 2 = 0$ (ii) $z^2 - 2z + 5 = 0$

(iii) $z^2 - 4z + 13 = 0$ (iv) $z^2 + 6z + 34 = 0$

(v) $4z^2 - 4z + 17 = 0$ (vi) $z^2 + 4z + 6 = 0$

⑦ Given that the complex numbers

$z_1 = a^2 + (3 + 2b)i$

$z_2 = (5a - 4) + b^2 i$

are equal, find the possible values of a and b.

Hence list the possible values of complex numbers z_1 and z_2.

⑧ A complex number $z = a + bi$, where a and b are real, is squared to give an answer of $-16 + 30i$. Find the possible values of a and b.

⑨ Find the square roots of the complex number $-40 + 42i$.

⑩ Figure 2.2 shows the graph of $y = x^2 - 4x + 3$.

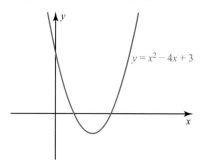

Figure 2.2

(i) Draw sketches of the curves $y = x^2 - 4x + 3$, $y = x^2 - 4x + 6$ and $y = x^2 - 4x + 8$ on the same axes.

(ii) Solve the equations

    (a) $x^2 - 4x + 3 = 0$

    (b) $x^2 - 4x + 6 = 0$

    (c) $x^2 - 4x + 8 = 0$

(iii) Describe the relationship between the roots of the three equation and how they relate to the graphs you sketched in part (i).

⑪ Given that $z = 2 + 3i$ is a root of the equation
$$z^2 + (a - i)z + 16 + bi = 0$$

where a and b are real, find a and b.

Explain why you cannot assume that the other root is $z = 2 - 3i$.

Given that the second root has the form $5 + ci$, find the other root of the equation.

2 Division of complex numbers

Complex conjugates

You have seen that the roots of a quadratic equation are almost the same, but have the opposite sign (+ and −) between the real and imaginary terms. For example, the roots of $x^2 - 4x + 13 = 0$ are $x = 2 + 3i$ and $x = 2 - 3i$. The pair of complex numbers $2 + 3i$ and $2 - 3i$ are called **conjugates**. Each is the conjugate of the other.

In general the complex number $x - yi$ is called the **complex conjugate**, or just the conjugate, of $x + yi$. The conjugate of a complex number z is denoted by z^*.

Example 2.3

Given that $z = 3 + 5i$, find

(i) $z + z^*$ (ii) zz^*

Solution

(i) $\quad z + z^* = (3 + 5i) + (3 - 5i)$

$\qquad\qquad = 6$

(ii) $\quad zz^* = (3 + 5i)(3 - 5i)$

$\qquad\qquad = 9 + 15i - 15i - 25i^2$

$\qquad\qquad = 9 + 25$

$\qquad\qquad = 34$

ACTIVITY 2.3

Prove that $z + z^*$ and zz are both real for all complex numbers z.

You can see from the example above that $z + z^*$ and zz^* are both real. This is an example of an important general result: that the sum of two complex conjugates is real and that their product is also real.

Dividing complex numbers

You probably already know that you can write an expression like $\dfrac{2}{3 - \sqrt{2}}$ as a fraction with a rational denominator by multiplying the numerator and denominator by $3 + \sqrt{2}$.

$$\frac{2}{3 - \sqrt{2}} = \frac{2}{3 - \sqrt{2}} \times \frac{3 + \sqrt{2}}{3 + \sqrt{2}} = \frac{6 + 2\sqrt{2}}{9 - 2} = \frac{6 + 2\sqrt{2}}{7}$$

Because zz^* is always real, you can use a similar method to write an expression like $\dfrac{2}{3 - 5i}$ as a fraction with a real denominator, by multiplying the numerator and denominator by $3 + 5i$. ←   3 + 5i is the complex conjugate of 3 − 5i.

This is the basis for dividing one complex number by another.

Example 2.4

Find the real and imaginary parts of $\dfrac{1}{5 + 2i}$.

Solution

Multiply the numerator and denominator by $5 - 2i$. ↗   5 − 2i is the conjugate of the denominator 5 + 2i.

$$\frac{1}{5 + 2i} = \frac{5 - 2i}{(5 + 2i)(5 - 2i)}$$

$$= \frac{5 - 2i}{25 + 4}$$

$$= \frac{5 - 2i}{29}$$

The real part is $\dfrac{5}{29}$ and the imaginary part is $-\dfrac{2}{29}$.

Example 2.5

Solve the equation $(2 + 3i)z = 9 - 4i$.

Discussion points

→ What are the values of $\frac{1}{i}$, $\frac{1}{i^2}$, $\frac{1}{i^3}$ and $\frac{1}{i^4}$?

→ Explain how you would work out the value of $\frac{1}{i^n}$ for any positive integer value n.

Solution

$(2 + 3i)z = 9 - 4i$

$\Rightarrow z = \dfrac{9 - 4i}{2 + 3i}$

$= \dfrac{(9 - 4i)(2 - 3i)}{(2 + 3i)(2 - 3i)}$

$= \dfrac{18 - 27i - 8i + 12i^2}{4 - 6i + 6i - 9i^2}$

$= \dfrac{6 - 35i}{13}$

$= \dfrac{6}{13} - \dfrac{35}{13}i$

> Multiply top and bottom by $2 - 3i$.

> Notice how the $-6i$ and $+6i$ terms will cancel to produce a real denominator.

Exercise 2.2

TECHNOLOGY

If your calculator handles complex numbers, you can use it to check your answers.

① Express these complex numbers in the form $x + yi$.

(i) $\dfrac{3}{7 - i}$ (ii) $\dfrac{3}{7 + i}$ (iii) $\dfrac{3i}{7 - i}$ (iv) $\dfrac{3i}{7 + i}$

② Express these complex numbers in the form $x + yi$.

(i) $\dfrac{3 + 5i}{2 - 3i}$ (ii) $\dfrac{2 - 3i}{3 + 5i}$ (iii) $\dfrac{3 - 5i}{2 + 3i}$ (iv) $\dfrac{2 + 3i}{3 - 5i}$

③ Simplify the following, giving your answers in the form $x + yi$.

(i) $\dfrac{(12 - 5i)(2 + 2i)}{4 - 3i}$

(ii) $\dfrac{12 - 5i}{(4 - 3i)^2}$

④ $z = 3 - 6i$, $w = -2 + 9i$ and $q = 6 + 3i$.

Write down the values of the following:

(i) $z + z^*$ (ii) ww^* (iii) $q^* + q$
(iv) z^*z (v) $w + w^*$ (vi) qq^*

⑤ Given that $z = 2 + 3i$ and $w = 6 - 4i$, find the following:

(i) $\text{Re}(z)$ (ii) $\text{Im}(z)$ (iii) z^*
(iv) w^* (v) $z^* + w^*$ (vi) $z^* - w^*$

⑥ Given that $z = 2 + 3i$ and $w = 6 - 4i$, find the following:

(i) $\text{Im}(z + z^*)$ (ii) $\text{Re}(w - w^*)$ (iii) $zz^* - ww^*$
(iv) $(z^3)^*$ (v) $(z^*)^3$ (vi) $zw^* - z^*w$

⑦ Given that $z_1 = 2 - 5i$, $z_2 = 4 + 10i$ and $z_3 = 6 - 5i$, find the following in the form $a + bi$, where a and b are rational numbers.

(i) $\dfrac{z_1 z_2}{z_3}$ (ii) $\dfrac{(z_3)^2}{z_1}$ (iii) $\dfrac{z_1 + z_2 - z_3}{(z_3)^2}$

⑧ Solve these equations.
  (i) $(1+i)z = 3+i$
  (ii) $(2-i)z + (2-6i) = 4-7i$
  (iii) $(3-4i)(z-1) = 10-5i$
  (iv) $(3+5i)(z+2-5i) = 6+3i$

⑨ Find the values of a and b such that $\dfrac{2-5i}{3+2i} = \dfrac{a+bi}{1-i}$.

⑩ The complex number $w = a + bi$, where a and b are real, satisfies the equation $(5-2i)w = 67 + 37i$.
  (i) Using the method of equating coefficients, find the values of a and b.
  (ii) Using division of complex numbers, find the values of a and b.

⑪ (i) For $z = 5-8i$ find $\dfrac{1}{z} + \dfrac{1}{z^*}$ in its simplest form.
  (ii) Write down the value of $\dfrac{1}{z} + \dfrac{1}{z^*}$ for $z = 5+8i$

⑫ For $z = x + yi$, find $\dfrac{1}{z} + \dfrac{1}{z^*}$ in terms of x and y.

⑬ Let $z_1 = x_1 + y_1i$ and $z_2 = x_2 + y_2i$.
  Show that $(z_1 + z_2)^* = z_1^* + z_2^*$.

⑭ Find real numbers a and b such that $\dfrac{a}{3+i} + \dfrac{b}{1+2i} = 1-i$.

⑮ Find all the numbers z, real or complex, for which $z^2 = 2z^*$.

⑯ The complex numbers z and w satisfy the following simultaneous equations.
$z + wi = 13$
$3z - 4w = 2i$
Find z and w, giving your answers in the form $a + bi$.

3 Representing complex numbers geometrically

Discussion point

➜ Why is it not possible to show a complex number on a number line?

A complex number $x + yi$ can be represented by the point with Cartesian coordinates (x, y).

For example, in Figure 2.3,
2 + 3i is represented by (2, 3)
−5 − 4i is represented by (−5, −4)
2i is represented by (0, 2)
7 is represented by (7, 0).

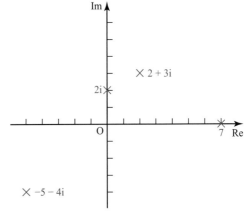

Figure 2.3

All real numbers are represented by points on the x-axis, which is therefore called the **real axis**. Purely imaginary numbers which have no real component (of the form $0 + y\mathrm{i}$) give points on the y-axis, which is called the **imaginary axis**.

These axes are labelled as Re and Im.

This geometrical illustration of complex numbers is called the **complex plane** or the **Argand diagram**.

> The Argand diagram is named after Jean-Robert Argand (1768–1822), a self-taught Swiss book-keeper who published an account of it in 1806.

ACTIVITY 2.4

(i) Copy Figure 2.3.
   For each of the four given points z, mark also the point $-z$.
   Describe the geometrical transformation which maps the point representing z to the point representing $-z$.

(ii) For each of the points z, mark the point z^*, the complex conjugate of z.
    Describe the geometrical transformation which maps the point representing z to the point representing z^*.

Representing the sum and difference of complex numbers

In Figure 2.4 the complex number $z = x + y\mathrm{i}$ is shown as a vector on an Argand diagram.

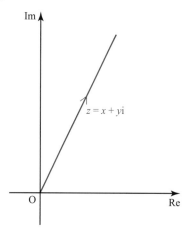

Figure 2.4

The use of vectors can be helpful in illustrating addition and subtraction of complex numbers on an Argand diagram. Figure 2.5 shows that the position vectors representing z_1 and z_2 form two sides of a parallelogram, the diagonal of which is the vector $z_1 + z_2$.

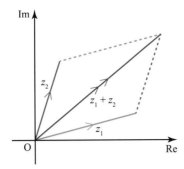

Figure 2.5

The addition can also be shown as a triangle of vectors, as in Figure 2.6.

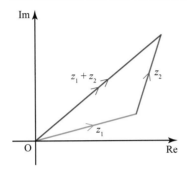

Figure 2.6

In Figure 2.7 you can see that $z_2 + w = z_1$ and so $w = z_1 - z_2$.

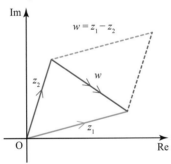

Figure 2.7

This shows that the complex number $z_1 - z_2$ is represented by the vector from the point representing z_2 to the point representing z_1, as shown in Figure 2.8.

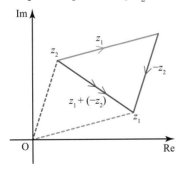

Figure 2.8

Notice the order of the points: the vector $z_1 - z_2$ starts at the point z_2 and goes to the point z_1.

Exercise 2.3

① Represent each of the following complex numbers on a single Argand diagram.
 (i) $3 + 2i$ (ii) $4i$ (iii) $-5 + i$
 (iv) -2 (v) $-6 - 5i$ (vi) $4 - 3i$

② Given that $z = 2 - 4i$, represent the following by points on a single Argand diagram.
 (i) z (ii) $-z$ (iii) z^* (iv) $-z^*$
 (v) iz (vi) $-iz$ (vii) iz^* (viii) $(iz)^*$

③ Given that $z = 10 + 5i$ and $w = 1 + 2i$, represent the following complex numbers on an Argand diagram.
 (i) z (ii) w (iii) $z + w$
 (iv) $z - w$ (v) $w - z$

④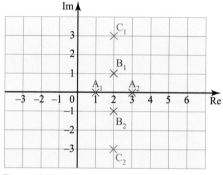

Figure 2.9

 (i) Find the quadratic equation which has roots A_1 and A_2.
 (ii) Find the quadratic equation which has roots B_1 and B_2.
 (iii) Find the quadratic equation which has roots C_1 and C_2.
 (iv) What do you notice about your answers to (i), (ii) and (iii)?

⑤ Give a geometrical proof that $(-z)^* = -(z^*)$.

⑥ Let $z = 1 + i$.
 (i) Find z^n for $n = -1, 0, 1, 2, 3, 4, 5$
 (ii) Plot each of the points z^n from part (i) on a single Argand diagram. Join each point to its predecessor and to the origin.
 (iii) Find the distance of each point from the origin.
 (iv) What do you notice?

⑦ Figure 2.10 shows the complex number $z = a + ib$. The distance of the point representing z from the origin is denoted by r.

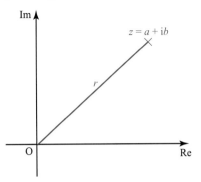

Figure 2.10

(i) Find an expression for r, and hence prove that $r^2 = zz^*$.

A second complex number, w, is given by $w = c + di$. The distance of the point representing w from the origin is denoted by s.

(ii) Write down an expression for s.

(iii) Find zw, and prove that the distance of the point representing zw from the origin is given by rs.

LEARNING OUTCOMES

When you have completed this chapter you should be able to:

➤ understand how complex numbers extend the number system
➤ solve quadratic equations with complex roots
➤ know what is meant by the terms real part, imaginary part and complex conjugate
➤ add, subtract, multiply and divide complex numbers
➤ solve problems involving complex numbers by equating real and imaginary parts
➤ represent a complex number on an Argand diagram
➤ represent addition and subtraction of two complex numbers on an Argand diagram.

FUTURE USES

■ In Chapter 5 you will look at how complex numbers can be used to describe sets of points in the Argand diagram.

KEY POINTS

1 Complex numbers are of the form $z = x + y\mathrm{i}$ with $\mathrm{i}^2 = -1$.
   x is called the real part, $\mathrm{Re}(z)$, and y is called the imaginary part, $\mathrm{Im}(z)$.
2 The conjugate of $z = x + y\mathrm{i}$ is $z^* = x - y\mathrm{i}$.
3 To add or subtract complex numbers, add or subtract the real and imaginary parts separately.
   $(x_1 + y_1\mathrm{i}) + (x_2 + y_2\mathrm{i}) = (x_1 + x_2) + (y_1 + y_2)\mathrm{i}$
4 To multiply complex numbers, expand the brackets then simplify using the fact that $\mathrm{i}^2 = -1$
5 To divide complex numbers, write as a fraction, then multiply top and bottom by the conjugate of the bottom and simplify the answer.
6 Two complex numbers $z_1 = x_1 + y_1\mathrm{i}$ and $z_2 = x_2 + y_2\mathrm{i}$ are equal only if $x_1 = x_2$ and $y_1 = y_2$.
7 The complex number $z = x + y\mathrm{i}$ can be represented geometrically as the point (x, y).

This is known as an Argand diagram.

3 Roots of polynomials

A **polynomial** is an expression like $4x^3 + x^2 - 4x - 1$. Its terms are all positive integer powers of a variable (in this case x) like x^2, or multiples of them like $4x^3$. There are no square roots, reciprocals, etc.

The **order** (or degree) of a polynomial is the highest power of the variable. So the order of $4x^3 + x^2 - 4x - 1$ is 3; this is why it is called a **cubic**.

You often need to solve polynomial equations, and it is usually helpful to think about the associated graph.

The following diagrams show the graphs of two cubic polynomial functions. The first example (in Figure 3.1) has three real roots (where the graph of the polynomial crosses the x-axis). The second example (in Figure 3.2) has only one real root. In this case there are also two **complex** roots.

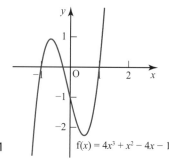

Figure 3.1 $f(x) = 4x^3 + x^2 - 4x - 1$

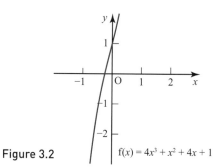

Figure 3.2 $f(x) = 4x^3 + x^2 + 4x + 1$

In general a polynomial equation of order n has n roots. However, some of these may be complex rather than real numbers and sometimes they coincide so that two or more distinct roots become one repeated root.

1 Polynomials

Discussion points

→ How would you solve the polynomial equation $4x^3 + x^2 - 4x - 1 = 0$?

→ What about $4x^3 + x^2 + 4x + 1 = 0$?

The following two statements are true for all polynomials:

■ A polynomial equation of order n has at most n real roots.

■ The graph of a polynomial function of order n has at most $n - 1$ turning points.

Here are some examples that illustrate these results.

Order 1 (a linear equation)

Example: $2x - 7 = 0$

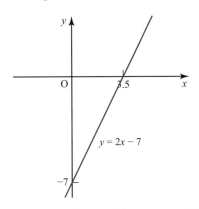

Figure 3.3 The graph is a straight line with no turning points. There is one real root at $x = 3.5$.

Order 2 (a quadratic equation)

Example: $x^2 - 4x + 4 = 0$

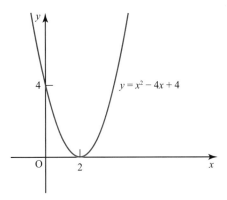

Figure 3.4 The curve has one turning point. There is one repeated root at $x = 2$.

Order 3 (a cubic equation)

Example: $x^3 - 1 = 0$

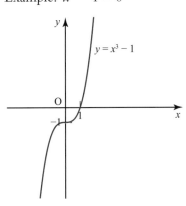

Figure 3.5 The two turning points of this curve coincide to give a point of inflection at $(0, -1)$. There is one real root at $x = 1$ and two complex roots at $x = \dfrac{-1 \pm \sqrt{3}i}{2}$.

Order 4 (a quartic equation)

Example: $x^4 - 3x^2 - 4 = 0$

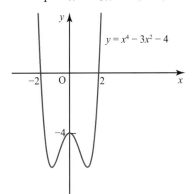

Figure 3.6 This curve has three turning points. There are two real roots at $x = -2$ and $x = 2$ and two complex roots at $x = \pm i$.

You will learn how how to find the complex roots of polynomial equations later in this chapter.

The same patterns continue for higher order polynomials.

The rest of this chapter explores some properties of polynomials, and ways to use these properties to avoid the difficulties of actually finding the roots of polynomials directly.

It is important that you recognise that the roots of polynomials may be complex. For this reason, in the work that follows, z is used as the variable (or unknown) instead of x to emphasise that the results apply regardless of whether the roots are complex or real.

Quadratic equations

TECHNOLOGY

You could use the equation solver on a calculator.

Discussion point

→ What is the connection between the sums and products of the roots, and the coefficients in the original equation?

ACTIVITY 3.1

Solve each of the following quadratic equations (by factorising or otherwise). Also write down the *sum* and *product* of the two roots.
What do you notice?

Equation	Two roots	Sum of roots	Product of roots
(i) $z^2 - 3z + 2 = 0$			
(ii) $z^2 + z - 6 = 0$			
(iii) $z^2 - 6z + 8 = 0$			
(iv) $z^2 - 3z - 10 = 0$			
(v) $2z^2 - 3z + 1 = 0$			
(vi) $z^2 - 4z + 5 = 0$			

The roots of polynomial equations are usually denoted by Greek letters such as α and β. ← α (alpha) and β (beta) are the first two letters of the Greek alphabet.

Always be careful to distinguish between:
a – the coefficient of z^2 and
α – one of the roots of the quadratic.

If you know the roots are α and β, you can write the equation

$$az^2 + bz + c = 0$$

in factorised form as

$$a(z - \alpha)(z - \beta) = 0. \quad \leftarrow \text{Assuming } a \neq 0$$

This gives the identity,

$$az^2 + bz + c \equiv a(z - \alpha)(z - \beta).$$

$$az^2 + bz + c \equiv a\left(z^2 - \alpha z - \beta z + \alpha\beta\right)$$

$$\equiv az^2 - a(\alpha + \beta)z + a\alpha\beta \quad \leftarrow \text{Multiplying out}$$

$$b = -a(\alpha + \beta) \Rightarrow \alpha + \beta = -\frac{b}{a}$$

     ← Equating coefficients of z

$$c = a\alpha\beta \Rightarrow \alpha\beta = \frac{c}{a}$$

     ← Equating constant terms

So the sum of the roots is

$$\alpha + \beta = -\frac{b}{a}$$

and the product of the roots is

$$\alpha\beta = \frac{c}{a}.$$

From these results you can obtain information about the roots without actually solving the equation.

ACTIVITY 3.2

The quadratic formula gives the roots of the quadratic equation $az^2 + bz + c = 0$ as

$$\alpha = \frac{-b + \sqrt{b^2 - 4ac}}{2a}, \quad \beta = \frac{-b - \sqrt{b^2 - 4ac}}{2a}.$$

Use these expressions to prove that $\alpha + \beta = -\dfrac{b}{a}$ and $\alpha\beta = \dfrac{c}{a}$.

Example 3.1

Find a quadratic equation with roots 5 and −3.

Solution

The sum of the roots is $5 + (-3) = 2$ $\Rightarrow -\dfrac{b}{a} = 2$

The product of the roots is $5 \times (-3) = -15$ $\Rightarrow \dfrac{c}{a} = -15$

Taking a to be 1 gives ←

$b = -2$ and $c = -15$

> You could choose any value for a but choosing 1 in this case gives the simplest form of the equation.

A quadratic equation with roots 5 and −3 is $z^2 - 2z - 15 = 0$.

Forming new equations

Using these properties of the roots sometimes allows you to form a new equation with roots that are related to the roots of the original equation. The next example illustrates this.

Example 3.2

The roots of the equation $2z^2 + 3z + 5 = 0$ are α and β.

(i) Find the values of $\alpha + \beta$ and $\alpha\beta$.

(ii) Find the quadratic equation with roots 2α and 2β.

Solution

(i) $\alpha + \beta = -\dfrac{3}{2}$ and

$\alpha\beta = \dfrac{5}{2}$

> These lines come from looking at the original quadratic, and quoting the facts $\alpha + \beta = -\dfrac{b}{a}$ and $\alpha\beta = \dfrac{c}{a}$.
> It might be confusing to introduce a, b and c here, since you need different values for them later in the question.

(ii) The sum of the new roots $= 2\alpha + 2\beta$

$$= 2(\alpha + \beta)$$

$$= 2 \times -\frac{3}{2}$$

$$= -3$$

The product of the new roots $= 2\alpha \times 2\beta$

$$= 4\alpha\beta$$

$$= 4 \times \frac{5}{2}$$

$$= 10$$

Let a, b and c be the coefficients in the new quadratic equation, then

$-\dfrac{b}{a} = -3$ and $\dfrac{c}{a} = 10$.

Taking $a = 1$ gives $b = 3$ and $c = 10$.

So a quadratic equation with the required roots is $z^2 + 3z + 10 = 0$.

Example 3.3

The roots of the equation $3z^2 - 4z - 1 = 0$ are α and β.
Find the quadratic equation with roots $\alpha + 1$ and $\beta + 1$.

Solution

$\alpha + \beta = \dfrac{4}{3}$ and

$\alpha\beta = -\dfrac{1}{3}$

The sum of the new roots $= \alpha + 1 + \beta + 1$

$$= \alpha + \beta + 2$$

$$= \frac{4}{3} + 2$$

$$= \frac{10}{3}$$

The product of the new roots $= (\alpha + 1)(\beta + 1)$

$$= \alpha\beta + (\alpha + \beta) + 1$$

$$= -\frac{1}{3} + \frac{4}{3} + 1$$

$$= 2$$

So $-\dfrac{b}{a} = \dfrac{10}{3}$ and $\dfrac{c}{a} = 2$.

> Choosing $a = 1$ would give a value for b which is not an integer. It is easier here to use $a = 3$.

Choose $a = 3$, then $b = -10$ and $c = 6$. ◄

So a quadratic equation with the required roots is $3z^2 - 10z + 6 = 0$.

ACTIVITY 3.3

Solve the quadratic equations from the previous two examples (perhaps using the equation solver on your calculator, or a computer algebra system):

(i) $2z^2 + 3z + 5 = 0 \qquad z^2 + 3z + 10 = 0$

(ii) $3z^2 - 4z - 1 = 0 \qquad 3z^2 - 10z + 6 = 0$

Verify that the relationships between the roots are correct.

Exercise 3.1

① Write down the sum and product of the roots of each of these quadratic equations.

(i) $2z^2 + 7z + 6 = 0$

(ii) $5z^2 - z - 1 = 0$

(iii) $7z^2 + 2 = 0$

(iv) $5z^2 + 24z = 0$

(v) $z(z + 8) = 4 - 3z$

(vi) $3z^2 + 8z - 6 = 0$

② Write down quadratic equations (in expanded form, with integer coefficients) with the following roots:

(i) $7, 3$

(ii) $4, -1$

(iii) $-5, -4.5$

(iv) $5, 0$

(v) 3 (repeated)

(vi) $3 - 2i, 3 + 2i$

③ The roots of $2z^2 + 5z - 9 = 0$ are α and β.
Find quadratic equations with these roots.

(i) 3α and 3β

(ii) $-\alpha$ and $-\beta$

(iii) $\alpha - 2$ and $\beta - 2$

(iv) $1 - 2\alpha$ and $1 - 2\beta$

④ Using the fact that $\alpha + \beta = -\dfrac{b}{a}$, and $\alpha\beta = \dfrac{c}{a}$, what can you say about the roots, α and β, of $az^2 + bz + c = 0$ in the following cases:

(i) a, b, c are all positive and $b^2 - 4ac > 0$

(ii) $b = 0$

(iii) $c = 0$

(iv) a and c have opposite signs

⑤ One root of $az^2 + bz + c = 0$ is twice the other. Prove that $2b^2 = 9ac$.

⑥ The roots of $az^2 + bz + c = 0$ are, α and β. Find quadratic equations with the following roots:

> You may wish to introduce different letters (say p, q and r instead of a, b and c) for the coefficients of your target equation.

　(i)　$k\alpha$ and $k\beta$

　(ii)　$k + \alpha$ and $k + \beta$

⑦ (i) A quadratic equation with *real* coefficients $ax^2 + bx + c = 0$ has complex roots z_1 and z_2. Explain how the relationships between roots and coefficients show that z_1 and z_2 must be complex conjugates.

　(ii) Find a quadratic equation with *complex* coefficients which has roots $2 + 3i$ and $3 - i$.

2 Cubic equations

There are corresponding properties for the roots of higher order polynomials.

To see how to generalise the properties you can begin with the cubics in a similar manner to the discussion of the quadratics. As before, it is conventional to use Greek letters to represent the three roots: α, β and γ (gamma, the third letter of the Greek alphabet).

You can write the general cubic as
$$az^3 + bz^2 + cz + d = 0$$
or in factorised form as
$$a(z - \alpha)(z - \beta)(z - \gamma) = 0.$$
This gives the identity
$$az^3 + bz^2 + cz + d \equiv a(z - \alpha)(z - \beta)(z - \gamma).$$

> Check this for yourself.

Multiplying out the right-hand side gives
$$az^3 + bz^2 + cz + d \equiv az^3 - a(\alpha + \beta + \gamma)z^2 + a(\alpha\beta + \beta\gamma + \gamma\alpha)z - a\alpha\beta\gamma.$$

Comparing coefficients of z^2:
$$b = -a(\alpha + \beta + \gamma) \Rightarrow \alpha + \beta + \gamma = -\frac{b}{a} \qquad \text{Sum of the roots:} \quad \sum\alpha$$

Comparing coefficients of z:
$$c = a(\alpha\beta + \beta\gamma + \gamma\alpha) \Rightarrow \alpha\beta + \beta\gamma + \gamma\alpha = \frac{c}{a} \quad \text{Sum of products of} \quad \sum\alpha\beta$$
pairs of roots:

Comparing constant terms:
$$d = -a\alpha\beta\gamma \Rightarrow \alpha\beta\gamma = -\frac{d}{a} \qquad \text{Product of the three} \quad \sum\alpha\beta\gamma$$
roots:

Note

Notation

It often becomes tedious writing out the sums of various combinations of roots, so shorthand notation is often used:

$\sum \alpha = \alpha + \beta + \gamma$ the sum of individual roots (however many there are)

$\sum \alpha\beta = \alpha\beta + \beta\gamma + \gamma\alpha$ the sum of the products of pairs of roots

$\sum \alpha\beta\gamma = \alpha\beta\gamma$ the sum of the products of triples of roots (in this case only one)

Provided you know the degree of the equation (e.g. cubic, quartic, etc,) it will be quite clear what this means. Functions like these are called symmetric functions of the roots, since exchanging any two of α, β, γ will not change the value of the function.

Using this notation you can shorten tediously long expressions. For example, for a cubic with roots α, β and γ,

$$\alpha^2\beta + \alpha\beta^2 + \beta^2\gamma + \beta\gamma^2 + \gamma^2\alpha + \gamma\alpha^2 = \sum \alpha^2\beta.$$

This becomes particularly useful when you deal with quartics in the next section.

Example 3.4

The roots of the equation $2z^3 - 9z^2 - 27z + 54 = 0$ form a geometric progression (i.e. they may be written as $\frac{a}{r}$, a, ar).

Solve the equation.

Solution

$\alpha\beta\gamma = -\dfrac{d}{a}$ $\Rightarrow \dfrac{a}{r} \times a \times ar = -\dfrac{54}{2}$

$\Rightarrow a^3 = -27$

$\Rightarrow a = -3$

$\sum \alpha = -\dfrac{b}{a}$ $\Rightarrow \dfrac{a}{r} + a + ar = \dfrac{9}{2}$

$\Rightarrow -3\left(\dfrac{1}{r} + 1 + r\right) = \dfrac{9}{2}$

$\Rightarrow 2\left(\dfrac{1}{r} + 1 + r\right) = -3$

$\Rightarrow 2 + 2r + 2r^2 = -3r$

$\Rightarrow 2r^2 + 5r + 2 = 0$

$\Rightarrow (2r + 1)(r + 2) = 0$

$\Rightarrow r = -2 \text{ or } r = -\dfrac{1}{2}$

Either value of r gives three roots: $\dfrac{3}{2}, -3, 6.$

Forming new equations: the substitution method

In the next example you are asked to form a new cubic equation with roots related to the roots of the original equation. Using the same approach as in the quadratic example is possible, but this gets increasingly complicated as the order of the equation increases. A substitution method is often a quicker alternative. The following example shows both methods for comparison.

Example 3.5

The roots of the cubic equation $2z^3 + 5z^2 - 3z - 2 = 0$ are α, β, γ.

Find the cubic equation with roots $2\alpha + 1, 2\beta + 1, 2\gamma + 1$.

Solution 1

$$\Sigma\alpha = \alpha + \beta + \gamma = -\frac{5}{2} \qquad \boxed{\Sigma\alpha = -\frac{b}{a}}$$

$$\Sigma\alpha\beta = \alpha\beta + \beta\gamma + \gamma\alpha = -\frac{3}{2} \qquad \boxed{\Sigma\alpha\beta = \frac{c}{a}}$$

$$\Sigma\alpha\beta\gamma = \alpha\beta\gamma = \frac{2}{2} = 1 \qquad \boxed{\Sigma\alpha\beta\gamma = -\frac{d}{a}}$$

For the new equation:

Sum of roots $= 2\alpha + 1 + 2\beta + 1 + 2\gamma + 1$
$$= 2(\alpha + \beta + \gamma) + 3$$
$$= -5 + 3 = -2$$

Product of the roots in pairs
$$= (2\alpha + 1)(2\beta + 1) + (2\beta + 1)(2\gamma + 1) + (2\gamma + 1)(2\alpha + 1)$$
$$= [4\alpha\beta + 2(\alpha + \beta) + 1] + [4\beta\gamma + 2(\beta + \gamma) + 1] + [4\gamma\alpha + 2(\gamma + \alpha) + 1]$$
$$= 4(\alpha\beta + \beta\gamma + \gamma\alpha) + 4(\alpha + \beta + \gamma) + 3$$
$$= 4 \times -\frac{3}{2} + 4 \times -\frac{5}{2} + 3$$
$$= -13$$

Product of roots $= (2\alpha + 1)(2\beta + 1))(2\gamma + 1)$
$$= 8\alpha\beta\gamma + 4(\alpha\beta + \beta\gamma + \gamma\alpha) + 2(\alpha + \beta + \gamma) + 1$$
$$= 8 \times 1 + 4 \times -\frac{3}{2} + 2 \times -\frac{5}{2} + 1$$
$$= -2$$

> Check this for yourself.

In the new equation, $-\frac{b}{a} = -2, \frac{c}{a} = -13, -\frac{d}{a} = -2.$

> These are all integers, so choose $a = 1$ and this gives the simplest integer coefficients.

The new equation is $z^3 + 2z^2 - 13z + 2 = 0$.

Solution 2 (substitution method)

This method involves a new variable $w = 2z + 1$. You write z in terms of w, and substitute into the original equation:

> This is a transformation of z in the same way as the new roots are a transformation of the original z roots.

$z = \dfrac{w - 1}{2}$ α, β, γ are the roots of $2z^3 + 5z^2 - 3z - 2 = 0$

$\Leftrightarrow$ $2\alpha + 1, 2\beta + 1, 2\gamma + 1$ are the roots of

$2\left(\dfrac{w - 1}{2}\right)^3 + 5\left(\dfrac{w - 1}{2}\right)^2 - 3\left(\dfrac{w - 1}{2}\right) - 2 = 0$

$\Leftrightarrow \dfrac{2}{8}(w - 1)^3 + \dfrac{5}{4}(w - 1)^2 - \dfrac{3}{2}(w - 1) - 2 = 0$

$\Leftrightarrow (w - 1)^3 + 5(w - 1)^2 - 6(w - 1) - 8 = 0$

$\Leftrightarrow w^3 - 3w^2 + 3w - 1 + 5w^2 - 10w + 5 - 6w + 6 - 8 = 0$

$\Leftrightarrow w^3 + 2w^2 - 13w + 2 = 0$

The substitution method can sometimes be much more efficient, although you need to take care with the expansion of the cubic brackets.

Exercise 3.2

① The roots of the cubic equation $2z^3 + 3z^2 - z + 7 = 0$ are α, β, γ. Find the following:

(i) $\sum \alpha$ (ii) $\sum \alpha\beta$

(iii) $\sum \alpha\beta\gamma$

② Find cubic equations (with integer coefficients) with the following roots:

(i) $1, 2, 4$ (ii) $2, -2, 3$
(iii) $0, -2, -1.5$ (iv) 2 (repeated), 2.5
(v) $-2, -3, 5$ (vi) $1, 2 + i, 2 - i$

③ The roots of each of these equations are in arithmetic progression (i.e. they may be written as $a - d$, a, $a + d$).
Solve each equation.

(i) $z^3 - 15z^2 + 66z - 80 = 0$ (ii) $9z^3 - 18z^2 - 4z + 8 = 0$

(iii) $z^3 - 6z^2 + 16 = 0$ (iv) $54z^3 - 189z^2 + 207z - 70 = 0$

④ The roots of the equation $z^3 + z^2 + 2z - 3 = 0$ are α, β, γ.

(i)   The substitution $w = z + 3$ is made. Write z in terms of w.

(ii)   Substitute your answer to part (i) for z in the equation $z^3 + z^2 + 2z - 3 = 0$

(iii)   Give your answer to part (ii) as a cubic equation in w with integer coefficients.

(iv)   Write down the roots of your equation in part (iii), in terms of α, β and γ.

⑤ The roots of the equation $z^3 - 2z^2 + z - 3 = 0$ are α, β, γ. Use the substitution $w = 2z$ to find a cubic equation in w with roots $2\alpha, 2\beta, 2\gamma$.

⑥ The roots of the equation $2z^3 + 4z^2 - 3z + 1 = 0$ are α, β, γ. Find cubic equations with these roots:

(i) $2 - \alpha, 2 - \beta, 2 - \gamma$ (ii) $3\alpha - 2, 3\beta - 2, 3\gamma - 2$

⑦ The roots of the equation $2z^3 - 12z^2 + kz - 15 = 0$ are in arithmetic progression.

Solve the equation and find k.

⑧ Solve $32z^3 - 14z + 3 = 0$ given that one root is twice another.

⑨ The equation $z^3 + pz^2 + 2pz + q = 0$ has roots $\alpha, 2\alpha, 4\alpha$.
Find all possible values of p, q, α.

⑩ The roots of $z^3 + pz^2 + qz + r = 0$ are $\alpha, -\alpha, \beta$, and $r \neq 0$.
Show that $r = pq$, and find all three roots in terms of p and q.

⑪ The cubic equation $8x^3 + px^2 + qx + r = 0$ has roots α and $\dfrac{1}{2\alpha}$ and β.

(i) Express p, q and r in terms of α and β.

(ii) Show that $2r^2 - pr + 4q = 16$.

(iii) Given that $p = 6$ and $q = -23$, find the two possible values of r and, in each case, solve the equation $8x^3 + 6x^2 - 23x + r = 0$.

⑫ Show that one root of $az^3 + bz^2 + cz + d = 0$ is the reciprocal of another root if and only if $a^2 - d^2 = ac - bd$.
Verify that this condition is satisfied for the equation
$21z^3 - 16z^2 - 95z + 42 = 0$ and hence solve the equation.

⑬ Find a formula connecting a, b, c and d which is a necessary and sufficient condition for the roots of the equation $az^3 + bz^2 + cz + d = 0$ to be in geometric progression.
Show that this condition is satisfied for the equation
$8z^3 - 52z^2 + 78z - 27 = 0$ and hence solve the equation.

3 Quartic equations

Quartic equations have four roots, denoted by the first four Greek letters: α, β, γ and δ (delta).

Discussion point

➜ By looking back at the two formulae for quadratics and the three formulae for cubics, predict the *four* formulae that relate the roots α, β, γ and δ to the coefficients a, b, c and d of the quartic equation $ax^4 + bx^3 + cx^2 + dx + e = 0$.

You may wish to check/derive these results yourself before looking at the derivation on the next page.

 Historical note

The formulae used to relate the coefficients of polynomials with sums and products of their roots are called Vieta's Formulae after François Viète (a Frenchman who commonly used a Latin version of his name: Franciscus Vieta). He was a lawyer by trade but made important progress (while doing mathematics in his spare time) on algebraic notation and helped pave the way for the more logical system of notation you use today.

Derivation of formulae

As before, the quartic equation

$$az^4 + bz^3 + cz^2 + dz + e = 0$$

can be written is factorised form as

$$a(z - \alpha)(z - \beta)(z - \gamma)(z - \delta) = 0.$$

This gives the identity

$$az^4 + bz^3 + cz^2 + dz + e \equiv a(z - \alpha)(z - \beta)(z - \gamma)(z - \delta).$$

Multiplying out the right-hand side gives

$$az^4 + bz^3 + cz^2 + dz + e \equiv az^4 - a(\alpha + \beta + \gamma + \delta)z^3$$
$$+ a(\alpha\beta + \alpha\gamma + \alpha\delta + \beta\gamma + \beta\delta + \gamma\alpha)z^2 - a(\alpha\beta\gamma + \beta\gamma\delta$$
$$+ \gamma\delta\alpha + \delta\alpha\beta)z + a\alpha\beta\gamma\delta.$$

Equating coefficients shows that

$$\sum \alpha = \alpha + \beta + \gamma + \delta = -\frac{b}{a}$$

The sum of the individual roots.

Check this for yourself.

$$\sum \alpha\beta = \alpha\beta + \alpha\gamma + \alpha\delta + \beta\gamma + \beta\delta + \gamma\delta = \frac{c}{a}$$

The sum of the products of roots in pairs.

$$\sum \alpha\beta\gamma = \alpha\beta\gamma + \beta\gamma\delta + \gamma\delta\alpha + \delta\alpha\beta = -\frac{d}{a}$$

The sum of the products of roots in threes.

$$\alpha\beta\gamma\delta = \frac{e}{a}$$

The product of the roots.

Example 3.6

The roots of the quartic equation $4z^4 + pz^3 + qz^2 - z + 3 = 0$ are $\alpha, -\alpha, \alpha + \lambda, \alpha - \lambda$ where α and λ are real numbers.

(i)   Express p and q in terms of α and λ.

(ii) Show that $\alpha = -\frac{1}{2}$, and find the values of p and q.

(iii) Give the roots of the quartic equation.

Solution

(i) $\sum \alpha = \alpha - \alpha + \alpha + \lambda + \alpha - \lambda = -\frac{p}{4}$

$$\Rightarrow 2\alpha = -\frac{p}{4}$$
$$\Rightarrow p = -8\alpha$$

Use the sum of the individual roots to find an expression for p.

$$\sum \alpha\beta = -\alpha^2 + \alpha(\alpha + \lambda) + \alpha(\alpha - \lambda) - \alpha(\alpha + \lambda) - \alpha(\alpha - \lambda)$$
$$+ (\alpha + \lambda)(\alpha - \lambda) = \frac{q}{4}$$

$$\Rightarrow -\lambda^2 = \frac{q}{4}$$
$$\Rightarrow q = -4\lambda^2$$

Use the sum of the product of the roots in pairs to find an expression for q.

(ii)
$$\sum \alpha\beta\gamma = -\alpha^2(\alpha + \lambda) - \alpha(\alpha + \lambda)(\alpha - \lambda) + \alpha(\alpha + \lambda)(\alpha - \lambda) - \alpha^2(\alpha - \lambda) = \frac{1}{4}$$

$$\Rightarrow -2\alpha^3 = \frac{1}{4}$$

$$\Rightarrow \alpha = -\frac{1}{2}$$

$$p = -8\alpha = -8 \times -\frac{1}{2} = 4$$

> Use the sum of the product of the roots in threes to find α (λ cancels out) and hence find p, using your answer to part (i).

$$\alpha\beta\gamma\delta = -\alpha^2(\alpha + \lambda)(\alpha - \lambda) = \frac{3}{4}$$

$$\Rightarrow -\alpha^2(\alpha^2 - \lambda^2) = \frac{3}{4}$$

$$\Rightarrow -\frac{1}{4}\left(\frac{1}{4} - \lambda^2\right) = \frac{3}{4}$$

$$\Rightarrow \frac{1}{4} - \lambda^2 = -3$$

$$\Rightarrow \lambda^2 = \frac{13}{4}$$

$$q = -4\lambda^2 = -4 \times \frac{13}{4} = -13$$

> Use the sum of the product of the roots and the value for α to find λ, and hence find q, using your answer to part (i).

> Substitute the values for α and λ to give the roots.

(iii) The roots of the equation are $\frac{1}{2}, -\frac{1}{2}, -\frac{1}{2} + \frac{1}{2}\sqrt{13}, -\frac{1}{2} - \frac{1}{2}\sqrt{13}$.

Exercise 3.3

① The roots of $2z^4 + 3z^3 + 6z^2 - 5z + 4 = 0$ are α, β, γ and δ.

Write down the following:

(i) $\sum \alpha$

(ii) $\sum \alpha\beta$

(iii) $\sum \alpha\beta\gamma$

(iv) $\sum \alpha\beta\gamma\delta$

② Find quartic equations (with integer coefficients) with the roots.

(i) $1, -1, 2, 4$

(ii) $0, 1.5, -2.5, -4$

(iii) 1.5 (repeated), -3 (repeated)

(iv) $1, -3, 1 + i, 1 - i$.

③ The roots of the quartic equation $2z^4 + 4z^3 - 3z^2 - z + 6 = 0$ are α, β, γ and δ.

Find quartic equations with these roots:

(i) $2\alpha, 2\beta, 2\gamma, 2\delta$

(ii) $\alpha - 1, \beta - 1, \gamma - 1, \delta - 1$.

④ The roots of the quartic equation $x^4 + 4x^3 - 8x + 4 = 0$ are α, β, γ and δ.

(i) By making a suitable substitution, find a quartic equation with roots $\alpha + 1, \ \beta + 1, \ \gamma + 1$ and $\delta + 1$.

(ii) Solve the equation found in part (i), and hence find the values of α, β, γ and δ.

⑤ The quartic equation $x^4 + px^3 - 12x + q = 0$, where p and q are real, has roots $\alpha, 3\alpha, \beta, -\beta$.

(i) By considering the coefficients of x^2 and x, find α and β, where $\beta > 0$.

(ii) Show that $p = 4$ and find the value of q.

(iii) By making the substitution $y = x - k$, for a suitable value of k, find a **cubic** equation in y, with integer coefficients, which has roots

$$-2\alpha, \beta - 3\alpha, -\beta - 3\alpha.$$

⑥ (i) Make conjectures about the five properties of the roots $\alpha, \beta, \gamma, \delta$ and ε (epsilon) of the general quintic $ax^5 + bx^4 + cx^3 + dx^2 + ex + f = 0$.

(ii) Prove your conjectures.

> **Note**
>
> For question 6, you should try the algebra by hand, thinking about keeping good presentation habits for long algebraic expansions. You may want to check any long expansions using CAS (computer algebra software). You then might also like to consider whether a 'proof' is still valid if it relies on a computer system to prove it – look up the history of *The Four Colour Theorem* to explore this idea further.

Prior Knowledge

You need to know how to use the factor theorem to solve polynomial equations, covered in MEI A Level Mathematics Year 1 (AS), Chapter 7.

4 Solving polynomial equations with complex roots

When solving polynomial equations with real coefficients, it is important to remember that any complex roots occur in conjugate pairs.

When there is a possibility of complex roots, it is common to express the polynomial in terms of z.

Example 3.7

The equation $z^3 + 7z^2 + 17z + 15 = 0$ has one integer root.

(i) Factorise $f(z) = z^3 + 7z^2 + 17z + 15$.

(ii) Solve $z^3 + 7z^2 + 17z + 15 = 0$.

(iii) Sketch the graph of $y = x^3 + 7x^2 + 17x + 15$.

Solution

(i) $f(1) = 1^3 + 7 \times 1^2 + 17 \times 1 + 15 = 40$ ←

> If there is an integer root, it must be a factor of 15. So try $z = \pm 1, \pm 3$, etc.

$f(-1) = (-1)^3 + 7 \times (-1)^2 + 17 \times (-1) + 15 = 4$

$f(3) = 3^3 + 7 \times 3^2 + 17 \times 3 + 15 = 156$

$f(-3) = (-3)^3 + 7 \times (-3)^2 + 17 \times (-3) + 15 = 0$ ←

> $f(-3) = 0$ so using the factor theorem, $(z + 3)$ is a factor.

So one root is $z = -3$, and $(z + 3)$ is a factor of $f(z)$.

Using algebraic division or by inspection, $f(z)$ can be written in the form:

$$f(z) = (z + 3)(z^2 + 4z + 5) \longleftarrow \boxed{\text{Check this for yourself}}$$

Now solve the quadratic equation $z^2 + 4z + 5 = 0$:

> using the quadratic formula.

$$z = \frac{-4 \pm \sqrt{4^2 - (4 \times 1 \times 5)}}{2} = \frac{-4 \pm \sqrt{-4}}{2} = \frac{-4 \pm 2i}{2} = -2 \pm i$$

So, fully factorised $f(z) = (z + 3)(z - (-2 + i))(z - (-2 - i))$

(ii) The roots are $z = -3$, $z = -2 \pm i$ $\longleftarrow$

> Note that there is one conjugate pair of complex roots and one real root.

(iii) Figure 3.7 shows the graph of the curve $y = f(x)$.

> You can see that the graph crosses the x-axis just once.

Figure 3.7

Sometimes you can use the relationships between roots and coefficients of polynomial equations to help you to find the roots. In Example 3.8, two solution methods are shown.

Example 3.8

Given that $z = 1 + 2i$ is a root of $4z^3 - 11z^2 + 26z - 15 = 0$, find the other roots.

Solution 1

As complex roots occur in conjugate pairs, the conjugate $z = 1 - 2i$ is also a root.

The next step is to find a quadratic equation $az^2 + bz + c = 0$ with roots $1 + 2i$ and $1 - 2i$.

$$-\frac{b}{a} = (1 + 2i) + (1 - 2i) = 2$$

$$\frac{c}{a} = (1 + 2i)(1 - 2i) = 1 + 4 = 5$$

Taking $a = 1$ gives $b = -2$ and $c = 5$

So the quadratic equation is $z^2 - 2z + 5 = 0$

$$4z^3 - 11z^2 + 26z - 15 = (z^2 - 2z + 5)(4z - 3)$$

The other roots are $z = 1 - 2i$ and $z = \frac{3}{4}$.

Solution 2

As complex roots occur in conjugate pairs, the conjugate $z = 1 - 2i$ is also a root.

The sum of the three roots is $\dfrac{11}{4}$ ← $\boxed{\alpha + \beta + \gamma = -\dfrac{b}{a}}$

$1 + 2i + 1 - 2i + \gamma = \dfrac{11}{4}$

$\gamma = \dfrac{11}{4} - 2 = \dfrac{3}{4}$

The other roots are $z = 1 - 2i$ and $z = \dfrac{3}{4}$.

Notice that Solution 2 is more efficient than Solution 1 in this case. You should look out for situations like this where using the relationships between roots and coefficients can be helpful.

Example 3.9

(i)   Solve $z^4 - 3z^2 - 4 = 0$.

(ii) Sketch the curve $y = x^4 - 3x^2 - 4$.

(iii) Show the roots of $z^4 - 3z^2 - 4 = 0$ on an Argand diagram.

Solution

(i) $z^4 - 3z^2 - 4 = 0$
    $(z^2 - 4)(z^2 + 1) = 0$ ← $\boxed{z^4 - 3z^2 - 4 \text{ is a quadratic in } z^2 \text{ and can be factorised.}}$
    $(z - 2)(z + 2)(z + i)(z - i) = 0$

The solution is $z = 2, -2, i, -i$.

(ii)

Figure 3.8

(iii)

Figure 3.9

Exercise 3.4

① 4 − 5i is one root of a quadratic equation with real coefficients.
   Write down the second root of the equation and hence find the equation.

② Verify that $2 + i$ is a root of $z^3 - z^2 - 7z + 15 = 0$, and find the other roots.

③ One root of $z^3 - 15z^2 + 76z - 140 = 0$ is an integer.
   Solve the equation and show all three roots on an Argand diagram.

④ The equation $z^3 - 2z^2 - 6z + 27 = 0$ has a real integer root in the range $-6 \le z \le 0$.
   (i)   Find the real root of the equation.
   (ii) Hence solve the equation and find the exact value of all three roots.

⑤ Given that 4 is a root of the equation $z^3 - z^2 - 3z - k = 0$, find the value of k and hence find the exact value of the other two roots of the equation.

⑥ Given that $1 - i$ is a root of $z^3 + pz^2 + qz + 12 = 0$, find the real numbers p and q, and state the other roots.

⑦ The three roots of a cubic equation are shown on the Argand diagram in Figure 3.10.

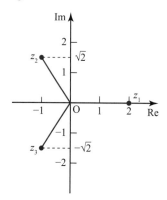

Figure 3.10

Find the equation in polynomial form.

⑧ One root of $z^4 - 10z^3 + 42z^2 - 82z + 65 = 0$ is $3 + 2i$.

Solve the equation and show the four roots on an Argand diagram.

⑨ You are given the complex number $w = 1 - i$.

(i) Express w^2, w^3 and w^4 in the form $a + bi$.

(ii) Given that $w^4 + 3w^3 + pw^2 + qw + 8 = 0$, where p and q are real numbers, find the values of p and q.

(iii) Hence find all four roots of the equation $z^4 + 3z^3 + pz^2 + qz + 8 = 0$, where p and q are the real numbers found in part (ii).

⑩ (i) Solve the equation $z^4 - 81 = 0$

(ii) Hence show the four fourth roots of 81 on an Argand diagram.

⑪ (i) Given that $\alpha = -1 + 2i$, express α^2 and α^3 in the form $a + bi$.

Hence show that α is a root of the cubic equation
$z^3 + 7z^2 + 15z + 25 = 0$

(ii) Find the other two roots of this cubic equation.

(iii) Illustrate the three roots of the cubic equation on an Argand diagram.

⑫ For each of these statements about polynomial equations with real coefficients, say whether the statement is TRUE or FALSE, and give an explanation.

(A) A cubic equation can have three complex roots.

(B) Some equations of order 6 have no real roots.

(C) A cubic equation can have a single root repeated three times.

(D) A quartic equation can have a repeated complex root.

⑬ Given that z = −2 + i is a root of the equation
$z^4 + az^3 + bz^2 + 10z + 25 = 0$, find the values of a and b, and solve the
equation.

⑭ The equation $z^4 - 8z^3 + 20z^2 - 72z + 99 = 0$ has a purely imaginary
root.

Solve the equation.

⑮ In this question, α is the complex number −1 + 3i.

(i) Find α^2 and α^3.

It is given that λ and μ are real numbers such that

$\lambda\alpha^3 + 8\alpha^2 + 34\alpha + \mu = 0$

(ii) Show that $\lambda = 3$, and find the value of μ.

(iii) Solve the equation $\lambda z^3 + 8z^2 + 34z + \mu = 0$, where λ and μ are as in
part (ii).

(iv) Illustrate the three roots on an Argand diagram.

⑯ Three of the roots of the quintic equation $z^5 + bz^4 + cz^3 + dz^2 + ez + f = 0$
are 3, −4i and 3 − i.

Find the values of the coefficients of the equation.

LEARNING OUTCOMES

When you have completed this chapter you should be able to:

➤ know the relationships between the roots and coefficients of quadratic, cubic
and quartic equations

➤ form new equations whose roots are related to the roots of a given equation
by a linear transformation

➤ understand that complex roots of polynomial equations with real coefficients
occur in conjugate pairs

➤ solve cubic and quartic equations with complex roots.

KEY POINTS

1 If α and β are the roots of the quadratic equation $az^2 + bz + c = 0$, then

$\alpha + \beta = -\dfrac{b}{a}$ and $\alpha\beta = \dfrac{c}{a}$.

2 If α, β and γ are the roots of the cubic equation $az^3 + bz^2 + cz + d = 0$, then

$\sum \alpha = \alpha + \beta + \gamma = -\dfrac{b}{a}$,

$\sum \alpha\beta = \alpha\beta + \beta\gamma + \gamma\alpha = \dfrac{c}{a}$ and,

$\alpha\beta\gamma = -\dfrac{d}{a}$.

3 If α, β, γ and δ are the roots of the quartic equation
$az^4 + bz^3 + cz^2 + dz + e = 0$, then

$$\Sigma \alpha = \alpha + \beta + \gamma + \delta = -\frac{b}{a},$$

$$\Sigma \alpha\beta = \alpha\beta + \alpha\gamma + \alpha\delta + \beta\gamma + \beta\delta + \gamma\delta = \frac{c}{a},$$

$$\Sigma \alpha\beta\gamma = \alpha\beta\gamma + \beta\gamma\delta + \gamma\delta\alpha + \delta\alpha\beta = -\frac{d}{a} \text{ and}$$

$$\alpha\beta\gamma\delta = \frac{e}{a}.$$

4 All of these formulae may be summarised using the shorthand sigma notation for elementary symmetric functions as follows:

$$\Sigma \alpha = -\frac{b}{a}$$

$$\Sigma \alpha\beta = \frac{c}{a}$$

$$\Sigma \alpha\beta\gamma = -\frac{d}{a}$$

$$\Sigma \alpha\beta\gamma\delta = \frac{e}{a}$$

(using the convention that polynomials of degree n are labelled

$az^n + bz^{n-1} + \ldots = 0$ and have roots α, β, γ)

5 A polynomial equation of degree n has n roots, taking into account complex roots and repeated roots. In the case of polynomial equations with real coefficients, complex roots always occur in conjugate pairs.

4 Sequences and series

Great things are not done by impulse, but by a series of small things brought together.

Vincent Van Gogh, 1882

Figure 4.1

Discussion point

➔ How would you describe the sequence of pictures of the moon shown in Figure 4.1?

Discussion point

→ How would you describe this sequence?

1 Sequences and series

A **sequence** is an ordered set of objects with an underlying rule.

For example:

2, 5, 8, 11, 14

A **series** is the sum of the terms of a numerical sequence:

2 + 5 + 8 + 11 + 14

Notation

There are a number of different notations which are commonly used in writing down sequences and series:

■ The terms of a sequence are often written as $a_1, a_2, a_3, \ldots$ or $u_1, u_2, u_3, \ldots$

■ The general term of a sequence may be written as a_r or u_r. (Sometimes the letters k or i are used instead of r.)

■ The last term is usually written as a_n or u_n.

■ The sum S_n of the first n terms of a sequence can be written using the symbol Σ (the Greek capital S, sigma).

$$S_n = a_1 + a_2 + a_3 + \ldots + a_n = \sum_{r=1}^{n} a_r$$

The numbers above and below the Σ are the limits of the sum. They show that the sum includes all the a_r from a_1 to a_n. The limits may be omitted if they are obvious, so that you would just write Σa_r or you might write $\sum_r a_r$ (meaning the sum of a_r for all values of r).

When discussing sequences you may find the following vocabulary helpful:

■ In an **increasing sequence**, each term is greater than the previous term.

■ In a **decreasing sequence**, each term is smaller than the previous term.

■ In an **oscillating sequence**, the terms lie above and below a middle number.

■ The terms of a **convergent sequence** get closer and closer to a limiting value.

Defining sequences

One way to define a sequence is by thinking about the relationship between one term and the next.

The sequence 2, 5, 8, 11, 14, ... can be written as

$u_1 = 2$ ← | You need to say where the sequence starts.

$u_{r+1} = u_r + 3$ ← | You find each term by adding 3 to the previous term.

This is called an **inductive** definition or **term-to-term** definition.

An alternative way to define a sequence is to describe the relationship between the term and its position.

In this case,

$$u_r = 3r - 1.$$

You can see that, for example, substituting $r = 2$ into this definition gives $u_2 = (3 \times 2) - 1 = 5$, which is the second term of the sequence.

This is called a **deductive** definition or **position-to-term** definition.

The series of positive integers

One of the simplest of all sequences is the sequence of the integers:

$$1, 2, 3, 4, 5, 6, \ldots$$

As simple as it is, it may not be immediately obvious how to calculate the sum of the first few integers, for example the sum of the first 100 integers.

$$\sum_{r=1}^{100} r = 1 + 2 + \ldots + 100$$

One way of reaching a total is illustrated below.

$$S_{100} = 1 + 2 + 3 + \ldots + 98 + 99 + 100 \longleftarrow \boxed{\text{Call the sum } S_{100}}$$

Rewrite S_{100} in reverse:

$$S_{100} = 100 + 99 + 98 + \ldots + 3 + 2 + 1$$

Adding these two lines together, by matching up each term with the one below it, produces pairings of 101 each time, while giving you $2S_{100}$ on the left-hand side.

$$
\begin{array}{rcllllllll}
S_{100} & = & 1 & + & 2 & + & 3 & + \ldots + & 98 & + 99 & + 100 \\
S_{100} & = & 100 & + & 99 & + & 98 & + \ldots + & 3 & + 2 & + 1 \\
\hline
2S_{100} & = & 101 & + & 101 & + & 101 & + \ldots + & 101 & + 101 & + 101
\end{array}
$$

There are 100 terms on the right-hand side (since you were originally adding 100 terms together), so simplify the right-hand side:

$$2S_{100} = 100 \times 101$$

and solve for S_{100}:

$$2S_{100} = 10\,100$$

$$S_{100} = 5050$$

The sum of the first 100 integers is 5050.

You can use this method to find a general result for the sum of the first n integers (call this S_n).

$$S_n = 1 + 2 + 3 + \ldots + (n - 2) + (n - 1) + n$$

$$S_n = n + (n - 1) + (n - 2) + \ldots + 3 + 2 + 1$$

$$2S_n = (n + 1) + (n + 1) + (n + 1) + \ldots + (n + 1) + (n + 1) + (n + 1)$$

$$2S_n = n(n + 1)$$

$$S_n = \frac{1}{2}n(n + 1).$$

This result is an important one and you will often need to use it.

TECHNOLOGY

You could use a spreadsheet to verify this result for different values of n.

> ### Note
>
> A common confusion occurs with the sigma notation when there is no r term present.
>
> For example,
>
> $$\sum_{r=1}^{5} 3 \longleftarrow \boxed{\text{This means 'The sum of 3, with } r \text{ changing from 1 to 5'.}}$$
>
> means
>
> $$3 + 3 + 3 + 3 + 3 = 15$$
>
> since there are five terms in the sum (it's just that there is no r term to change anything each time).
>
> In general:
>
> $$\sum_{r=1}^{n} 1 = 1 + 1 + \dots + 1 + 1$$
>
> with n repetitions of the number 1.
>
> So,
>
> $$\sum_{r=1}^{n} 1 = n$$
>
> This apparently obvious result is important and you will often need to use it.

You can use the results $\displaystyle\sum_{r=1}^{n} r = \frac{1}{2}n(n+1)$ and $\displaystyle\sum_{r=1}^{n} 1 = n$ to find the sum of other series.

Example 4.1

For the series $2 + 5 + 8 + \dots + 500$:

(i)   Find a formula for the rth term, u_r.

(ii)   How many terms are in this series?

(iii) Find the sum of the series using the reverse/add method.

(iv)   Express the sum using sigma notation, and use this to confirm your answer to part (iii).

Solution

(i)   The terms increase by 3 each time and start at 2. So $u_r = 3r - 1$.

(ii)   Let the number of terms be n. The last term (the nth term) is 500.

$$u_n = 3n - 1$$
$$3n - 1 = 500$$
$$3n = 501$$
$$n = 167$$

There are 167 terms in this series.

(iii) $S = 2 + 5 + \dots + 497 + 500$

$S = 500 + 497 + \dots + 5 + 2$

$2S = 167 \times 502$

$S = 41\,917$

(iv) $S = \sum\limits_{r=1}^{167}(3r - 1)$

$S = \sum\limits_{r=1}^{167}3r - \sum\limits_{r=1}^{167}1$

$S = 3\sum\limits_{r=1}^{167}r - \sum\limits_{r=1}^{167}1$

$S = 3 \times \dfrac{1}{2} \times 167 \times 168 - 167$ ← Using the results $\sum\limits_{r=1}^{n}r = \dfrac{1}{2}n(n + 1)$

and $\sum\limits_{r=1}^{n}1 = n$

$S = 41917$

Example 4.2

Calculate the sum of the integers from 100 to 200 inclusive.

Solution

$\sum\limits_{r=100}^{200}r = \sum\limits_{1}^{200}r - \sum\limits_{1}^{99}r$ ← Start with all the integers from 1 to 200, and subtract the integers from 1 to 99, leaving those from 100 to 200.

$= \dfrac{1}{2} \times 200 \times 201 - \dfrac{1}{2} \times 99 \times 100$

$= 20\,100 - 4950$

$= 15\,150$

Exercise 4.1

① For each of the following definitions, write down the first five terms of the sequence and describe the sequence.

   (i) $u_r = 5r + 1$

   (ii) $v_r = 3 - 6r$

   (iii) $p_r = 2^{r+2}$

   (iv) $q_r = 10 + 2 \times (-1)^r$

   (v) $a_{r+1} = 2a_r + 1, \quad a_1 = 2$

   (vi) $u_r = \dfrac{5}{r}$

② For the sequence $1, 5, 9, 13, 17, \ldots$

   (i)   write down the next four terms of the sequence

   (ii) write down an inductive rule for the sequence, in the form
       $u_1 = \ldots, u_{r+1} = \ldots$

   (iii) write down a deductive rule for the general term of the sequence, in the form $u_r = \ldots$

③ For each of the following sequences.

   (a) write down the next four terms of the sequence

   (b) write down an inductive rule for the sequence

   (c) write down a deductive rule for the general term of the sequence

   (d) find the 20th term of the sequence.

(i) $10, 8, 6, 4, 2, \ldots$

(ii) $1, 2, 4, 8, 16, \ldots$

(iii) $50, 250, 1250, 6250, \ldots$

④ Find the sum of the series $\displaystyle\sum_{1}^{5} u_r$ for each of the following:

(i) $u_r = 2 + r$

(ii) $u_r = 3 - 11r$

(iii) $u_r = 3^r$

(iv) $u_r = 7.5 \times (-1)^r$

⑤ For $S = 50 + 44 + 38 + 32 + \ldots + 14$

(i)   Express S in the form $\displaystyle\sum_{r=1}^{n} u_r$

where n is an integer, and u_r is an algebraic expression for the rth term of the series.

(ii)   Hence, or otherwise, calculate the value of S.

⑥ Given $u_r = 6r + 2$, calculate $\displaystyle\sum_{r=11}^{30} u_r$.

⑦ The general term of a sequence is given by $u_r = (-1)^r \times 5$.

(i)   Write down the first six terms of the sequence and describe it.

(ii)   Find the sum of the series $\displaystyle\sum_{r=1}^{n} u_r$:

(a) when n is even

(b) when n is odd.

(iii)   Find an algebraic expression for the sum to n terms, whatever the value of n.

⑧ A sequence is given by

$b_{r+2} = b_r + 2,\ b_1 = 0,\ b_2 = 100$

(i)   Write down the first six terms of the sequence and describe it.

(ii)   Find the smallest odd value of r for which $b_r \geq 200$.

(iii)   Find the largest even value of r for which $b_r \leq 200$.

⑨ A sawmill receives an order requesting many logs of various specific lengths, that must come from the same particular tree. The log lengths must start at 5 cm long and increase by 2 cm each time, up to a length of 53 cm.

The saw blade destroys 1 cm (in length) of wood (turning it to sawdust) at every cut. What is the minimum height of tree required to fulfil this order?

⑩ Find the sum of the integers from n to its square (inclusive). Express your answer in a fully factorised form.

⑪ Write down the first five terms of the following sequence:

$$c_{r+1} = \begin{cases} 3c_r + 1 & \text{if } c_r \text{ is odd} \\ \dfrac{c_r}{2} & \text{if } c_r \text{ is even} \end{cases} \qquad c_1 = 10$$

You can find out more about this sequence by a web search for the Collatz conjecture.

Try some other starting values (e.g. $c_1 = 6$ or 13) and make a conjecture about the behaviour of this sequence for any starting value.

2 Using standard results

In the previous section you used two important results:

$$\sum_{r=1}^{n} 1 = n$$

$$\sum_{r=1}^{n} r = \frac{1}{2}n(n+1)$$ ← [The sum of the integers.]

There are similar results for the sum of the first n squares, and the first n cubes.

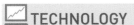
TECHNOLOGY

You could use a spreadsheet to verify these results for different values of n.

The sum of the squares: $$\sum_{r=1}^{n} r^2 = \frac{1}{6}n(n+1)(2n+1)$$

The sum of the cubes: $$\sum_{r=1}^{n} r^3 = \frac{1}{4}n^2(n+1)^2$$

These are important results. You will prove they are true later in the chapter.

These results can be used to sum other series, as shown in the following examples.

| **Example 4.3** | (i)   Write out the first three terms of the sequence $u_r = r^2 + 2r - 1$. |

(ii)   Find $\displaystyle\sum_{r=1}^{n} u_r$.

(iii)   Use your answers from part (i) to check that your answer to part (ii) works for $n = 3$.

> **Solution**
> (i) $2, 7, 14$
>
> (ii)
> $$\sum_{r=1}^{n} u_r = \sum_{r=1}^{n} (r^2 + 2r - 1)$$
>
> $$= \sum_{r=1}^{n} r^2 + 2\sum_{r=1}^{n} r - \sum_{r=1}^{n} 1$$
>
> $$= \frac{1}{6}n(n+1)(2n+1) + 2 \times \frac{1}{2}n(n+1) - n$$
>
> $$= \frac{1}{6}n\big[(n+1)(2n+1) + 6(n+1) - 6\big]$$
>
> $$= \frac{1}{6}n\big(2n^2 + 3n + 1 + 6n + 6 - 6\big)$$
>
> $$= \frac{1}{6}n\big(2n^2 + 9n + 1\big)$$

(iii) $n = 3$

$$\frac{1}{6}n\left(2n^2 + 9n + 1\right) = \frac{1}{6} \times 3 \times (18 + 27 + 1)$$

$$= \frac{1}{2} \times 46$$

$$= 23$$

$$2 + 7 + 14 = 23$$

> It is a good idea to check your results like this, if you can.

Example 4.4

(i)   Write the sum of this series using Σ notation.

$$(1 \times 3) + (2 \times 4) + (3 \times 5) + \ldots + n\left(n + 2\right)$$

(ii)   Hence find an expression for the sum in terms of n.

Solution

(i) $\displaystyle\sum_{r=1}^{n} r(r + 2)$

(ii)
$$\sum_{r=1}^{n} r(r + 2) = \sum_{r=1}^{n} (r^2 + 2r)$$

$$= \sum_{r=1}^{n} r^2 + 2\sum_{r=1}^{n} r$$

$$= \frac{1}{6}n(n + 1)(2n + 1) + 2 \times \frac{1}{2}n(n + 1)$$

$$= \frac{1}{6}n(n + 1)[2n + 1 + 6]$$

$$= \frac{1}{6}n(n + 1)(2n + 7)$$

Exercise 4.2

① (i)   Write out the first three terms of the sequence $u_r = 2r - 1$.

   (ii)   Find an expression for $\displaystyle\sum_{r=1}^{n}(2r - 1)$.

   (iii)   Use part (i) to check part (ii).

② (i)   Write out the first three terms of the sequence $u_r = r(3r + 1)$.

   (ii)   Find an expression for $\displaystyle\sum_{r=1}^{n} r(3r + 1)$.

   (iii)   Use part (i) to check part (ii).

③ (i)   Write out the first three terms of the sequence $u_r = (r + 1)r^2$.

   (ii)   Find an expression for $\displaystyle\sum_{r=1}^{n}(r + 1)r^2$.

   (iii)   Use part (i) to check part (ii).

④ Find $\displaystyle\sum_{r=1}^{n}(4r^3 - 6r^2 + 4r - 1)$.

⑤ Find $(1 \times 2) + (2 \times 3) + (3 \times 4) + \ldots + n(n + 1)$.

⑥ Find $(1 \times 2 \times 3) + (2 \times 3 \times 4) + (3 \times 4 \times 5) + \ldots + n(n + 1)(n + 2)$.

⑦ Find the sum of integers above n, up to and including $2n$, giving your answer in a fully factorised form.

⑧ Find the sum of the cubes of the integers larger than n, up to and including $3n$, giving your answer in a fully factorised form.

⑨ On a particularly artistic fruit stall, a pile of oranges is arranged to form a truncated square pyramid. Each layer is a square, with the lengths of the side of successive layers reducing by one orange (as in Figure 4.2).

The bottom layer measures $2n \times 2n$ oranges, and there are n layers.

(i) Prove that the number of oranges used is $\dfrac{1}{6}n(2n + 1)(7n + 1)$.

(ii) How many complete layers can the person setting up the stall use for this arrangement, given their stock of 1000 oranges? How many oranges are left over?

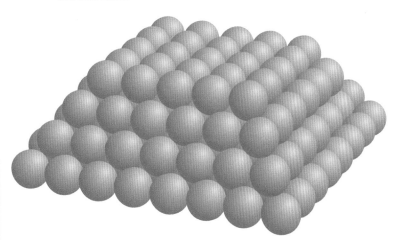

Figure 4.2

⑩ You have £20 000 to invest for one year. You put it in the following bank account:

'Flexible Saver': 1.5% interest APR

- Interest calculated monthly (i.e. $\frac{1.5}{12}$% of balance each month).

- Interest paid annually, into a separate account.

- No limits on withdrawals or balance.

Your bank then informs you of a new savings account, which you are allowed to open as well as the Flexible Saver.

'Regular Saver': 5% interest APR

- Interest calculated monthly (i.e. $\frac{5}{12}$% each month).

- Interest paid annually, into a separate account.

- Maximum £1000 balance increase per month.

(i) Assuming you initially have your money in the Flexible Saver, but transfer as much as you can into a Regular Saver each month, calculate how much extra money you will earn, compared to what would happen if you just left it in the Flexible Saver all year.

(ii) Generalise your result – given an investment of I (in thousands of pounds), and a time of n months – what interest will you earn?

(Assume $n < I$, or you'll run out of funds to transfer.)

3 The method of differences

Sometimes it is possible to find the sum of a series by subtracting it from a related series, with most of the terms cancelling out. This is called the method of differences and is shown in the following example.

Example 4.5

Calculate the value of the series: $5 + 10 + 20 + 40 + \ldots + 2560 + 5120$

Solution

Each term is double the previous one.

> In fact, the sequence is $u_r = 5 \times 2^{r-1}$ but you won't need that here.

Call the sum S.

$S = 5 + 10 + 20 + \ldots + 2560 + 5120$

Double it:

$2S = 10 + 20 + 40 + \ldots + 5120 + 10\,240$

Subtract the first line from the second and notice that most terms cancel. In fact, only two remain.

$2S - S = 10\,240 - 5$

$S = 10\,235$

> This is the sum you needed.

This example worked because of the doubling of the terms.

Calculating the sums of much more complicated series can also use this technique, if each term can be expressed as the difference of two (or more) terms. Look at the following examples carefully to see the idea, paying particular attention to the way the series are laid out to help find the cancelling terms.

Example 4.6

(i) Show that $\dfrac{1}{r} - \dfrac{1}{r+1} = \dfrac{1}{r(r+1)}$.

(ii) Hence find $\dfrac{1}{1 \times 2} + \dfrac{1}{2 \times 3} + \dfrac{1}{3 \times 4} + \ldots + \dfrac{1}{30 \times 31}$.

Solution

(i) $\text{LHS} = \dfrac{1}{r} - \dfrac{1}{r+1} = \dfrac{(r+1) - r}{r(r+1)}$

$= \dfrac{1}{r(r+1)}$

$= \text{RHS}$ as required

(ii) $\dfrac{1}{1 \times 2} + \dfrac{1}{2 \times 3} + \dfrac{1}{3 \times 4} + \dots + \dfrac{1}{30 \times 31} = \displaystyle\sum_{r=1}^{30} \dfrac{1}{r(r+1)}$

$= \displaystyle\sum_{r=1}^{30} \left(\dfrac{1}{r} - \dfrac{1}{r+1} \right)$

Using the result from part (i)

start writing out the sum, but it is helpful to lay it out like this to see which parts cancel.

$= 1 - \dfrac{1}{2}$
$+ \dfrac{1}{2} - \dfrac{1}{3}$
$+ \dfrac{1}{3} - \dfrac{1}{4}$
$+ \dots\dots$
$+ \dfrac{1}{29} - \dfrac{1}{30}$
$+ \dfrac{1}{30} - \dfrac{1}{31}$

The terms in the red loops cancel out – so all the terms in the green box vanish.

$= 1 - \dfrac{1}{31}$

$= \dfrac{30}{31}$

Discussion point

→ What happens to this series when n becomes very large?

Notice that the result in the example can easily be generalised for a sequence of any length. If the sequence has n terms, then the terms would still cancel in pairs, leaving the first term, 1, and the last term, $-\dfrac{1}{n+1}$.

The sum of the terms would therefore be

$$1 - \dfrac{1}{n+1} = \dfrac{n+1-1}{n+1} = \dfrac{n}{n+1} \, .$$

The cancelling of nearly all the terms is similar to the way in which the interior sections of a collapsible telescope disappear when it is compressed, so a sum like this is sometimes described as a **telescoping sum**.

The next example uses a telescoping sum to prove a familiar result.

Example 4.7

(i)   Show that $(2r + 1)^2 - (2r - 1)^2 = 8r$.

(ii)   Hence find $\displaystyle\sum_{r=1}^{n} 8r$.

(iii)   Deduce that $\displaystyle\sum_{r=1}^{n} r = \frac{1}{2}n(n + 1)$.

Solution

(i) $(2r + 1)^2 - (2r - 1)^2 = \left(4r^2 + 4r + 1\right) - \left(4r^2 - 4r + 1\right)$

$= 8r$

as required.

(ii) $\displaystyle\sum_{r=1}^{n} 8r = \sum_{r=1}^{n}\left[(2r + 1)^2 - (2r - 1)^2\right]$

$= 3^2 - 1^2$

$+ 5^2 - 3^2$

$+ 7^2 - 5^2$

$+ \ldots$

> The only terms remaining are the 2nd and the 2nd to last.

$+ (2(n - 1) + 1)^2 - 2(n - 1) - 1)^2$

$+ 2(n + 1)^2 - (2n - 1)^2$

$= (2n + 1)^2 - 1^2$

$= 4n^2 + 4n + 1 - 1$

$= 4n^2 + 4n$

(iii)   Since $\displaystyle\sum_{r=1}^{n} 8r = 4n^2 + 4n$

so $\displaystyle\sum_{r=1}^{n} r = \frac{1}{2}n^2 + \frac{1}{2}n$

> This result was also proved on page 74 using a different method.

$= \frac{1}{2}n(n + 1)$

as required.

Example 4.8

(i) Show that $\dfrac{2}{r} - \dfrac{3}{r+1} + \dfrac{1}{r+2} = \dfrac{r+4}{r(r+1)(r+2)}$.

(ii) Hence find $\displaystyle\sum_{r=1}^{n} \dfrac{r+4}{r(r+1)(r+2)}$.

Solution

(i)
$$\dfrac{2}{r} - \dfrac{3}{r+1} + \dfrac{1}{r+2} = \dfrac{2(r+1)(r+2) - 3r(r+2) + r(r+1)}{r(r+1)(r+2)}$$

$$= \dfrac{2r^2 + 6r + 4 - 3r^2 - 6r + r^2 + r}{r(r+1)(r+2)}$$

$$= \dfrac{r+4}{r(r+1)(r+2)}$$

(ii)
$$\sum_{r=1}^{n} \dfrac{r+4}{r(r+1)(r+2)} = \sum_{r=1}^{n}\left(\dfrac{2}{r} - \dfrac{3}{r+1} + \dfrac{1}{r+2}\right)$$

$$= 2 - \dfrac{3}{2} + \dfrac{1}{3}$$
$$+ \dfrac{2}{2} - \dfrac{3}{3} + \dfrac{1}{4}$$
$$+ \dfrac{2}{3} - \dfrac{3}{4} - \dfrac{1}{5}$$
$$+ \ldots - \ldots + \ldots$$
$$+ \ldots - \ldots + \ldots$$
$$+ \dfrac{2}{n-2} - \dfrac{3}{n-1} + \dfrac{1}{n}$$
$$+ \dfrac{2}{n-2} - \dfrac{3}{n} + \dfrac{1}{n+1}$$
$$+ \dfrac{2}{n} - \dfrac{3}{n+1} + \dfrac{1}{n+2}$$

> The terms in the red loops cancel out – so all the terms in the green box vanish.

Most of the terms cancel, leaving

$$\sum_{r=1}^{n} \dfrac{r+4}{r(r+1)(r+2)} = 2 - \dfrac{3}{2} + \dfrac{2}{2} + \dfrac{1}{n+1} - \dfrac{3}{n+1} + \dfrac{1}{n+2}$$

$$= \dfrac{3}{2} - \dfrac{2}{n+1} + \dfrac{1}{n+2}$$

Note

The terms which do not cancel form a symmetrical pattern, three at the start and three at the end.

> **Discussion points**
>
> → Show that the final expression in the previous example can be simplified to give $\dfrac{n(3n+7)}{2(n+1)(n+2)}$.
>
> → What happens to the series as n becomes very large?

Exercise 4.3

① This question is about the series $1 + 3 + 5 + \ldots + (2n-1)$.

You can write this as $\displaystyle\sum_{r=1}^{n}(2r-1)$.

  (i) Show that $r^2 - (r-1)^2 = 2r - 1$.

  (ii) Write out the first three terms and the last three terms of
  $$\sum_{r=1}^{n}\left(r^2 - (r-1)^2\right).$$

  (iii) Hence find $\displaystyle\sum_{r=1}^{n}(2r-1)$.

  (iv) Show that using the standard formulae to find $\displaystyle\sum_{r=1}^{n}(2r-1)$ gives the same result as in (iii).

② This question is about the series $\dfrac{2}{1\times 3} + \dfrac{2}{3\times 5} + \dfrac{2}{5\times 7} + \ldots + \dfrac{2}{19\times 21}$.

  (i) Show that the general term of the series is $\dfrac{2}{(2r-1)(2r+1)}$, and find the values of r for the first term and the last term of the series.

  (ii) Show that $\dfrac{1}{2r-1} - \dfrac{1}{2r+1} = \dfrac{2}{(2r-1)(2r+1)}$.

  (iii) Hence find $\dfrac{2}{1\times 3} + \dfrac{2}{3\times 5} + \dfrac{2}{5\times 7} + \ldots + \dfrac{2}{19\times 21}$.

③ (i) Show that $(r+1)^2(r+2) - r^2(r+1) = (r+1)(3r+2)$.

  (ii) Hence find $(2\times 5) + (3\times 8) + (4\times 11) + \ldots + (n+1)(3n+2)$.

  (iii) Show that you can obtain the same result by using the standard formulae to find the sum of this series.

  (iv) Using trial and improvement, find the smallest value of n for which the sum is greater than one million.

④ (i) Show that $\dfrac{1}{r^2} - \dfrac{1}{(r+1)^2} = \dfrac{2r+1}{r^2(r+1)^2}$.

  (ii) Hence find $\displaystyle\sum_{r=1}^{n}\dfrac{2r+1}{r^2(r+1)^2}$.

⑤ (i) Show that $\dfrac{1}{2r} - \dfrac{1}{2(r+2)} = \dfrac{1}{r(r+2)}$.

  (ii) Hence find $\displaystyle\sum_{r=1}^{n}\dfrac{1}{r(r+2)}$.

  (iii) Find the value of this sum for $n = 100$, $n = 1000$ and $n = 10\,000$ and comment on your answer.

⑥ (i) Show that $-\dfrac{1}{r+2} + \dfrac{3}{r+3} - \dfrac{2}{r+4} = \dfrac{r}{(r+2)(r+3)(r+4)}$.

   (ii) Hence find $\displaystyle\sum_{r=1}^{12} \dfrac{r}{(r+2)(r+3)(r+4)}$.

⑦ (i) Show that $\dfrac{1}{2r} - \dfrac{1}{r+1} + \dfrac{1}{2(r+2)} = \dfrac{1}{r(r+1)(r+2)}$.

   (ii) Hence find $\displaystyle\sum_{r=1}^{n} \dfrac{1}{r(r+1)(r+2)}$.

   (iii) Find the value of this sum for $n = 100$ and $n = 1000$, and comment on your answer.

In Questions 8 and 9 you will prove the standard results for Σr^2 and Σr^3.

⑧ (i) Show that $(2r+1)^3 - (2r-1)^3 = 24r^2 + 2$.

   (ii) Hence find $\displaystyle\sum_{r=1}^{n}\left(24r^2 + 2\right)$.

   (iii) Deduce that $\displaystyle\sum_{r=1}^{n} r^2 = \frac{1}{6}n(n+1)(2n+1)$.

⑨ (i) Show that $(2r+1)^4 - (2r-1)^4 = 64r^3 + 16r$.

   (ii) Hence find $\displaystyle\sum_{r=1}^{n}\left(64r^3 + 16r\right)$.

   (iii) Deduce that $\displaystyle\sum_{r=1}^{n} r^3 = \frac{1}{4}n^2(n+1)^2$.

   (You may use the standard result for Σr.)

⑩ (i) Show that $\dfrac{2}{r^2 - 1}$ can be written as $\dfrac{1}{r-1} - \dfrac{1}{r+1}$.

   (ii) Hence find the values of A and B in the identity
$$\frac{1}{r^2 - 1} = \frac{A}{r-1} + \frac{B}{r+1}$$

   (iii) Find $\displaystyle\sum_{r=2}^{n} \dfrac{1}{r^2 - 1}$.

   (iv) What is the value of this sum as n becomes very large?

4 Proof by induction

Discussion point

➜ Is this a valid argument?

The oldest person to have ever lived, with documentary evidence, is believed to be a French woman called Jeanne Calment who died aged 122, in 1997.

Emily is an old woman who claims to have broken the record. A reporter asked her, 'How do you know you're 122 years old?'

She replied, 'Because I was 121 last year.'

The sort of argument that Emily was trying to use is called inductive reasoning. If all the elements are present it can be used in proof by induction. This is the subject of the rest of this chapter. It is a very beautiful form of proof but it is also very delicate; if you miss out any of the steps in the argument, as Emily did, you invalidate your whole proof.

ACTIVITY 4.1

Work out the first four terms of this pattern:

$$\frac{1}{1 \times 2} =$$

$$\frac{1}{1 \times 2} + \frac{1}{2 \times 3} =$$

$$\frac{1}{1 \times 2} + \frac{1}{2 \times 3} + \frac{1}{3 \times 4} =$$

$$\frac{1}{1 \times 2} + \frac{1}{2 \times 3} + \frac{1}{3 \times 4} + \frac{1}{4 \times 5} =$$

Activity 4.1 illustrates one common way of solving problems in mathematics. Looking at a number of particular cases may show a pattern, which can be used to form a **conjecture** (i.e. a theory about a possible general result).

Conjectures are often written algebraically.

The conjecture can then be tested in further particular cases.

In this case, the sum of the first n terms of the sequence can be written as

$$\frac{1}{1 \times 2} + \frac{1}{2 \times 3} + \frac{1}{3 \times 4} + \dots + \frac{1}{n(n + 1)}.$$

The activity shows that the conjecture

$$\frac{1}{1 \times 2} + \frac{1}{2 \times 3} + \frac{1}{3 \times 4} + \dots + \frac{1}{n(n + 1)} = \frac{n}{n + 1}$$

is true for $n = 1, 2, 3$ and 4.

Try some more terms, say, the next two.

If you find a **counter-example** at any point (a case where the conjecture is not true) then the conjecture is definitely disproved. If, on the other hand, the further cases agree with the conjecture then you may feel that you are on the right lines, but you can never be mathematically certain that trying another particular case might not reveal a counter-example: the conjecture is supported by more evidence but not proved.

The ultimate goal is to prove this conjecture is true for *all* positive integers. But it is not possible to prove this conjecture by deduction from known results. A different approach is needed: **mathematical induction**.

In Activity 4.1 you established that the conjecture is true for particular cases of n ($n = 1, 2, 3, 4, 5$ and 6).

Now, assume that the conjecture is true for a particular integer, $n = k$ say, so that

$$\frac{1}{1 \times 2} + \frac{1}{2 \times 3} + \frac{1}{3 \times 4} + \dots + \frac{1}{k(k + 1)} = \frac{k}{k + 1}$$

and use this assumption to check what happens for the next integer, $n = k + 1$.

If the conjecture is true then you should get

$$\frac{1}{1\times 2} + \frac{1}{2\times 3} + \frac{1}{3\times 4} + \ldots + \frac{1}{k(k+1)} + \frac{1}{(k+1)(k+2)} = \frac{(k+1)}{(k+1)+1}$$

$$= \frac{k+1}{k+2}$$

Replacing k by $k+1$ in the result $\frac{k}{k+1}$

This is your target result. It is what you need to establish.

Look at the left-hand side (LHS). You can see that the first k terms are part of the assumption.

$$\frac{1}{1\times 2} + \frac{1}{2\times 3} + \frac{1}{3\times 4} + \ldots + \frac{1}{k(k+1)} + \frac{1}{(k+1)(k+2)} \quad \text{(the LHS)}$$

$$= \frac{k}{k+1} + \frac{1}{(k+1)(k+2)} \qquad \boxed{\text{Using the assumption}}$$

$$= \frac{k(k+2)+1}{(k+1)(k+2)} \qquad \boxed{\text{getting a common denominator}}$$

$$= \frac{k^2 + 2k + 1}{(k+1)(k+2)} \qquad \boxed{\text{expanding the top bracket}}$$

$$= \frac{(k+1)^2}{(k+1)(k+2)} \qquad \boxed{\text{factorising the top quadratic}}$$

$$= \frac{k+1}{k+2} \qquad \boxed{\text{cancelling the } (k+1) \text{ factor – since } k \neq -1}$$

$$\boxed{\text{which is the required result.}}$$

These steps show that *if* the conjecture is true for $n = k$, *then* it is true for $n = k + 1$.

Since you have already proved it is true for $n = 1$, you can deduce that it is therefore true for $n = 2$ (by taking $k = 2$).

You can continue in this way (e.g. take $n = 2$ and deduce it is true for $n = 3$) as far as you want to go. Since you can reach *any* positive integer n you have now proved the conjecture is true for *every positive integer*.

This method of **proof by mathematical induction** (often shortened to **proof by induction**) is a bit like the process of climbing a ladder:

If you can

1 get on the ladder (the bottom rung), and
2 get from one rung to the next,
   then you can climb as far up the ladder as you like.

Figure 4.3

The corresponding steps in the previous proof are

1 showing the conjecture is true for $n = 1$, and
2 showing that *if* it is true for a particular value ($n = k$ say), *then* it is true for the next one ($n = k + 1$).

(Notice the *if… then…* structure to this step.)

You should conclude any argument by mathematical induction with a statement of what you have shown.

Steps in mathematical induction

To prove something by mathematical induction you need to state a conjecture to begin with. Then there are five elements needed to try to prove the conjecture is true.

This can be done before or after finding the target expression, but you may find it easier to find the target expression first so that you know what you are working towards.

- Proving that it is true for a starting value (e.g. $n = 1$).

- Finding the target expression:
  using the result for $n = k$ to find the equivalent result for $n = k + 1$.

To find the target expression you replace k with $k + 1$ in the result for $n = k$.

- Proving that:
  if it is true for $n = k$, *then* it is true for $n = k + 1$.

This ensures the argument is properly rounded off. You will often use the word 'therefore'.

- Arguing that since it is true for $n = 1$, it is also true for $n = 1 + 1 = 2$, and so for $n = 2 + 1 = 3$ and for all subsequent values of n.

- Concluding the argument by writing down the result and stating that it has been proved.

Example 4.9

(the sum of the squares of the first n integers)

Prove that, for all positive integers n:

$$1^2 + 2^2 + 3^2 + \ldots + n^2 = \frac{1}{6}n(n + 1)(2n + 1)$$

 Note

- -

You have already had the opportunity to prove this result using the method of differences, in Question 8 of Exercise 4.3.

Solution

When $n = 1$,   LHS $= 1^2 = 1$ RHS $= \frac{1}{6} \times 1 \times 2 \times 3 = 1$

So it is true for $n = 1$.

Assume the result is true for $n = k$, so

$$1^2 + 2^2 + \ldots + k^2 = \frac{1}{6}k(k + 1)(2k + 1)$$

Target expression:

$$1^2 + 2^2 + 3^2 + \ldots + k^2 + (k + 1)^2 = \frac{1}{6}(k + 1)[(k + 1) + 1][(2(k + 1) + 1]$$

$$= \frac{1}{6}(k + 1)(k + 2)(2k + 3)$$

You want to prove that the result is true for $n = k + 1$
(if the assumption is true).

Look at the LHS of the result you want to prove:
$$1^2 + 2^2 + 3^2 + \ldots + k^2 + (k + 1)^2$$
Use the assumed result for $n = k$, to replace the first k terms.

$$= \frac{1}{6}k(k + 1)(2k + 1) + (k + 1)^2 \longleftarrow \boxed{\text{The } (k + 1)\text{th. term.}}$$

$$\boxed{\text{The first } k \text{ terms.}}$$

$$= \frac{1}{6}(k + 1)\big[k(2k + 1) + 6(k + 1)\big]$$

$\boxed{\text{Take out a factor } \frac{1}{6}(k + 1).\\ \text{You can see from the}\\ \text{target expression that}\\ \text{this will be helpful.}}$ $$= \frac{1}{6}(k + 1)(2k^2 + 7k + 6)$$

$$= \frac{1}{6}(k + 1)(k + 2)(2k + 3)$$

$\boxed{\text{This is the same as the target}\\ \text{expression, as required.}}$

If the result is true for $n = k$, then it is true for $n = k + 1$.

Since it is true for $n = k$, it is true for all positive integer values of n.

Therefore the result that $1 + 2^2 + \ldots + n^2 = \frac{1}{6}n(n + 1)(2n + 1)$ is true.

ACTIVITY 4.2

Jane is investigating the sum of the first n even numbers.
She writes
$$2 + 4 + 6 + \ldots + 2n = \left(n + \frac{1}{2}\right)^2.$$

(i) Prove that *if* this result is true when $n = k$, *then* it is true when $n = k + 1$.
Explain why Jane's conjecture is *not* true for all positive integers n.

(ii) Suggest a different conjecture for the sum of the first n even numbers, that is true for $n = 1$ but not for other values of n. At what point does an attempt to use proof by induction on this result break down?

Exercise 4.4

① (i) Show that the result $1 + 3 + 5 + \ldots + (2n - 1) = n^2$ is true for the case $n = 1$.

(ii) Assume that $1 + 3 + 5 + \ldots + (2k - 1) = k^2$ and use this to prove that:
$$1 + 3 + \ldots + (2k - 1) + (2k + 1) = (k + 1)^2.$$

(iii) Explain how parts (i) and (ii) together prove the sum of the first n odd integers is n^2.

② (i) Show that the result $1 + 5 + 9 + \ldots + (4n - 3) = n(2n - 1)$ is true for the case $n = 1$.

(ii) Assume that $1 + 5 + 9 + \ldots + (4k - 3) = k(2k - 1)$
and use this to prove that:
$$1 + 5 + \ldots + (4k - 3) + (4(k + 1) - 3) = (k + 1)(2(k + 1) - 1).$$

(iii) Explain how parts (i) and (ii) together prove that:
$$1 + 5 + 9 + \ldots + (4n - 3) = n(2n - 1)$$

Prove the following results by induction.

③ $1 + 2 + 3 + \ldots + n = \frac{1}{2}n(n + 1)$

(the sum of the first n integers)

> You have already seen two proofs of this result, on pages 73 and 83.

④ $\sum_{r=1}^{n} r^3 = \frac{1}{4}n^2(n + 1)^2$

(the sum of the first n cubes)

> You have already had the opportunity to prove this result using the method of differences, in Question 9 of Exercise 4.3.

⑤ $2^1 + 2^2 + 2^3 + 2^4 + \ldots + 2^n = 2(2^n - 1)$

⑥ $\sum_{r=0}^{n} x^r = \frac{1 - x^{n+1}}{1 - x}$ $(x \neq 1)$

⑦ $(1 \times 2 \times 3) + (2 \times 3 \times 4) + \ldots + n(n + 1)(n + 2) = \frac{1}{4}n(n + 1)(n + 2)(n + 3)$

⑧ $\sum_{r=1}^{n}(3r + 1) = \frac{1}{2}n(3n + 5)$

⑨ $\frac{1}{3} + \frac{1}{15} + \frac{1}{35} + \ldots + \frac{1}{4n^2 - 1} = \frac{n}{2n + 1}$

⑩ $\left(1 - \frac{1}{2^2}\right)\left(1 - \frac{1}{3^2}\right)\left(1 - \frac{1}{4^2}\right)\ldots\left(1 - \frac{1}{n^2}\right) = \frac{n + 1}{2n}$ for $n \geq 2$

⑪ $1 \times 1! + 2 \times 2! + 3 \times 3! + \ldots + n \times n! = (n + 1)! - 1$

⑫ (i) Prove by induction that

$$\sum_{r=1}^{n}(5r^4 + r^2) = \frac{1}{2}n^2(n + 1)^2(2n + 1).$$

(ii) Using the result in part (i), and the formula for $\sum_{r=1}^{n} r^2$, show that

$$\sum_{r=1}^{n} r^4 = \frac{1}{30}n(n + 1)(2n + 1)(3n^2 + 3n - 1).$$

5 Other proofs by induction

So far, you have used induction to prove results involving the sums of series. It can also be used in other situations.

You have seen that induction can be used to prove a given result for the sum of a series in which the terms have been given using a deductive definition. In the next example you will see how induction can be used to prove a given result for the general term of a sequence, when the terms of a sequence have been given inductively.

Example 4.10

A sequence is defined by $u_{n+1} = 4u_n - 3, u_1 = 2$.

Prove that $u_n = 4^{n-1} + 1$.

Solution

For $n = 1, u_1 = 4^0 + 1 = 1 + 1 = 2$, so the result is true for $n = 1$.

Assume that the result is true for $n = k$, so that $u_k = 4^{k-1} + 1$.

> Target expression:
> $u_{k+1} = 4^k + 1$.

For $n = k + 1$, $u_{k+1} = 4u_k - 3$

$$= 4\left(4^{k-1} + 1\right) - 3$$

$$= 4 \times 4^{k-1} + 4 - 3$$

$$= 4^k + 1$$

If the result is true for $n = k$, then it is true for $n = k + 1$.

Since it is true for $n = 1$, it is true for all positive integer values of n.
Therefore the result $u_n = 4^{n-1} + 1$ is true.

You can sometimes use induction to prove results involving powers of matrices.

Example 4.11

Given $\mathbf{A} = \begin{pmatrix} 4 & 1 \\ 3 & 2 \end{pmatrix}$, prove by induction that

$$\mathbf{A}^n = \frac{1}{4}\begin{pmatrix} 3 \times 5^n + 1 & 5^n - 1 \\ 3 \times 5^n - 3 & 5^n + 3 \end{pmatrix}.$$

Solution

Let $n = 1$ LHS $= \mathbf{A}^1 = \begin{pmatrix} 4 & 1 \\ 3 & 2 \end{pmatrix}$

RHS $= \frac{1}{4}\begin{pmatrix} 3 \times 5 + 1 & 5 - 1 \\ 3 \times 5 - 3 & 5 + 3 \end{pmatrix}$

$$= \frac{1}{4}\begin{pmatrix} 16 & 4 \\ 12 & 8 \end{pmatrix}$$

$$= \begin{pmatrix} 4 & 1 \\ 3 & 2 \end{pmatrix}$$

$$= \text{LHS as required}$$

Assume true for $n = k$, i.e.

$$\mathbf{A}^k = \frac{1}{4}\begin{pmatrix} 3 \times 5^k + 1 & 5^k - 1 \\ 3 \times 5^k - 3 & 5^k + 3 \end{pmatrix}$$

> Target expression:
> $$\mathbf{A}^{k+1} = \frac{1}{4}\begin{pmatrix} 3 \times 5^{k+1} + 1 & 5^{k+1} - 1 \\ 3 \times 5^{k+1} - 3 & 5^{k+1} + 3 \end{pmatrix}$$

You want to prove it is true for $n = k + 1$.

$$\mathbf{A}^{k+1} = \mathbf{A}^k \mathbf{A}$$

$$= \frac{1}{4}\begin{pmatrix} 3 \times 5^k + 1 & 5^k - 1 \\ 3 \times 5^k - 3 & 5^k + 3 \end{pmatrix}\begin{pmatrix} 4 & 1 \\ 3 & 2 \end{pmatrix}$$

$$= \frac{1}{4}\begin{pmatrix} 12 \times 5^k + 4 + 3 \times 5^k - 3 & 3 \times 5^k + 1 + 2 \times 5^k - 2 \\ 12 \times 5^k - 12 + 3 \times 5^k + 9 & 3 \times 5^k - 3 + 2 \times 5^k + 6 \end{pmatrix}$$

Multiplying matrices.

$$= \frac{1}{4}\begin{pmatrix} 15 \times 5^k + 1 & 5 \times 5^k - 1 \\ 15 \times 5^k - 3 & 5 \times 5^k + 3 \end{pmatrix}$$

Using $15 = 3 \times 5$.

$$= \frac{1}{4}\begin{pmatrix} 3 \times 5^{k+1} + 1 & 5^{k+1} - 1 \\ 3 \times 5^{k+1} - 3 & 5^{k+1} + 3 \end{pmatrix}$$

This is the target matrix.

as required.

If it is true for $n = k$, then it is true for $n = k + 1$

Since it is true for $n = 1$, it is true for all $n \geq 1$.

Therefore the result $\mathbf{A}^n = \frac{1}{4}\begin{pmatrix} 3 \times 5^n + 1 & 5^n - 1 \\ 3 \times 5^n - 3 & 5^n + 3 \end{pmatrix}$ is true.

Exercise 4.5

① A sequence is defined by $u_{n+1} = 3u_n + 2, u_1 = 2$.

   Prove by induction that $u_n = 3^n - 1$.

② A sequence is defined by $u_{n+1} = 2u_n - 1, u_1 = 2$.

   Prove by induction that $u_n = 2^{n-1} + 1$.

③ Given that $\mathbf{M} = \begin{pmatrix} 2 & 0 \\ 0 & 3 \end{pmatrix}$, prove by induction that $\mathbf{M}^n = \begin{pmatrix} 2^n & 0 \\ 0 & 3^n \end{pmatrix}$.

④ A sequence is defined by $u_{n+1} = 4u_n - 6, u_1 = 3$.

   Prove by induction that $u_n = 4^{n-1} + 2$.

⑤ (i) Given that $\mathbf{M} = \begin{pmatrix} 1 & 1 \\ 0 & 1 \end{pmatrix}$, prove by induction that $\mathbf{M}^n = \begin{pmatrix} 1 & n \\ 0 & 1 \end{pmatrix}$.

   (ii) Describe the transformations represented by $\mathbf{M}$ and by $\mathbf{M}^n$.

⑥ A sequence is defined by $u_{n+1} = \dfrac{u_n}{u_n + 1}$, $u_1 = 1$.

   (i)   Find the values of u_2, u_3 and u_4.

   (ii)   Suggest a general formula for u_n, and prove your conjecture by induction.

⑦ You are given the matrix $\mathbf{A} = \begin{pmatrix} -1 & -4 \\ 1 & 3 \end{pmatrix}$.

   (i)   Calculate $\mathbf{A}^2$ and $\mathbf{A}^3$.

   (ii)   Show that the formula $\mathbf{A}^n = \begin{pmatrix} 1 - 2n & -4n \\ n & 1 + 2n \end{pmatrix}$ is consistent with the given value of $\mathbf{A}$ and your calculations for $n = 2$ and $n = 3$.

   (iii) Prove by induction that the formula for $\mathbf{A}^n$ is correct when n is a positive integer.

⑧ You are given the matrix $\mathbf{M} = \begin{pmatrix} -1 & 2 \\ 3 & 1 \end{pmatrix}$.

   (i)   Calculate $\mathbf{M}^2$, $\mathbf{M}^3$ and $\mathbf{M}^4$.

   (ii)   Write down separate conjectures for formulae for $\mathbf{M}^n$, for even n (i.e. $\mathbf{M}^{2m}$) and for odd n (i.e. $\mathbf{M}^{2m+1}$)

   (iii) Prove each conjecture by induction, and hence write down what $\mathbf{M}^n$ is for any $n \geq 1$.

⑨ Let $F_n = 2^{(2^n)} + 1$.

   (i)   Calculate F_0, F_1, F_2, F_3, and F_4.

   (ii)   Prove, by induction, that $F_0 \times F_1 \times F_2 \times \ldots \times F_{n-1} = F_n - 2$.

   (iii) Use part (ii) to prove that F_i and F_j are coprime (for $i \neq j$).

   (iv) Use part (iii) to prove there are infinitely many prime numbers.

The F_n numbers are called Fermat Numbers. The first five are prime: the Fermat Primes. Nobody (yet) knows if any other Fermat Numbers are prime.

●

LEARNING OUTCOMES

When you have completed this chapter you should be able to:

➤ know what is meant by a sequence and a series

➤ find the sum of a series using standard formulae for $\sum r$, $\sum r^2$ and $\sum r^3$

➤ find the sum of a series using the method of differences

➤ use proof by induction to prove given results for the sum of a series

➤ use proof by induction to prove given results for the nth term of a sequence

➤ use proof by induction to prove given results for the nth power of a matrix.

KEY POINTS

1   The terms of a sequence are often written as $a_1, a_2, a_3, \ldots$ or $u_1, u_2, u_3, \ldots$
    The general term of a sequence may be written as a_r or u_r (sometimes the letters k or i are used instead of r). The last term is usually written as a_n or u_n.

2   A series is the sum of the terms of a sequence. The sum S_n of the first n terms of a sequence can be written using the symbol Σ (the Greek capital S, sigma).

$$S_n = a_1 + a_2 + a_3 + \ldots + a_n = \sum_{r=1}^{n} a_r$$

The numbers above and below the Σ are the limits of the sum. They show that the sum includes all the terms a_r from a_1 to a_n.

3   Some series can be expressed as combinations of these standard results:

$$\sum_{r=1}^{n} r = \frac{1}{2}n(n+1) \qquad \sum_{r=1}^{n} r^2 = \frac{1}{6}n(n+1)(2n+1) \qquad \sum_{r=1}^{n} r^3 = \frac{1}{4}n^2(n+1)^2$$

4   Some series can be summed by using the method of differences. If the terms of the series can be written as the difference of terms of another series, then many terms may cancel out. This is called a telescoping sum.

5   To prove by induction that a statement involving an integer n is true for all $n \geq n_0$, you need to:

■   prove that the result is true for an initial value of n_0, typically $n = 1$

■   find the target expression:
    use the result for $n = k$ to find the equivalent result for $n = k + 1$.

■   prove that:
    if it is true for $n = k$, *then* it is true for $n = k + 1$.

■   argue that since it is true for $n = 1$, it is also true for $n = 1 + 1 = 2$, and so for $n = 2 + 1 = 3$ and for all subsequent values of n.

■   conclude the argument with a precise statement about what has been proved.

FUTURE USES

■   In the A Level Further Mathematics textbook you will see how functions such as e^x and $\sin x$ can be written as infinite series using Maclaurin series.

■   You will also meet series expansions of other functions using Maclaurin series.

■   You will look at some further types of proof by induction in the A Level Further Mathematics textbook.

For questions 1 to 4 you must show non-calculator methods in your answer.

① (i) The complex number w is given by $w = 1 + 2i$. On a single Argand diagram plot the points which represent the four complex numbers $w, w^2, w - w^*$ and $\dfrac{1}{w} + \dfrac{1}{w^*}$. [5 marks]

(ii) Which two of the numbers $w, w^2, w - w^*$ and $\dfrac{1}{w} + \dfrac{1}{w^*}$ have the same imaginary part? [1 mark]

② You are given that one of the roots of the cubic equation $z^3 - 9z^2 + 28z - 30 = 0$ is an integer and that another is $3 + i$.

Solve the cubic equation. [5 marks]

③ Ezra is investigating whether the formula for solving quadratic equations works if the coefficients of the quadratic are not real numbers. Here is the beginning of his working for one particular quadratic equation.

$$(2+i)z^2 + 6z + (2-i) = 0$$

$$z = \frac{-b \pm \sqrt{b^2 - 4ac}}{2}$$

$$= \frac{-6 \pm \sqrt{36 - 4(2+i)(2-i)}}{2(2+i)}$$

$$= \dots$$

(i) Finish off Ezra's working. Show that both of the answers given by this method are of the form $\lambda(2-i)$, where λ is real, stating the value of λ in each case. [4 marks]

(ii) How should Ezra check that his answers are indeed roots of the equation? [1 mark]

④ The cubic equation $x^3 + 3x^2 - 6x - 8 = 0$ has roots α, β, γ.

(i) Find a cubic equation with roots $\alpha + 1, \beta + 1, \gamma + 1$. [4 marks]

(ii) Solve the equation you found as your answer to part (i). [3 marks]

(iii) Solve the equation $x^3 + 3x^2 - 6x - 8 = 0$. [2 marks]

PS ⑤ (i) What transformation is represented by the matrix $\mathbf{B} = \begin{pmatrix} 0 & -1 \\ 1 & 0 \end{pmatrix}$? [2 marks]

(ii) By considering transformations, or otherwise, find a matrix $\mathbf{A}$ such that $\mathbf{A}^2 = \mathbf{B}$. [3 marks]

MP **PS** ⑥ You are given that the quadratic equation $az^2 + bz + c = 0$ has roots δ and $\delta + 1$.

By considering the sum and product of its roots, or otherwise, prove that $b^2 - 4ac = a^2$. [5 marks]

MP ⑦ A sequence is defined by the relationship $u_{k+1} = 2u_k - k+1$ with $u_1 = 3$.

(i) Write down the first five terms of the sequence. [1 mark]

(ii) Prove by induction that $u_n = 2^n + n$. [6 marks]

⑧ The matrix $\mathbf{R}$ is given by $\mathbf{R} = \begin{pmatrix} -\dfrac{3}{5} & \dfrac{4}{5} \\ \dfrac{4}{5} & \dfrac{3}{5} \end{pmatrix}$. The transformation corresponding to **R** is denoted R. The unit square OIPJ has coordinates O(0, 0), I(1, 0), P(1, 1), J(0, 1).

(i) Plot, on the same diagram, the unit square and its image O'I'P'J under R. [2 marks]

(ii) Find the equation of the line of invariant points for R. [3 marks]

(iii) Verify that the line which is perpendicular to this line of invariant points, and which passes through the origin, is an invariant line. [3 marks]

(iv) Mark on your diagram in part (i) two points on the unit square which are invariant under R. [2 marks]

⑨ (i) Show that

$$\frac{1}{6}(r + 3)(r + 4)(r + 5) - \frac{1}{6}(r + 2)(r + 3)(r + 4) = \frac{1}{2}(r + 3)(r + 4).$$

[2 marks]

(ii) Use the result in part (i) to show that

$$\sum_{r=1}^{n} \frac{1}{2}(r + 3)(r + 4) = \frac{1}{6}(n + 3)(n + 4)(n + 5) - 10.$$

[4 marks]

(iii) Find the sum of the first 20 terms of the series
$4 \times 5 + 5 \times 6 + 6 \times 7 + \ldots$ [2 marks]

5 Complex numbers and geometry

The power of mathematics is often to change one thing into another, to change geometry into language.

Marcus du Sautoy

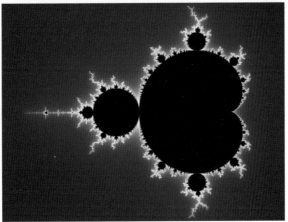

Figure 5.1 The Mandlebrot set

Discussion point

→ Figure 5.1 is an Argand diagram showing the Mandlebrot set. The black area shows all the complex numbers that satisfy a particular rule. Find out about the rule which defines whether or not a particular complex number is in the Mandlebrot set.

1 The modulus and argument of a complex number

Figure 5.2 shows the point representing $z = x + y\mathrm{i}$ on an Argand diagram.

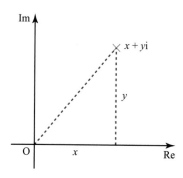

Figure 5.2

> Using Pythagoras' theorem.

The distance of this point from the origin is $\sqrt{x^2 + y^2}$.

This distance is called the modulus of z, and is denoted by $|z|$.

So, for the complex number $z = x + y\mathrm{i}$, $|z| = \sqrt{x^2 + y^2}$.

Notice that since $zz^* = (x + \mathrm{i}y)(x - \mathrm{i}y) = x^2 + y^2$, then $|z|^2 = zz^*$.

Example 5.1

Represent each of the following complex numbers on an Argand diagram. Find the modulus of each complex number, giving exact answers in their simplest form.

$$z_1 = -5 + \mathrm{i} \qquad z_2 = 6 \qquad z_3 = -5 - 5\mathrm{i} \qquad z_4 = -4\mathrm{i}$$

Solution

Figure 5.3

$$|z_1| = \sqrt{(-5)^2 + 1} = \sqrt{26}$$

$$|z_2| = \sqrt{6^2 + 0^2} = \sqrt{36} = 6$$

$$|z_3| = \sqrt{(-5)^2 + (-5)^2} = \sqrt{50} = 5\sqrt{2}$$

$$|z_4| = \sqrt{0^2 + (-4)^2} = \sqrt{16} = 4$$

Notice that the modulus of a real number $z = a$ is equal to a and the modulus of an imaginary number $z = bi$ is equal to b.

Figure 5.4 shows the complex number z on an Argand diagram. The length r represents the modulus of the complex number and the angle θ is called the argument of the complex number.

Prior Knowledge

You need to be familiar with radians, which are covered in the A Level Mathematics book. There is a brief introduction on page 169 of this book.

When describing complex numbers, it is usual to give the angle θ in radians.

Figure 5.4

The argument is measured anticlockwise from the positive real axis. By convention the argument is measured in radians.

However, this angle is not uniquely defined since adding any multiple of 2π to θ gives the same direction. To avoid confusion, it is usual to choose that value of θ for which $-\pi < \theta \leq \pi$, as shown in Figure 5.5.

This is called the **principal argument** of z and is denoted by $\arg z$. Every complex number except zero has a unique principal argument.

The argument of zero is undefined.

Discussion point

→ For the complex number $z = x + y$i, is it true that $\arg z$ is given by $\arctan\left(\dfrac{y}{x}\right)$?

Figure 5.5 shows the complex numbers $z_1 = 2 - 3$i and $z_2 = -2 + 3$i. For both z_1 and z_2, $\dfrac{y}{x} = -\dfrac{3}{2}$ and a calculator gives $\arctan\left(-\dfrac{3}{2}\right) = -0.98$ rad.

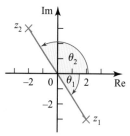

Figure 5.5

The argument of z_1 is the angle θ_1 and this is indeed -0.98 radians. However, the argument of z_2 is the angle θ_2 which is in the second quadrant. It is given by $\pi - 0.98 = 2.16$ radians.

Always draw a diagram when finding the argument of a complex number. This tells you in which quadrant the complex number lies.

Example 5.2

For each of these complex numbers, find the argument of the complex number, giving your answers in radians in exact form or to 3 significant figures as appropriate.

(i) $z_1 = -5 + i$ (ii) $z_2 = 2\sqrt{3} - 2i$ (iii) $z_3 = -5 - 5i$ (iv) $z_4 = -4i$

Solution

(i) $z_1 = -5 + i$

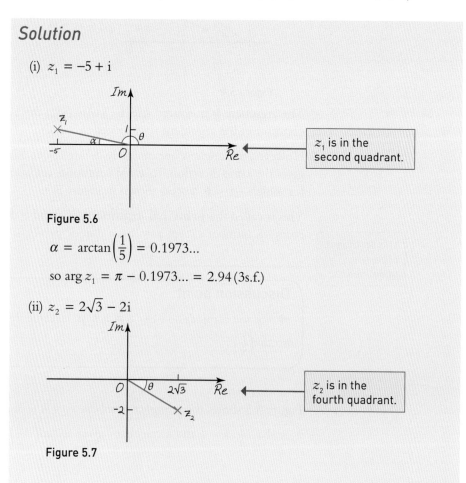

Figure 5.6

z_1 is in the second quadrant.

$$\alpha = \arctan\left(\frac{1}{5}\right) = 0.1973...$$

so $\arg z_1 = \pi - 0.1973... = 2.94\,(3\text{s.f.})$

(ii) $z_2 = 2\sqrt{3} - 2i$

z_2 is in the fourth quadrant.

Figure 5.7

$$\theta = \arctan\left(\frac{2}{2\sqrt{3}}\right) = \frac{\pi}{6}$$

As it is measured in a clockwise direction,

$\arg z_2 = -\dfrac{\pi}{6}$.

(iii) $z_3 = -5 - 5i$

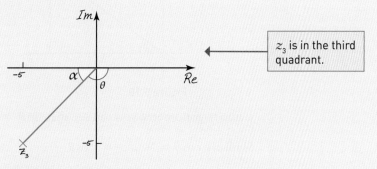

Figure 5.8

z_3 is in the third quadrant.

$$\alpha = \arctan\left(\frac{5}{5}\right) = \frac{\pi}{4}$$

So, $\theta = \pi - \dfrac{\pi}{4} = \dfrac{3\pi}{4}$

Since it is measured in a clockwise direction,

$\arg z_3 = -\dfrac{3\pi}{4}$.

(iv) $z_4 = -4i$

Figure 5.9

z_4 lies on the negative imaginary axis.

On the negative imaginary axis, the argument is $-\dfrac{\pi}{2}$

$\arg z_4 = -\dfrac{\pi}{2}$.

The modulus-argument form of a complex number

In Figure 5.10, you can see the relationship between the components of a complex number and its modulus and argument.

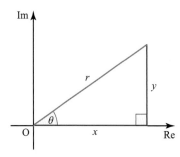

Figure 5.10

Using trigonometry, you can see that $\sin\theta = \dfrac{y}{r}$ and so $y = r\sin\theta$.

Similarly, $\cos\theta = \dfrac{x}{r}$ so $x = r\cos\theta$.

Therefore, the complex number $z = x + y\mathrm{i}$ can be written

$$z = r\cos\theta + r\sin\theta\,\mathrm{i}$$

or

$$z = r(\cos\theta + \mathrm{i}\sin\theta).$$

> The modulus–argument form of a complex number is sometimes called the *polar* form, as the modulus of a complex number is its distance from the origin, which is also called the *pole*.

This is called the **modulus-argument form** of the complex number and is sometimes written as (r, θ).

You may have noticed in the earlier calculations that values of sin, cos and tan for some angles are exact and can be expressed in surds. You will see these values in the following activity – they are worth memorising as this will help make some calculations quicker.

ACTIVITY 5.1

Copy and complete this table. Use the diagrams in Figure 5.11 to help you.

Give your answers as exact values (involving surds where appropriate), rather than as decimals.

	$\dfrac{\pi}{6}$	$\dfrac{\pi}{4}$	$\dfrac{\pi}{3}$
sin			
cos			
tan			

Table 5.1

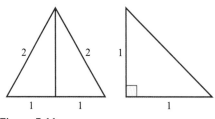

Figure 5.11

ACTIVITY 5.2

Most calculators can convert complex numbers given in the form (x, y) to the form (r, θ) (called *rectangular to polar*, and often shown as $R \rightarrow P$) and from (r, θ) to (x, y) (*polar to rectangular*, $P \rightarrow R$).

Find out how to use these facilities on your calculator.

Does your calculator always give the correct θ, or do you sometimes have to add or subtract 2π?

Example 5.3

Write the following complex numbers in modulus-argument form.

(i) $z_1 = \sqrt{3} + 3i$ (ii) $z_2 = -3 + \sqrt{3}i$

(iii) $z_3 = \sqrt{3} - 3i$ (iv) $z_4 = -3 - \sqrt{3}i$

Solution

Figure 5.12 shows the four complex numbers z_1, z_2, z_3 and z_4.

For each complex number, the modulus is $\sqrt{\left(\sqrt{3}\right)^2 + 3^2} = 2\sqrt{3}$

$$\alpha_1 = \arctan\left(\frac{3}{\sqrt{3}}\right) = \frac{\pi}{3}$$

$$\Rightarrow \arg z_1 = \frac{\pi}{3} \text{, so } z_1 = 2\sqrt{3}\left(\cos\frac{\pi}{3} + i\sin\frac{\pi}{3}\right)$$

By symmetry, $\arg z_3 = -\frac{\pi}{3}$, so $z_3 = 2\sqrt{3}\left(\cos\left(-\frac{\pi}{3}\right) + i\sin\left(-\frac{\pi}{3}\right)\right)$

$$\alpha_2 = \arctan\left(\frac{\sqrt{3}}{3}\right) = \frac{\pi}{6}$$

$$\Rightarrow \arg z_2 = \pi - \frac{\pi}{6} = \frac{5\pi}{6} \text{, so } z_2 = 2\sqrt{3}\left(\cos\frac{5\pi}{6} + i\sin\frac{5\pi}{6}\right)$$

By symmetry, $\arg z_4 = -\frac{5\pi}{6}$, so $z_4 = 2\sqrt{3}\left(\cos\left(-\frac{5\pi}{6}\right) + i\sin\left(-\frac{5\pi}{6}\right)\right)$

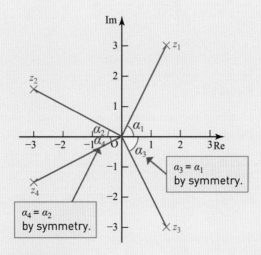

Figure 5.12

Exercise 5.1

① The Argand diagram in Figure 5.13 shows three complex numbers.

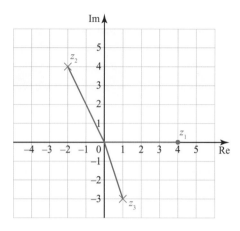

Figure 5.13

Write each of the numbers z_1, z_2 and z_3 in the form:

(i) $a + b\mathrm{i}$

(ii) $r(\cos\theta + \mathrm{i}\sin\theta)$, giving answers exactly or to 3 significant figures where appropriate.

② Find the modulus and argument of each of the following complex numbers, giving your answer exactly or to 3 significant figures where appropriate.

(i) $3 + 2\mathrm{i}$ (ii) $-5 + 2\mathrm{i}$ (iii) $-3 - 2\mathrm{i}$ (iv) $2 - 5\mathrm{i}$

③ Find the modulus and argument of each of the complex numbers on this Argand diagram.

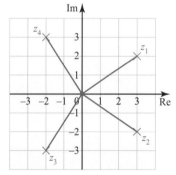

Figure 5.14

Describe the transformations that map z_1 onto each of the other points on the diagram.

④ Write each of the following complex numbers in the form $x + y\mathrm{i}$, giving surds in your answer where appropriate.

(i) $4\left(\cos\left(-\dfrac{\pi}{2}\right) + \mathrm{i}\sin\left(-\dfrac{\pi}{2}\right)\right)$

(ii) $7\left(\cos\dfrac{3\pi}{4} + \mathrm{i}\sin\dfrac{3\pi}{4}\right)$

(iii) $3\left(\cos\dfrac{5\pi}{6} + i\sin\dfrac{5\pi}{6}\right)$

(iv) $5\left(\cos\left(-\dfrac{\pi}{6}\right) + i\sin\left(-\dfrac{\pi}{6}\right)\right)$

⑤ For each complex number, find the modulus and argument, and hence write the complex number in modulus-argument form.

Give the argument in radians, either as a multiple of π or correct to 3 significant figures.

(i) 1   (ii) -2 (iii) $3i$ (iv) $-4i$

⑥ For each of the complex numbers below, find the modulus and argument, and hence write the complex number in modulus-argument form.

Give the argument in radians as a multiple of π.

(i) $1 + i$ (ii) $-1 + i$ (iii) $-1 - i$ (iv) $1 - i$

⑦ For each complex number, find the modulus and principal argument, and hence write the complex number in modulus-argument form.

Give the argument in radians, either as a multiple of π or correct to 3 significant figures.

(i) $6\sqrt{3} + 6i$ (ii) $3 - 4i$ (iii) $-12 + 5i$

(iv) $4 + 7i$ (v) $-58 - 93i$

⑧ Express each of these complex numbers in the form $r(\cos\theta + i\sin\theta)$ giving the argument in radians, either as a multiple of π or correct to 3 significant figures.

(i) $\dfrac{2}{3 - i}$ (ii) $\dfrac{3 - 2i}{3 - i}$ (iii) $\dfrac{-2 - 5i}{3 - i}$

⑨ Represent each of the following complex numbers on a separate Argand diagram and write it in the form $x + yi$, giving surds in your answer where appropriate.

(i) $|z| = 2$, $\arg z = \dfrac{\pi}{2}$ (ii) $|z| = 3$, $\arg z = \dfrac{\pi}{3}$

(iii) $|z| = 7$, $\arg z = \dfrac{5\pi}{6}$ (iv) $|z| = 1$, $\arg z = -\dfrac{\pi}{4}$

(v) $|z| = 5$, $\arg z = -\dfrac{2\pi}{3}$ (vi) $|z| = 6$, $\arg z = -2$

⑩ Given that $\arg(5 + 2i) = \alpha$, find the argument of each of the following in terms of α.

(i) $-5 - 2i$ (ii) $5 - 2i$ (iii) $-5 + 2i$

(iv) $2 + 5i$ (v) $-2 + 5i$

⑪ The complex numbers z_1 and z_2 are shown on the Argand diagram in Figure 5.15.

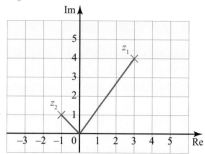

Figure 5.15

(i) Find the modulus and argument of each of the two numbers.

(ii) (a) Find $z_1 z_2$ and $\dfrac{z_1}{z_2}$.

(b) Find the modulus and argument of each of $z_1 z_2$ and $\dfrac{z_1}{z_2}$.

(iii) What rules can you deduce about the modulus and argument of the two complex numbers and the answers to part (ii)(b)?

2 Multiplying and dividing complex numbers in modulus-argument form

Prior knowledge

You need to be familiar with the compound angle formulae. These are covered in the A Level Mathematics book, and a brief introduction is given on page 172 of this book.

ACTIVITY 5.3

What is the geometrical effect of multiplying one complex number by another? To explore this question, start with the numbers $z_1 = 2 + 3i$ and $z_2 = iz_1$.

(i) Plot the vectors z_1 and z_2 on the same Argand diagram, and describe the geometrical transformation that maps the vector z_1 to the vector z_2.

(ii) Repeat part (i) with $z_1 = 2 + 3i$ and $z_2 = 2iz_1$.

(iii) Repeat part (i) with $z_1 = 2 + 3i$ and $z_2 = (1 + i)z_1$.

You will have seen in Activity 5.3 that multiplying one complex number by another involves a combination of an enlargement and a rotation.

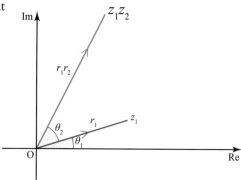

Figure 5.16

You obtain the vector $z_1 z_2$ by enlarging the vector z_1 by the scale factor $|z_2|$, and rotate it anticlockwise through an angle of $\arg z_2$.

So to multiply complex numbers in modulus-argument form, you *multiply* their moduli and *add* their arguments.

$$|z_1 z_2| = |z_1||z_2|$$

$$\arg(z_1 z_2) = \arg z_1 + \arg z_2$$

> You may need to add or subtract 2π to give the principal argument.

You can prove these results using the compound angle formulae.

$$z_1 z_2 = r_1(\cos\theta_1 + i\sin\theta_1) \times r_2(\cos\theta_2 + i\sin\theta_2)$$
$$= r_1 r_2(\cos\theta_1\cos\theta_2 + i\cos\theta_1\sin\theta_2 + i\sin\theta_1\cos\theta_2 - \sin\theta_1\sin\theta_2)$$
$$= r_1 r_2[(\cos\theta_1\cos\theta_2 - \sin\theta_1\sin\theta_2) + i(\cos\theta_1\sin\theta_2 + \sin\theta_1\cos\theta_2)]$$

> The identity $\cos(\theta_1 + \theta_2)$.

> The identity $\sin(\theta_1 + \theta_2)$.

$$= r_1 r_2[(\cos(\theta_1 + \theta_2)) + i\sin(\theta_1 + \theta_2)]$$

So, $|z_1 z_2| = r_1 r_2$ and $\arg(z_1 z_2) = \theta_1 + \theta_2$.

Dividing complex numbers works in a similar way. You obtain the vector $\dfrac{z_1}{z_2}$ by enlarging the vector z_1 by the scale factor $\dfrac{1}{|z_2|}$, and rotate it *clockwise* through an angle of $\arg z_2$.

> This is equivalent to rotating it anticlockwise through an angle of $-\arg z_2$.

So, to divide complex numbers in modulus-argument form, you *divide* their moduli and *subtract* their arguments.

$$\left|\frac{z_1}{z_2}\right| = \frac{|z_1|}{|z_2|}$$

$$\arg\left(\frac{z_1}{z_2}\right) = \arg z_1 - \arg z_2$$

You can prove this easily from the multiplication results by letting $\dfrac{z_1}{z_2} = w$, so that $z_1 = wz_2$.

Then $|z_1| = |w||z_2|$, so $|w| = \dfrac{|z_1|}{|z_2|}$

and $\arg z_1 = \arg w + \arg z_2$, so $\arg w = \arg z_1 - \arg z_2$.

Example 5.4

The complex numbers w and z are given by $w = 2\left(\cos\dfrac{\pi}{4} + i\sin\dfrac{\pi}{4}\right)$ and $z = 5\left(\cos\dfrac{5\pi}{6} + i\sin\dfrac{5\pi}{6}\right)$.

Find (i) wz and (ii) $\dfrac{w}{z}$ in modulus-argument form. Illustrate each of these on a separate Argand diagram.

Solution

$$|w| = 2 \quad \arg w = \frac{\pi}{4}$$

$$|z| = 5 \quad \arg w = \frac{5\pi}{6}$$

(i) $|wz| = |w||z| = 2 \times 5 = 10$

$$\arg w + \arg z = \frac{\pi}{4} + \frac{5\pi}{6} = \frac{13\pi}{12}$$

> This is not in the range $-\pi < \theta \leq \pi$.

so $\arg(wz) = \dfrac{13\pi}{12} - 2\pi = -\dfrac{11}{12}\pi$ ← Subtract 2π to obtain the principal argument.

$$wz = 10\left(\cos\left(-\dfrac{11\pi}{12}\right) + i\sin\left(-\dfrac{11\pi}{12}\right)\right)$$

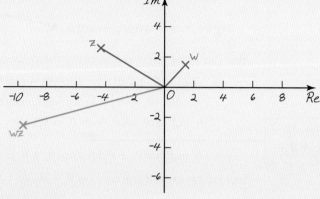

Figure 5.17

(ii) $\dfrac{|w|}{|z|} = \dfrac{|w|}{|z|} = \dfrac{2}{5}$

$\arg w - \arg z = \dfrac{\pi}{4} - \dfrac{5\pi}{6} = -\dfrac{7\pi}{12}$

$$wz = \dfrac{2}{5}\left(\cos\left(-\dfrac{7\pi}{12}\right) + i\sin\left(-\dfrac{7\pi}{12}\right)\right)$$

Figure 5.18

Exercise 5.2

① The complex numbers w and z shown in the Argand diagram are $w = 1 + i$ and $z = 1 - \sqrt{3}i$

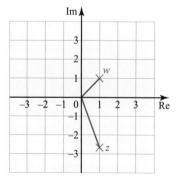

Figure 5.19

(i) Find the modulus and argument of each of the complex numbers w and z.

(ii) Hence write down the modulus and argument of

    (a) wz

    (b) $\dfrac{w}{z}$

(iii) Show the points w, z, wz and $\dfrac{w}{z}$ on a copy of the Argand diagram.

② Given that $z = 2\left(\cos\dfrac{\pi}{4} + \mathrm{i}\sin\dfrac{\pi}{4}\right)$ and $w = 3\left(\cos\dfrac{\pi}{3} + \mathrm{i}\sin\dfrac{\pi}{3}\right)$, find the following complex numbers in modulus-argument form

   (i) wz (ii) $\dfrac{w}{z}$ (iii) $\dfrac{z}{w}$ (iv) $\dfrac{1}{z}$

③ The complex numbers z and w are defined as follows:

$z = -3 + 3\sqrt{3}\mathrm{i}$

$|w| = 18$, $\arg w = -\dfrac{\pi}{6}$

Write down the values of

   (i) $\arg z$ (ii) $|z|$ (iii) $\arg(zw)$ (iv) $|zw|$.

④ Given that $z = 6\left(\cos\dfrac{\pi}{6} + \mathrm{i}\sin\dfrac{\pi}{6}\right)$ and $w = 2\left(\cos\left(-\dfrac{\pi}{4}\right) + \mathrm{i}\sin\left(-\dfrac{\pi}{4}\right)\right)$, find the following complex numbers in modulus-argument form:

   (i) w^2 (ii) z^5 (iii) $w^3 z^4$

   (iv) $5\mathrm{i}z$ (v) $(1+\mathrm{i})w$

⑤ Find the multiplication scale factor and the angle of rotation which maps

   (i) the vector $2 + 3\mathrm{i}$ to the vector $5 - 2\mathrm{i}$

   (ii) the vector $-4 + \mathrm{i}$ to the vector $3\mathrm{i}$.

⑥ Prove that, in general, $\arg\left(\dfrac{1}{z}\right) = -\arg z$. What are the exceptions to this rule?

⑦ (i) Find the real and imaginary parts of $\dfrac{-1+\mathrm{i}}{1+\sqrt{3}\mathrm{i}}$.

   (ii) Express $-1 + \mathrm{i}$ and $1 + \sqrt{3}\mathrm{i}$ in modulus-argument form.

   (iii) Hence show that $\cos\dfrac{5\pi}{12} = \dfrac{\sqrt{3}-1}{2\sqrt{2}}$, and find an exact expression for $\sin\dfrac{5\pi}{12}$.

⑧ Prove that for three complex numbers $w = r_1(\cos\theta_1 + \mathrm{i}\sin\theta_1)$, $z = r_2(\cos\theta_2 + \mathrm{i}\sin\theta_2)$ and $p = r_3(\cos\theta_3 + \mathrm{i}\sin\theta_3)$, $|wzp| = |w||z||p|$ and $\arg(wzp) = \arg w + \arg z + \arg p$.

3 Loci in the Argand diagram

A locus is the set of locations that a point can occupy when constrained by a given rule. The plural of locus is loci.

Loci of the form $|z - a| = r$

Figure 5.20 shows the positions for two general complex numbers $z_1 = x_1 + y_1 \mathrm{i}$ and $z_2 = x_2 + y_2 \mathrm{i}$.

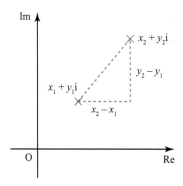

Figure 5.20

You saw earlier that the complex number $z_2 - z_1$ can be represented by the vector from the point representing z_1 to the point representing z_2 (see Figure 5.20). This is the key to solving many questions about sets of points in an Argand diagram, as shown in the following example.

Example 5.5

Draw Argand diagrams showing the following sets of points z for which

(i) $|z| = 5$

(ii) $|z - 3| = 5$

(iii) $|z - 4\mathrm{i}| = 5$

(iv) $|z - 3 - 4\mathrm{i}| = 5$

Solution
(i) $|z| = 5$

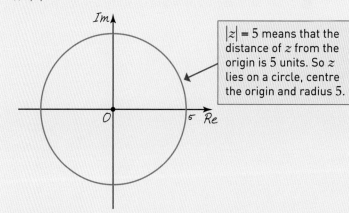

$|z| = 5$ means that the distance of z from the origin is 5 units. So z lies on a circle, centre the origin and radius 5.

Figure 5.21

(ii) $|z - 3| = 5$

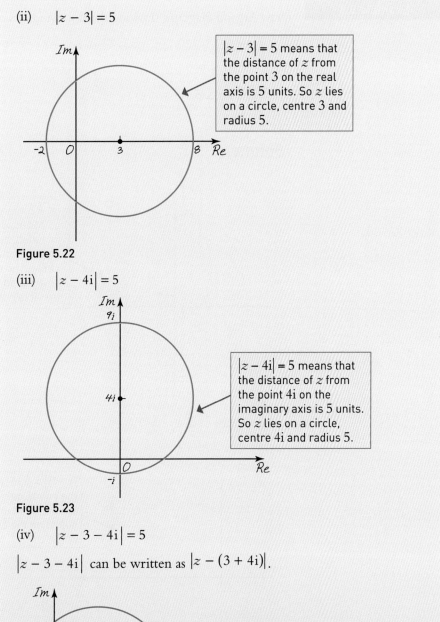

$|z - 3| = 5$ means that the distance of z from the point 3 on the real axis is 5 units. So z lies on a circle, centre 3 and radius 5.

Figure 5.22

(iii) $|z - 4i| = 5$

$|z - 4i| = 5$ means that the distance of z from the point 4i on the imaginary axis is 5 units. So z lies on a circle, centre 4i and radius 5.

Figure 5.23

(iv) $|z - 3 - 4i| = 5$

$|z - 3 - 4i|$ can be written as $|z - (3 + 4i)|$.

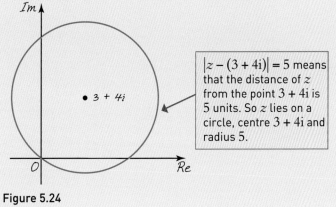

$|z - (3 + 4i)| = 5$ means that the distance of z from the point 3 + 4i is 5 units. So z lies on a circle, centre 3 + 4i and radius 5.

Figure 5.24

Generally, a locus in an Argand diagram of the form $|z - a| = r$ is a circle, centre a and radius r.

In the example above, each locus is the set of points on the circumference of the circle. It is possible to define a region in the Argand diagram in a similar way.

Example 5.6

Draw Argand diagrams showing the following sets of points z for which

(i) $|z| < 5$

(ii) $|z - 3| > 5$

(iii) $|z - 4i| \leq 5$

Solution

(i) $|z| < 5$

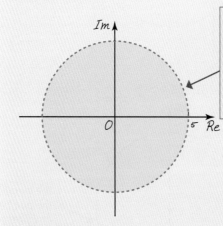

$|z| < 5$ means that all the points inside the circle are included, but not the points on the circumference of the circle. The circle is shown as a dotted line to indicate that it is not part of the locus.

Figure 5.25

(ii) $|z - 3| > 5$

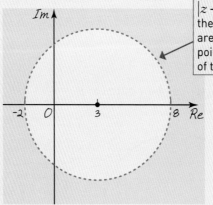

$|z - 3| > 5$ means that all the points outside the circle are included, but not the points on the circumference of the circle.

Figure 5.26

(iii) $|z - 4i| \leq 5$

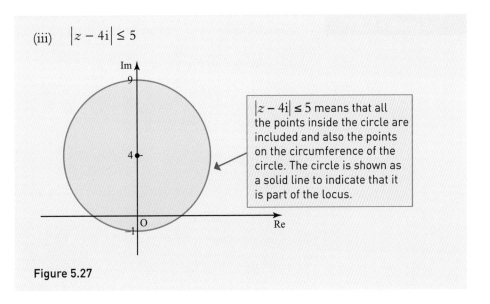

$|z - 4i| \leq 5$ means that all the points inside the circle are included and also the points on the circumference of the circle. The circle is shown as a solid line to indicate that it is part of the locus.

Figure 5.27

Loci of the form arg $(z - a) = \theta$

ACTIVITY 5.4

(i)   Plot some points which have argument $\frac{\pi}{4}$.

Use your points to sketch the locus of $\arg z = \frac{\pi}{4}$.

Is the point $-2 - 2i$ on this locus?

How could you describe the locus?

(ii)   Which of the following complex numbers satisfy $\arg(z - 2) = \frac{\pi}{4}$?

(a) $z = 4$

(b) $z = 3 + i$

(c) $z = 4i$

(d) $z = 8 + 6i$

(e) $z = 1 - i$

Describe and sketch the locus of points which satisfy $\arg(z - 2) = \frac{\pi}{4}$.

In Activity 5.4 you looked at the loci of points of the form $\arg(z - a) = \frac{\pi}{4}$ where a is a fixed complex number. On the Argand diagram the locus looks like this.

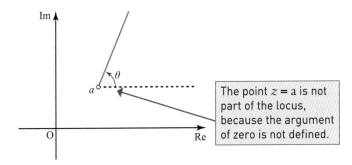

The point $z = a$ is not part of the locus, because the argument of zero is not defined.

Figure 5.28

The locus is a half line of points from the point a and with angle measured θ from the positive horizontal axis, as shown in Figure 5.28.

Example 5.7

Sketch the locus of z in an Argand diagram when

(i) $\arg(z - 3) = \dfrac{2\pi}{3}$

(ii) $\arg(z + 2i) = \dfrac{\pi}{6}$

(iii) $\arg(z - 1 + 4i) = -\dfrac{\pi}{4}$.

Solution

(i) This is a half line starting from $z = 3$, at an angle $\dfrac{2\pi}{3}$.

Figure 5.29

(ii) This can be written in the form $\arg(z - (-2i)) = \dfrac{\pi}{6}$ so it is a half line starting from $-2i$ at an angle $\dfrac{\pi}{6}$.

Figure 5.30

(iii) This can be written $\arg(z - (1 - 4i)) = -\dfrac{\pi}{4}$ so it is a half line starting from $1 - 4i$ at an angle $-\dfrac{\pi}{4}$.

Figure 5.31

Example 5.8

Sketch diagrams that represent the regions represented by

(i) $0 \le \arg(z - 3i) \le \dfrac{\pi}{3}$

(ii) $-\dfrac{\pi}{4} < \arg(z - 3 + 4i) < \dfrac{\pi}{4}$.

Solution

(i)   This is the region between the two half lines starting at $z = 3i$, at angle 0 and angle $\dfrac{\pi}{3}$.

Figure 5.32

(ii) $\arg(z - 3 + 4i)$ can be written $\arg(z - (3 - 4i))$ so this is the region between two half lines starting at $3 - 4i$ at angles $-\dfrac{\pi}{4}$ and $\dfrac{\pi}{4}$.

The lines are not included in the locus.

Figure 5.33

Loci of the form $|z - a| = |z - b|$

ACTIVITY 5.5

On an Argand diagram, mark the points $3 + 4i$ and $-1 + 2i$. Identify some points that are the same distance from both points.

Use your diagram to describe and sketch the locus $|z - 3 - 4i| = |z + 1 - 2i|$.

Generally, the locus $|z - a| = |z - b|$ represents the locus of all points which lie on the perpendicular bisector between the points represented by the complex numbers a and b.

Example 5.9

Show each of the following sets of points on an Argand diagram.

(i) $|z - 3 - 4i| = |z + 1 - 2i|$

(ii) $|z - 3 - 4i| < |z + 1 - 2i|$

(iii) $|z - 3 - 4i| \geq |z + 1 - 2i|$

Solution

(i) The condition can be written as $|z - (3 + 4i)| = |z - (-1 + 2i)|$.

The distance of z from the point $3 + 4i$ is equal to the distance of z from the point $-1 + 2i$, so the locus is the perpendicular bisector of these two points.

Figure 5.34

(ii) $|z - 3 - 4i| < |z + 1 - 2i|$

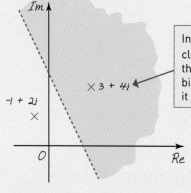

In this case the locus includes all the points closer to the point $3 + 4i$ than to $-1 + 2i$. So the locus is the shaded area. The perpendicular bisector itself is not included in the locus, so it is shown as a dotted line.

Figure 5.35

(iii) $\left|z - 3 - 4i\right| \geq \left|z + 1 - 2i\right|$

In this case the locus includes all the points closer to the point $-1 + 2i$ than to $3 + 4i$, and also all the points which are the same distance from the two points. So the locus is the shaded area as well as the perpendicular bisector, which is shown as a solid line to indicate that it is part of the locus.

Figure 5.36

Example 5.10

Draw, on the same Argand diagram, the loci

(i) $\left|z - 3 - 4i\right| = 5$

(ii) $\left|z\right| = \left|z - 4i\right|$.

Shade the region that satisfies both $\left|z - 3 - 4i\right| \leq 5$ and $\left|z\right| \leq \left|z - 4i\right|$.

Solution

(i) $\left|z - 3 - 4i\right|$ can be written as $\left|z - (3 + 4i)\right|$ so (i) is a circle centre $3 + 4i$ with radius 5.

(ii) $\left|z\right| = \left|z - 4i\right|$ represents the perpendicular bisector of the line between the points $z = 0$ and $z = 4i$.

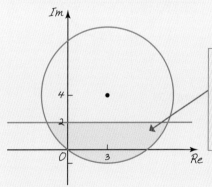

$\left|z - 3 - 4i\right| \leq 5$ represents the circumference and the inside of the circle. $\left|z\right| \leq \left|z - 4i\right|$ represents the side of the perpendicular bisector that is nearer to the origin including the perpendicular bisector itself. The shaded area represents the region for which both conditions are true.

Figure 5.37

 Don't get confused between loci of the forms $\left|z - a\right| = r$ and $\left|z - a\right| = \left|z - b\right|$.

$\left|z - a\right| = r$ represents a circle, centred on the complex number a, with radius r.

$\left|z - a\right| = \left|z - b\right|$ represents the perpendicular bisector of the line between the points a and b.

Exercise 5.3

① For each of parts (i) to (iv), draw an Argand diagram showing the set of points z for which the given condition is true.

(i) $\left|z\right| = 2$ (ii) $\left|z - 2\mathrm{i}\right| = 2$

(iii) $\left|z - 2\right| = 2$ (iv) $\left|z + \sqrt{2} + \sqrt{2}\mathrm{i}\right| = 2$

② For each of parts (i) to (iv), draw an Argand diagram showing the set of points z for which the given condition is true.

(i) $\arg z = \dfrac{\pi}{3}$ (ii) $\arg\left(z + 1 + \sqrt{3}\mathrm{i}\right) = \dfrac{\pi}{3}$

(iii) $\arg\left(z - 1 + \sqrt{3}\mathrm{i}\right) = \dfrac{2\pi}{3}$ (iv) $\arg\left(z - 1 - \sqrt{3}\mathrm{i}\right) = -\dfrac{2\pi}{3}$

③ For each of parts (i) to (iv), draw an Argand diagram showing the set of points z for which the given condition is true.

(i) $\left|z - 8\right| = \left|z - 4\right|$ (ii) $\left|z - 2 - 4\mathrm{i}\right| = \left|z - 6 - 8\mathrm{i}\right|$

(iii) $\left|z + 5 - 2\mathrm{i}\right| = \left|z + 3\mathrm{i}\right|$ (iv) $\left|z + 3 + 5\mathrm{i}\right| = \left|z - \mathrm{i}\right|$

④ Write down the loci for the sets of points z that are represented in each of these Argand diagrams.

(i)

Figure 5.38

(ii)

Figure 5.39

(iii)

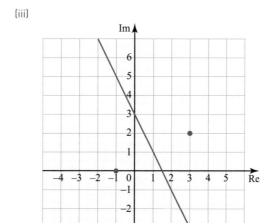

Figure 5.40

(5) Write down, in terms of z, the loci for the regions that are represented in each of these Argand diagrams.

(i)

Figure 5.41

(ii)

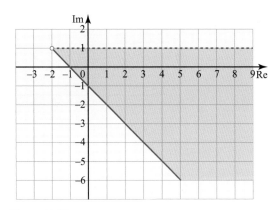

Figure 5.42

(iii)

Figure 5.43

⑥ Draw an Argand diagram showing the set of points z for which $\left|z - 12 + 5i\right| \leq 7$. Use the diagram to prove that, for these z, $6 \leq \left|z\right| \leq 20$.

⑦ For each of parts (i) to (iii), draw an Argand diagram showing the set of points z for which the given condition is true.

(i) $\arg(z - 3 + i) \leq -\dfrac{\pi}{6}$

(ii) $0 \leq \arg(z - 3i) \leq \dfrac{3\pi}{4}$

(iii) $-\dfrac{\pi}{4} < \arg(z + 5 - 3i) < \dfrac{\pi}{3}$

⑧ On an Argand diagram shade in the regions represented by the following inequalities.

(i) $\left|z - 3\right| \leq 2$

(ii) $\left|z - 6i\right| > \left|z + 2i\right|$

(iii) $2 \leq \left|z - 3 - 4i\right| \leq 4$

(iv) $\left|z + 3 + 6i\right| \leq \left|z - 2 - 7i\right|$.

⑨ Shade on an Argand diagram the region satisfied by the inequalities $\left|z - 1 + i\right| \leq 1$ and $-\dfrac{\pi}{3} < \arg z < 0$.

⑩

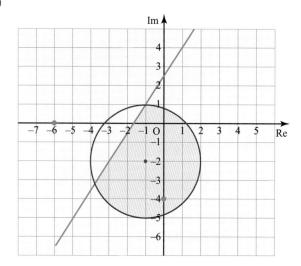

Figure 5.44

(i) For this Argand diagram, write down in terms of z

    (a) the loci of the set of points on the circle

    (b) the loci of the set of points on the straight line.

(ii) Using inequalities, express in terms of z the shaded region on the Argand diagram.

⑪ Sketch on the same Argand diagram

    (i) the locus of points $\left| z - 2 + 2i \right| = 3$

    (ii) the locus of points $\arg(z - 2 + 2i) = -\dfrac{\pi}{4}$

    (iii) the locus of points $\arg(z - 2 + 2i) = \dfrac{\pi}{2}$.

Shade the region defined by the inequalities $\left| z - 2 + 2i \right| \leq 3$ and $-\dfrac{\pi}{4} \leq \arg(z - 2 + 2i) \leq \dfrac{\pi}{2}$.

⑫ You are given the complex number $w = -\sqrt{3} + 3i$.

    (i) Find $\arg w$ and $\left| w - 2i \right|$.

    (ii) On an Argand diagram, shade the region representing complex numbers z which satisfy both of these inequalities:

$$\left| z - 2i \right| \leq 2 \text{ and } \frac{\pi}{2} \leq \arg z \leq \frac{2\pi}{3}$$

Indicate the point on your diagram which corresponds to w.

⑬ Sketch a diagram that represents the regions represented by

$$\left| z - 2 - 2i \right| \leq 2 \textbf{ and } 0 \leq \arg(z - 2i) \leq \frac{\pi}{4}.$$

⑭ By using an Argand diagram, determine if it is possible to find values of z for which $\left| z - 2 + i \right| \geq 10$ and $\left| z + 4 + 2i \right| \leq 2$ simultaneously.

⑮ What are the greatest and least values of $\left| z + 3 - 2i \right|$ if $\left| z - 5 + 4i \right| \leq 3$?

⑯ You are given that $\left| z - 3 \right| = 2\left| z - 3 + 9i \right|$.

    (i) Show, using algebra with $z = x + yi$, that the locus of z is a circle and state the centre and radius of the circle.

    (ii) Sketch the locus of the circle on an Argand diagram.

LEARNING OUTCOMES

When you have completed this chapter you should be able to:

➤ find the modulus of a complex number
➤ find the principal argument of a complex number using radians
➤ express a complex number in modulus-argument form
➤ multiply and divide complex numbers in modulus-argument form
➤ represent multiplication and division of two complex numbers on an Argand diagram
➤ represent and interpret sets of complex numbers as loci on an Argand diagram:
  ➤ circles of the form $|z - a| = r$
  ➤ half-lines of the form $\arg(z - a) = \theta$
  ➤ lines of the form $|z - a| = |z - b|$
➤ represent and interpret regions defined by inequalities based on the above.

KEY POINTS

1 The modulus of $z = x + y\mathrm{i}$ is $|z| = \sqrt{x^2 + y^2}$. This is the distance of the point z from the origin on the Argand diagram.

2 The argument of z is the angle θ, measured in radians, between the line connecting the origin and the point z and the positive real axis.

3 The principal argument of z, $\arg z$, is the angle θ, measured in radians, for which $-\pi < \theta \leq \pi$, between the line connecting the origin and the point z and the positive real axis.

4 For a complex number z, $zz* = |z|^2$.

5 The modulus–argument form of z is $z = r(\cos\theta + \mathrm{i}\sin\theta)$, where $r = |z|$ and $\theta = \arg z$. This is often written as (r, θ)

6 For two complex numbers z_1 and z_2:

$|z_1 z_2| = |z_1||z_2|$ $\arg(z_1 z_2) = \arg z_1 + \arg z_2$

$\left|\dfrac{z_1}{z_2}\right| = \dfrac{|z_1|}{|z_2|}$ $\arg\left(\dfrac{z_1}{z_2}\right) = \arg z_1 - \arg z_2$

7 The distance between the points z_1 and z_2 in an Argand diagram is $|z_1 - z_2|$.

8 $|z - a| = r$ represents a circle, centre a and radius r.
   $|z - a| < r$ represents the interior of the circle, and $|z - a| > r$ represents the exterior of the circle.

9 $\arg(z - a) = \theta$ represents a half line starting at $z = a$ at an angle of θ from the positive real direction.

10 $|z - a| = |z - b|$ represents the perpendicular bisector of the points a and b.

FUTURE USES

■ Work on complex numbers will be developed further in A Level Further Mathematics.

■ Complex numbers will be needed for work on differential equations in A Level Further Mathematics, in particular in modelling oscillations (simple harmonic motion).

6 Matrices and their inverses

The grand thing is to be able to reason backwards.
Arthur Conan Doyle

Discussion points

➔ What is the same about each of the triangles in the diagram?

➔ How many of the yellow triangles are needed to cover the large purple triangle?

Figure 6.1 Sierpinsky triangle.

The diagram in Figure 6.1 is called a Sierpinsky triangle. The pattern can be continued with smaller and smaller triangles.

1 The determinant of a matrix

Figure 6.2 shows the unit square, labelled OIPJ, and the parallelogram OI′P′J′ formed when OIPJ is transformed using the matrix $\begin{pmatrix} 5 & 4 \\ 1 & 2 \end{pmatrix}$.

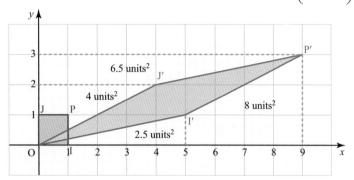

Figure 6.2

What effect does the transformation have on the area of OIPJ?

The area of OIPJ is 1 unit^2.

To find the area of OI′P′J′, a rectangle has been drawn surrounding it. The area of the rectangle is $9 \times 3 = 27$ units^2. The part of the rectangle that is not inside OI′P′J′ has been divided up into two triangles and two trapezia and their areas are shown on the diagram.

So, area OI′P′J′ $= 27 - 2.5 - 8 - 6.5 - 4 = 6$ units^2.

The interesting question is whether you could predict this answer from the numbers in the matrix $\begin{pmatrix} 5 & 4 \\ 1 & 2 \end{pmatrix}$.

You can see that $5 \times 2 - 4 \times 1 = 6$. Is this just a coincidence?

To answer that question you need to transform the unit square by the general 2×2 matrix $\begin{pmatrix} a & b \\ c & d \end{pmatrix}$ and see whether the area of the transformed figure is $(ad - bc)$ units^2. The answer is, 'Yes', and the proof is left for you to do in the activity below.

ACTIVITY 6.1

The unit square is transformed by the matrix $\begin{pmatrix} a & b \\ c & d \end{pmatrix}$.

Prove that the resulting shape is a parallelogram with area $(ad - bc)$ units^2.

It is now evident that the quantity $(ad - bc)$ is the area scale factor associated with the transformation matrix $\begin{pmatrix} a & b \\ c & d \end{pmatrix}$. It is called the **determinant** of the matrix.

Example 6.1

A shape S has area $8\,\text{cm}^2$. S is mapped to a shape T under the transformation represented by the matrix $\mathbf{M} = \begin{pmatrix} 1 & -2 \\ 3 & 0 \end{pmatrix}$.

Find the area of shape T.

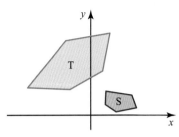

Figure 6.3

Note

In Example 6.1, it does not matter what shape S looks like; for any shape S with area $8\,\text{cm}^2$, the area of the image T will always be $48\,\text{cm}^2$.

Solution

$$\det\begin{pmatrix} 1 & -2 \\ 3 & 0 \end{pmatrix} = (1 \times 0) - (-2 \times 3) = 0 + 6 = 6$$

> The area scale factor of the transformation is 6 ...

$$\text{Area of T} = 8 \times 6$$
$$= 48\,\text{cm}^2$$

> ... and so the area of the original shape is multiplied by 6.

Example 6.2

(i) Draw a diagram to show the image of the unit square OIPJ under the transformation represented by the matrix $\mathbf{M} = \begin{pmatrix} 2 & 3 \\ 4 & 1 \end{pmatrix}$.

(ii) Find det $\mathbf{M}$.

(iii) Use your answer to part (ii) to find the area of the transformed shape.

Solution

(i) $$\begin{pmatrix} 2 & 3 \\ 4 & 1 \end{pmatrix}\begin{pmatrix} 0 & 1 & 1 & 0 \\ 0 & 0 & 1 & 1 \end{pmatrix} = \begin{pmatrix} 0 & 2 & 5 & 3 \\ 0 & 4 & 5 & 1 \end{pmatrix}$$

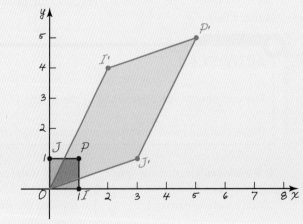

Figure 6.4

(ii) $\det\begin{pmatrix} 2 & 3 \\ 4 & 1 \end{pmatrix} = (2 \times 1) - (3 \times 4) = 2 - 12 = -10$

(iii) The area of the transformed shape is 10 square units.

Notice that the determinant is negative. Since area cannot be negative, the area of the transformed shape is 10 square units.

The sign of the determinant does have significance. If you move anticlockwise around the original unit square you come to vertices O, I, P, J in that order. However, moving anticlockwise about the image reverses the order of the vertices i.e. O, J′, P′, I′. This reversal in the order of the vertices produces the negative determinant.

Discussion point

Which of the following transformations reverse the order of the vertices?

➜ (i)   rotation

➜ (ii) reflection

➜ (iii) enlargement

Check your answers by finding the determinants of matrices representing these transformations.

Example 6.3

Given that $\mathbf{P} = \begin{pmatrix} 2 & 1 \\ 0 & 1 \end{pmatrix}$ and $\mathbf{Q} = \begin{pmatrix} 2 & 1 \\ 1 & 2 \end{pmatrix}$, find

(i)   det **P**

(ii) det **Q**

(iii) det **PQ**.

What do you notice?

Solution

(i)   det **P** = 2 − 0 = 2

(ii) det **Q** = 4 − 1 = 3

(iii) $\mathbf{PQ} = \begin{pmatrix} 2 & 1 \\ 0 & 1 \end{pmatrix}\begin{pmatrix} 2 & 1 \\ 1 & 2 \end{pmatrix} = \begin{pmatrix} 5 & 4 \\ 1 & 2 \end{pmatrix}$ det (**PQ**) = 10 − 4 = 6

The determinant of **PQ** is given by det **P** × det **Q**.

The example above illustrates the general result that $\det(\mathbf{MN}) = \det\mathbf{M} \times \det\mathbf{N}$.

Remember that a transformation **MN** means 'apply **N**, then apply **M**'.

This result makes sense in terms of transformations. In Example 6.3, applying **Q** involves an area scale factor of 3, and applying **P** involves an area scale factor of 2. So applying **Q** followed by **P**, represented by the matrix **PQ**, involves an area scale factor of 6.

The work so far has been restricted to 2 × 2 matrices. All square matrices have determinants; for a 3 × 3 matrix the determinant represents a volume scale factor. However, a non-square matrix does not have a determinant.

Discussion points

→ Find out how to calculate the determinant of square matrices using your calculator.

→ Use your calculator to find the determinant of the matrix $\begin{pmatrix} 2 & 0 & 0 \\ 0 & 2 & 0 \\ 0 & 0 & 2 \end{pmatrix}$.

→ Describe the transformation represented by the matrix $\begin{pmatrix} 2 & 0 & 0 \\ 0 & 2 & 0 \\ 0 & 0 & 2 \end{pmatrix}$ and explain the significance of the determinant.

Example 6.4

A transformation is represented by the matrix $\mathbf{A} = \begin{pmatrix} -1 & 0 & 0 \\ 0 & 1 & 0 \\ 0 & 0 & 1 \end{pmatrix}$.

(i)   Describe the transformation represented by **A**.

(ii) Using a calculator, find the determinant of **A**.

(iii) Decide whether the transformation represented by **A** preserves or reverses the orientation.

Explain how this is connected to your answer to part (ii).

Solution

(i)   Matrix **A** represents a reflection in the plane $x = 0$.

(ii) Using a calculator, det **A** = −1.

(iii) Matrix **A** represents a reflection, so the orientation is reversed. This is confirmed by the negative determinant.

> The first column of **A** shows that the unit vector **i** is mapped to −**i**, and the other columns show that the unit vectors **j** and **k** are mapped to themselves.

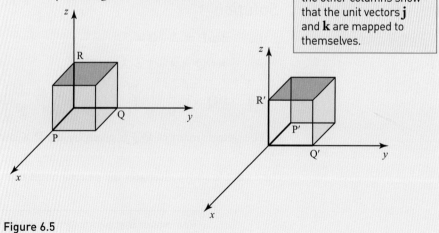

Figure 6.5

Matrices with determinant zero

Figure 6.6 shows the image of the unit square OIPJ under the transformation represented by the matrix $\mathbf{T} = \begin{pmatrix} 6 & 4 \\ 3 & 2 \end{pmatrix}$.

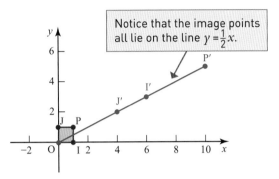

> Notice that the image points all lie on the line $y = \frac{1}{2}x$.

Figure 6.6

The determinant of $\mathbf{T} = (6 \times 2) - (4 \times 3) = 12 - 12 = 0$.

This means that the area scale factor of the transformation is zero, so any shape is transformed into a shape with area zero.

In this case, the image of a point (p, q) is given by

$$\begin{pmatrix} 6 & 4 \\ 3 & 2 \end{pmatrix} \begin{pmatrix} p \\ q \end{pmatrix} = \begin{pmatrix} 6p + 4q \\ 3p + 2q \end{pmatrix} = \begin{pmatrix} 2(3p + 2q) \\ 3p + 2q \end{pmatrix}.$$

You can see that for all the possible image points, the y-coordinate is half the x-coordinate, showing that all the image points lie on the line $y = \frac{1}{2}x$.

In this transformation, more than one point maps to the same image point.

For example, $(4, 0) \to (24, 12)$

$(0, 6) \to (24, 12)$

$(1, 4.5) \to (24, 12)$.

Discussion point

→ What is the effect of a transformation represented by a 3 × 3 matrix with determinant zero?

Exercise 6.1

① For each of the following matrices:

(a) draw a diagram to show the image of the unit square under the transformation represented by the matrix

(b) find the area of the image in part (a)

(c) find the determinant of the matrix.

(i) $\begin{pmatrix} 3 & -2 \\ 4 & 1 \end{pmatrix}$ (ii) $\begin{pmatrix} 4 & 0 \\ -1 & 4 \end{pmatrix}$ (iii) $\begin{pmatrix} 4 & -8 \\ 1 & -2 \end{pmatrix}$ (iv) $\begin{pmatrix} 5 & -7 \\ -3 & 2 \end{pmatrix}$

② The matrix $\begin{pmatrix} x - 3 & -3 \\ 2 & x - 5 \end{pmatrix}$ has determinant 9.

Find the possible values of x.

③ (i) Write down the matrices **A**, **B**, **C** and **D** which represent:

A – a reflection in the x-axis

B – a reflection in the y-axis

C – a reflection in the line $y = x$

D – a reflection in the line $y = -x$

(ii) Show that each of the matrices **A**, **B**, **C** and **D** has determinant of −1.

(iii) Draw diagrams for each of the transformations **A**, **B**, **C** and **D** to demonstrate that the images of the vertices labelled anticlockwise on the unit square OIPJ are reversed to a clockwise labelling.

④ A triangle has area $6\,\text{cm}^2$. The triangle is transformed by means of the

matrix $\begin{pmatrix} 2 & 3 \\ -3 & 1 \end{pmatrix}$.

Find the area of the image of the triangle.

⑤ The two-way stretch with matrix $\begin{pmatrix} a & 0 \\ 0 & d \end{pmatrix}$ preserves the area (i.e. the area

of the image is equal to the area of the original shape).

What is the relationship connecting a and d?

⑥ Figure 6.7 shows the unit square transformed by a shear.

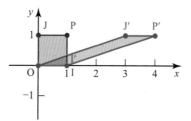

Figure 6.7

(i) Write down the matrix which represents this transformation.

(ii) Show that under this transformation the area of the image is always equal to the area of the object.

⑦ A transformation in three dimensions is represented by the matrix

$$\mathbf{A} = \begin{pmatrix} 2 & 3 & 1 \\ -1 & 1 & 0 \\ 0 & 4 & 2 \end{pmatrix}.$$

A cuboid has volume $5\,\text{cm}^3$. What is the volume of the image of the cuboid under the transformation represented by **A**?

⑧ $\mathbf{M} = \begin{pmatrix} 5 & 3 \\ 4 & 2 \end{pmatrix}$ and $\mathbf{N} = \begin{pmatrix} 3 & 2 \\ -2 & 1 \end{pmatrix}$.

(i) Find the determinants of **M** and **N**.

(ii) Find the matrix **MN** and show that $\det(\mathbf{MN}) = \det \mathbf{M} \times \det \mathbf{N}$.

⑨ The plane is transformed by the matrix $\mathbf{M} = \begin{pmatrix} 4 & -6 \\ 2 & -3 \end{pmatrix}$.

(i) Draw a diagram to show the image of the unit square under the transformation represented by $\mathbf{M}$.

(ii) Describe the effect of the transformation and explain this with reference to the determinant of $\mathbf{M}$.

⑩ The plane is transformed by the matrix $\mathbf{N} = \begin{pmatrix} 5 & -10 \\ -1 & 2 \end{pmatrix}$.

(i) Find the image of the point (p, q).

(ii) Hence show that the whole plane is mapped to a straight line and find the equation of this line.

(iii) Find the determinant of $\mathbf{N}$ and explain its significance.

⑪ A matrix $\mathbf{T}$ maps all points on the line $x + 2y = 1$ to the point $(1, 3)$.

(i) Find the matrix $\mathbf{T}$ and show that it has determinant of zero.

(ii) Show that $\mathbf{T}$ maps all points on the plane to the line $y = 3x$.

(iii) Find the coordinates of the point to which all points on the line $x + 2y = 3$ are mapped.

⑫ The plane is transformed using the matrix $\begin{pmatrix} a & b \\ c & d \end{pmatrix}$ where $ad - bc = 0$.

Prove that the general point P(x, y) maps to P$'$ on the line $cx - ay = 0$.

⑬ The point P is mapped to P$'$ on the line $3y = x$ so that PP$'$ is parallel to the line $y = 3x$.

(i) Find the equation of the line parallel to $y = 3x$ passing through the point P with coordinates (s, t).

(ii) Find the coordinates of P$'$, the point where this line meets $3y = x$.

(iii) Find the matrix of the transformation which maps P to P$'$ and show that the determinant of this matrix is zero.

2 The inverse of a matrix

The identity matrix

Whenever you multiply a 2×2 matrix $\mathbf{M}$ by $\begin{pmatrix} 1 & 0 \\ 0 & 1 \end{pmatrix}$ the product is $\mathbf{M}$. It makes no difference whether you **pre-multiply**, for example,

$$\begin{pmatrix} 1 & 0 \\ 0 & 1 \end{pmatrix} \begin{pmatrix} 4 & -2 \\ 6 & 3 \end{pmatrix} = \begin{pmatrix} 4 & -2 \\ 6 & 3 \end{pmatrix}$$

or **post-multiply**

$$\begin{pmatrix} 4 & -2 \\ 6 & 3 \end{pmatrix} \begin{pmatrix} 1 & 0 \\ 0 & 1 \end{pmatrix} = \begin{pmatrix} 4 & -2 \\ 6 & 3 \end{pmatrix}.$$

The matrix $\begin{pmatrix} 1 & 0 \\ 0 & 1 \end{pmatrix}$ is known as the 2 × 2 identity matrix.

Identity matrices are often denoted by the letter **I**.

For multiplication of matrices, **I** behaves in the same way as the number 1 when dealing with the multiplication of real numbers.

The transformation represented by the identity matrix maps every points to itself.

Similarly, the 3 × 3 identity matrix is $\begin{pmatrix} 1 & 0 & 0 \\ 0 & 1 & 0 \\ 0 & 0 & 1 \end{pmatrix}$.

Example 6.5

(i) Write down the matrix **A** which represents a rotation of 90° anticlockwise about the origin.

(ii) Write down the matrix **B** which represents a rotation of 90° clockwise about the origin.

(iii) Find the product **AB** and comment on your answer.

Solution

(i) $\mathbf{A} = \begin{pmatrix} 0 & -1 \\ 1 & 0 \end{pmatrix}$

(ii) $\mathbf{B} = \begin{pmatrix} 0 & 1 \\ -1 & 0 \end{pmatrix}$

(iii) $\mathbf{AB} = \begin{pmatrix} 0 & -1 \\ 1 & 0 \end{pmatrix}\begin{pmatrix} 0 & 1 \\ -1 & 0 \end{pmatrix} = \begin{pmatrix} 1 & 0 \\ 0 & 1 \end{pmatrix}$

AB represents a rotation of 90° clockwise followed by a rotation of 90° anticlockwise. The result of this is to return to the starting point.

To undo the effect of a rotation through 90° anticlockwise about the origin, you need to carry out a rotation through 90° clockwise about the origin. These two transformations are inverses of each other.

Similarly, the matrices which represent these transformations are inverses of each other.

In Example 6.5, $\mathbf{B} = \begin{pmatrix} 0 & 1 \\ -1 & 0 \end{pmatrix}$ is the inverse of $\mathbf{A} = \begin{pmatrix} 0 & -1 \\ 1 & 0 \end{pmatrix}$, and vice versa.

Finding the inverse of a matrix

If the product of two square matrices, **M** and **N**, is the identity matrix **I**, then **N** is the inverse of **M**. You can write this as $\mathbf{N} = \mathbf{M}^{-1}$.

Generally, if $\mathbf{M} = \begin{pmatrix} a & b \\ c & d \end{pmatrix}$ you need to find an inverse matrix $\begin{pmatrix} p & q \\ r & s \end{pmatrix}$ such that $\begin{pmatrix} a & b \\ c & d \end{pmatrix}\begin{pmatrix} p & q \\ r & s \end{pmatrix} = \begin{pmatrix} 1 & 0 \\ 0 & 1 \end{pmatrix}$.

ACTIVITY 6.3

Multiply $\begin{pmatrix} a & b \\ c & d \end{pmatrix}$ by $\begin{pmatrix} d & -b \\ -c & a \end{pmatrix}$.

What do you notice?

Use your result to write down the inverse of the general matrix $\mathbf{M} = \begin{pmatrix} a & b \\ c & d \end{pmatrix}$.
How does the determinant $|\mathbf{M}|$ relate to the matrix $\mathbf{M}^{-1}$?

You should have found in the activity that the inverse of the matrix

$\mathbf{M} = \begin{pmatrix} a & b \\ c & d \end{pmatrix}$ is given by

$$\mathbf{M}^{-1} = \frac{1}{ad-bc}\begin{pmatrix} d & -b \\ -c & a \end{pmatrix}.$$

If the determinant is zero then the inverse matrix does not exist and the matrix is said to be **singular**. If det $\mathbf{M} \neq 0$ the matrix is said to be **non-singular**.

If a matrix is singular, then it maps all points on the plane to a straight line. So an infinite number of points are mapped to the same point on the straight line. It is therefore not possible to find the inverse of the transformation, because an inverse matrix would map a point on that straight line to just one other point, not to an infinite number of them.

A special case is the zero matrix, which maps all points to the origin.

Example 6.6

$$\mathbf{A} = \begin{pmatrix} 11 & 3 \\ 6 & 2 \end{pmatrix}$$

(i) Find $\mathbf{A}^{-1}$.

(ii) The point P is mapped to the point Q (5, 2) under the transformation represented by $\mathbf{A}$. Find the coordinates of P.

Solution

(i) det $\mathbf{A} = (11 \times 2) - (3 \times 6) = 4$

$$\mathbf{A}^{-1} = \frac{1}{4}\begin{pmatrix} 2 & -3 \\ -6 & 11 \end{pmatrix}$$

(ii) $\mathbf{A}^{-1}\begin{pmatrix} 5 \\ 2 \end{pmatrix} = \frac{1}{4}\begin{pmatrix} 2 & -3 \\ -6 & 11 \end{pmatrix}\begin{pmatrix} 5 \\ 2 \end{pmatrix}$

$\mathbf{A}$ maps P to Q, so $\mathbf{A}^{-1}$ maps Q to P.

$$= \frac{1}{4}\begin{pmatrix} 4 \\ -8 \end{pmatrix}$$

$$= \begin{pmatrix} 1 \\ -2 \end{pmatrix}$$

The coordinates of P are (1, −2).

As matrix multiplication is generally non-commutative, it is interesting to find out if $\mathbf{MM}^{-1} = \mathbf{M}^{-1}\mathbf{M}$. The next activity investigates this.

ACTIVITY 6.4

(i) In Example 6.6 you found that the inverse of $\mathbf{A} = \begin{pmatrix} 11 & 3 \\ 6 & 2 \end{pmatrix}$ is

$\mathbf{A}^{-1} = \dfrac{1}{4}\begin{pmatrix} 2 & -3 \\ -6 & 11 \end{pmatrix}$.

Show that $\mathbf{AA}^{-1} = \mathbf{A}^{-1}\mathbf{A} = \mathbf{I}$.

(ii) If the matrix $\mathbf{M} = \begin{pmatrix} a & b \\ c & d \end{pmatrix}$, write down $\mathbf{M}^{-1}$ and show that $\mathbf{MM}^{-1} = \mathbf{M}^{-1}\mathbf{M} = \mathbf{I}$.

The result $\mathbf{MM}^{-1} = \mathbf{M}^{-1}\mathbf{M} = \mathbf{I}$ is important as it means that the inverse of a matrix, if it exists, is unique. This is true for all square matrices, not just 2×2 matrices.

Discussion points

→ How would you reverse the effect of a rotation followed by a reflection?

→ How would you write down the inverse of a matrix product $\mathbf{MN}$ in terms of $\mathbf{M}^{-1}$ and $\mathbf{N}^{-1}$?

TECHNOLOGY

Investigate how to use your calculator to find the inverse of 2×2 and 3×3 matrices.

Check using your calculator that multiplying a matrix by its inverse gives the identity matrix.

The inverse of a product of matrices

Suppose you want to find the inverse of the product $\mathbf{MN}$, where $\mathbf{M}$ and $\mathbf{N}$ are non-singular matrices. This means that you need to find a matrix $\mathbf{X}$ such that
$$\mathbf{X}(\mathbf{MN}) = \mathbf{I}.$$

$\mathbf{X}(\mathbf{MN}) = \mathbf{I} \Rightarrow \mathbf{XMNN}^{-1} = \mathbf{IN}^{-1}$ Post multiply by $\mathbf{N}^{-1}$

$\Rightarrow \mathbf{XM} = \mathbf{IN}^{-1}$ Using $\mathbf{NN}^{-1} = \mathbf{I}$

$\Rightarrow \mathbf{XMM}^{-1} = \mathbf{N}^{-1}\mathbf{M}^{-1}$ Post multiply by $\mathbf{M}^{-1}$

$\Rightarrow \mathbf{X} = \mathbf{N}^{-1}\mathbf{M}^{-1}$ Using $\mathbf{MM}^{-1} = \mathbf{I}$

So $(\mathbf{MN})^{-1} = \mathbf{N}^{-1}\mathbf{M}^{-1}$ for matrices $\mathbf{M}$ and $\mathbf{N}$ of the same order. This means that when working backwards, you must reverse the second transformation before reversing the first transformation.

① For the matrix $\begin{pmatrix} 5 & -1 \\ -2 & 0 \end{pmatrix}$

(i) find the image of the point $(3, 5)$

(ii) find the inverse matrix

(iii) find the point which maps to the image $(3, -2)$.

② Determine whether the following matrices are singular or non-singular. For those that are non-singular, find the inverse.

(i) $\begin{pmatrix} 6 & 3 \\ -4 & 2 \end{pmatrix}$ (ii) $\begin{pmatrix} 6 & 3 \\ 4 & 2 \end{pmatrix}$ (iii) $\begin{pmatrix} 11 & 3 \\ 3 & 11 \end{pmatrix}$ (iv) $\begin{pmatrix} 11 & 11 \\ 3 & 3 \end{pmatrix}$

(v) $\begin{pmatrix} 2 & -7 \\ 0 & 0 \end{pmatrix}$ (vi) $\begin{pmatrix} -2a & 4a \\ 4b & -8b \end{pmatrix}$ (vii) $\begin{pmatrix} -2 & 4a \\ 4b & -8 \end{pmatrix}$

③ Using a calculator, find whether the following matrices are singular or non-singular. For those that are non-singular find the inverse.

(i) $\begin{pmatrix} 2 & 4 & 9 \\ -1 & -3 & 0 \\ 4 & -2 & -7 \end{pmatrix}$ (ii) $\begin{pmatrix} 4 & 0 & -1 \\ 2 & -3 & 5 \\ -4 & 6 & -10 \end{pmatrix}$ (iii) $\begin{pmatrix} 1 & 0 & 3 \\ 8 & -2 & -1 \\ 3 & 5 & 11 \end{pmatrix}$

④ $\mathbf{M} = \begin{pmatrix} 5 & 6 \\ 2 & 3 \end{pmatrix}$ and $\mathbf{N} = \begin{pmatrix} 8 & 5 \\ -2 & -1 \end{pmatrix}$.

Calculate the following:

(i) $\mathbf{M}^{-1}$ (iii) $\mathbf{MN}$ (v) $(\mathbf{MN})^{-1}$ (vii) $\mathbf{M}^{-1}\mathbf{N}^{-1}$

(ii) $\mathbf{N}^{-1}$ (iv) $\mathbf{NM}$ (vi) $(\mathbf{NM})^{-1}$ (viii) $\mathbf{N}^{-1}\mathbf{M}^{-1}$

⑤ The diagram shows the unit square OIPJ mapped to the image OI′P′J′ under a transformation represented by a matrix $\mathbf{M}$.

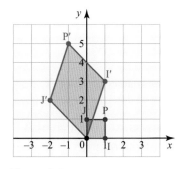

Figure 6.8

(i) Find the inverse of $\mathbf{M}$.

(ii) Use matrix multiplication to show that $\mathbf{M}^{-1}$ maps OI′P′J′ back to OIPJ.

⑥ The matrix $\begin{pmatrix} 1-k & 2 \\ -1 & 4-k \end{pmatrix}$ is singular.

Find the possible values of k.

⑦ Given that $\mathbf{M} = \begin{pmatrix} 2 & 3 \\ -1 & 4 \end{pmatrix}$ and $\mathbf{MN} = \begin{pmatrix} 7 & 2 & -9 & 10 \\ 2 & -1 & -12 & 17 \end{pmatrix}$, find the matrix $\mathbf{N}$.

⑧ Triangle T has vertices at $(1, 0)$, $(0, 1)$ and $(-2, 0)$.

It is transformed to triangle T′ by the matrix $\mathbf{M} = \begin{pmatrix} 3 & 1 \\ 1 & 1 \end{pmatrix}$.

(i) Find the coordinates of the vertices of T′.

Show the triangles T and T′ on a single diagram.

(ii) Find the ratio of the area of T′ to the area of T.

Comment on your answer in relation to the matrix $\mathbf{M}$.

(iii) Find $\mathbf{M}^{-1}$ and verify that this matrix maps the vertices of T′ to the vertices of T.

⑨ $\mathbf{M} = \begin{pmatrix} a & b \\ c & d \end{pmatrix}$ is a singular matrix.

(i) Show that $\mathbf{M}^2 = (a + d)\mathbf{M}$.

(ii) Find a formula which expresses $\mathbf{M}^n$ in terms of $\mathbf{M}$, where n is a positive integer.

Comment on your results.

⑩ Given that $\mathbf{PQR} = \mathbf{I}$, show algebraically that

(i) $\mathbf{Q} = \mathbf{P}^{-1}\mathbf{R}^{-1}$

(ii) $\mathbf{Q}^{-1} = \mathbf{RP}$.

Given that $\mathbf{P} = \begin{pmatrix} 3 & 1 \\ 1 & 2 \end{pmatrix}$ and $\mathbf{R} = \begin{pmatrix} 12 & -3 \\ 2 & -1 \end{pmatrix}$

(iii) use part (i) to find the matrix $\mathbf{Q}$

(iv) calculate the matrix $\mathbf{Q}^{-1}$

(v) verify that your answer to part (ii) is correct by calculating $\mathbf{RP}$ and comparing it with your answer to part (iv).

⑪ $\mathbf{A} = \begin{pmatrix} 1 & 7 & 4 \\ 0 & 1 & 2 \\ 0 & 0 & 1 \end{pmatrix}$, $\mathbf{B} = \begin{pmatrix} 1 & 0 & 0 \\ 3 & 1 & 0 \\ -1 & -4 & 1 \end{pmatrix}$ and $\mathbf{C} = \mathbf{AB}$.

(i) Calculate the matrix $\mathbf{C}$.

(ii) Work out the matrix product $\mathbf{A}\begin{pmatrix} 1 & a & b \\ 0 & 1 & c \\ 0 & 0 & 1 \end{pmatrix}$.

(iii) Using the answer to part (ii), find $\mathbf{A}^{-1}$.

(iv) Using a calculator, find $\mathbf{B}^{-1}$.

(v) Using your results from parts (iii) and (iv), find $\mathbf{C}^{-1}$.

⑫ The matrix $\mathbf{M} = \begin{pmatrix} k - 1 & k - 1 & 0 \\ 1 & k + 1 & -2 \\ k - 1 & k - 2 & 1 \end{pmatrix}$ has inverse

$\mathbf{M}^{-1} = \begin{pmatrix} k & -1 & -2 \\ -\dfrac{5}{2} & k - 2 & k - 1 \\ -\dfrac{7}{2} & 1 & k \end{pmatrix}$.

Find the value of k.

3 Using matrices to solve simultaneous equations

There are a number of methods to solve a pair of linear simultaneous equations of the form

$$3x + 2y = 17$$
$$2x - 5y = 24$$

These include elimination, substitution or graphical methods.

An alternative method involves the use of inverse matrices. This method has the advantage that it can more easily be extended to solving a set of n equations in n variables.

Example 6.7

Use a matrix method to solve the simultaneous equations

$$3x + 2y = 17$$
$$2x - 5y = 24$$

Solution

$$\begin{pmatrix} 3 & 2 \\ 2 & -5 \end{pmatrix} \begin{pmatrix} x \\ y \end{pmatrix} = \begin{pmatrix} 17 \\ 24 \end{pmatrix}.$$ ← Write the equations in matrix form.

The inverse of the matrix $\begin{pmatrix} 3 & 2 \\ 2 & -5 \end{pmatrix}$ is $-\dfrac{1}{19}\begin{pmatrix} -5 & -2 \\ -2 & 3 \end{pmatrix}$.

$$-\frac{1}{19}\begin{pmatrix} -5 & -2 \\ -2 & 3 \end{pmatrix}\begin{pmatrix} 3 & 2 \\ 2 & -5 \end{pmatrix}\begin{pmatrix} x \\ y \end{pmatrix} = -\frac{1}{19}\begin{pmatrix} -5 & -2 \\ -2 & 3 \end{pmatrix}\begin{pmatrix} 17 \\ 24 \end{pmatrix}$$

Pre-multiply both sides of the matrix equation by the inverse matrix.

$$\begin{pmatrix} x \\ y \end{pmatrix} = -\frac{1}{19}\begin{pmatrix} -133 \\ 38 \end{pmatrix} = \begin{pmatrix} 7 \\ -2 \end{pmatrix}$$

As $\mathbf{M}^{-1}\mathbf{Mp} = \mathbf{p}$ the left-hand side simplifies to $\begin{pmatrix} x \\ y \end{pmatrix}$.

The solution is $x = 7$, $y = -2$.

Geometrical interpretation in two dimensions

Two equations in two unknowns can be represented in a plane by two straight lines. The number of points of intersection of the lines determines the number of solutions to the equations.

There are three different possibilities.

Case 1

Example 6.7 shows that two simultaneous equations can have a unique solution. Graphically, this is represented by a single point of intersection.

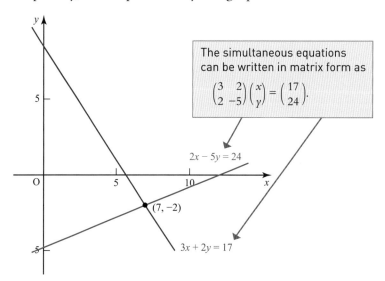

The simultaneous equations can be written in matrix form as
$$\begin{pmatrix} 3 & 2 \\ 2 & -5 \end{pmatrix}\begin{pmatrix} x \\ y \end{pmatrix} = \begin{pmatrix} 17 \\ 24 \end{pmatrix}.$$

$2x - 5y = 24$

$(7, -2)$

$3x + 2y = 17$

Figure 6.9

This is the case where $\det \mathbf{M} \neq 0$ and so the inverse matrix $\mathbf{M}^{-1}$ exists, allowing the equations to be solved.

Case 2

If two lines are parallel they do not have a point of intersection. For example, the lines

$x + 2y = 10$

$x + 2y = 4$

are parallel.

The equations can be written in matrix form as
$$\begin{pmatrix} 1 & 2 \\ 1 & 2 \end{pmatrix}\begin{pmatrix} x \\ y \end{pmatrix} = \begin{pmatrix} 10 \\ 4 \end{pmatrix}.$$

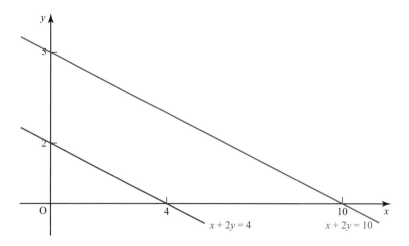

$x + 2y = 4$ $x + 2y = 10$

Figure 6.10

The matrix $\mathbf{M} = \begin{pmatrix} 1 & 2 \\ 1 & 2 \end{pmatrix}$ has determinant zero and hence the inverse matrix does not exist.

Case 3

More than one solution is possible in cases where the lines are **coincident**, i.e. lie on top of each other. For example, the two lines

$$x + 2y = 10$$
$$3x + 6y = 30$$

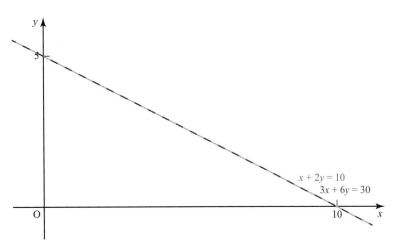

The equations can be written in matrix form as

$$\begin{pmatrix} 1 & 2 \\ 3 & 6 \end{pmatrix}\begin{pmatrix} x \\ y \end{pmatrix} = \begin{pmatrix} 10 \\ 30 \end{pmatrix}.$$

are coincident. You can see this because the equations are multiples of each other.

Figure 6.11

In this case the matrix **M** is $\begin{pmatrix} 1 & 2 \\ 3 & 6 \end{pmatrix}$ and $\det \mathbf{M} = 0$.

There are infinitely many solutions to these equations.

ACTIVITY 6.5

(i) Write the three simultaneous equations

$$2x - 2y + 3z = 4$$
$$5x + y - z = -6$$
$$3x + 4y - 2z = 1$$

as a matrix equation.

Use a matrix method and your calculator to solve the simultaneous equations.

(ii) Repeat part (i) for the three simultaneous equations

$$2x - 2y + 3z = 4$$
$$5x + y - z = -6$$
$$3x + 3y - 4z = 1$$

What happens in this case?

Try to solve the equations algebraically. Comment on your answer.

Exercise 6.3

① (i) Find the inverse of the matrix $\begin{pmatrix} 3 & -1 \\ 2 & 3 \end{pmatrix}$.

(ii) Hence use a matrix method to solve the simultaneous equations
$$3x - y = 2$$
$$2x + 3y = 5$$

② Use matrices to solve the following pairs of simultaneous equations.

(i) $3x + 2y = 4$
$x - 2y = 4$

(ii) $3x - 2y = 9$
$x - 4y = -2$

③ (i) Use a calculator to find the inverse of the matrix $\begin{pmatrix} 3 & 1 & 1 \\ -5 & -2 & 3 \\ 1 & 1 & 1 \end{pmatrix}$.

(ii) Hence use a matrix method to solve the simultaneous equations
$$3x + y + z = -2$$
$$-5x - 2y + 3z = -1$$
$$x + y + z = 2$$

④ Use a matrix method to solve these simultaneous equations. (You should use a calculator to find the inverse matrix.)
$$x + 5y + z = 0$$
$$2x - 3y - 4z = 7$$
$$3x + 2y - 6z = 4$$

⑤ For each of the following pair of equations, describe the intersections of the pair of straight lines represented by the simultaneous equations.

(i) $3x + 5y = 18$
$2x + 4y = 11$

(ii) $3x + 6y = 18$
$2x + 4y = 12$

(iii) $3x + 6y = 18$
$2x + 4y = 15$

⑥ Find the two values of k for which the equations
$$2x + ky = 3$$
$$kx + 8y = 6$$

do not have a unique solution.

How many solutions are there in each case?

⑦ (i) Find **AB** where $\mathbf{A} = \begin{pmatrix} 5 & -2 & k \\ 3 & -4 & -5 \\ -2 & 3 & 4 \end{pmatrix}$

and $\mathbf{B} = \begin{pmatrix} -1 & 3k+8 & 4k+10 \\ -2 & 2k+20 & 3k+25 \\ 1 & -11 & -14 \end{pmatrix}$.

Hence write down the inverse matrix $\mathbf{A}^{-1}$, stating the condition on the value of k required for the inverse to exist.

(ii) Using the result from part (i) solve the equation

$$\begin{pmatrix} 5 & -2 & k \\ 3 & -4 & -5 \\ -2 & 3 & 4 \end{pmatrix} \begin{pmatrix} x \\ y \\ z \end{pmatrix} = \begin{pmatrix} 28 \\ 0 \\ m \end{pmatrix}$$

when $k = 8$ and $m = 2$.

⑧ Find the conditions on a and b for which the simultaneous equations
$ax + by = 1$

$bx + ay = b$

have a unique solution.

Solve the equations when $a = -3$ giving your answers in terms of b.

Find the value of b for which the solution will lie on the line $y = -x$.

LEARNING OUTCOMES

When you have completed this chapter you should be able to:

➤ find the determinant of a 2 × 2 matrix

➤ know what is meant by a singular matrix

➤ understand that the determinant of a 2 × 2 matrix represents the area scale factor of the corresponding transformation, and understand the significance of the sign of the determinant

➤ find the inverse of a non-singular 2 × 2 matrix

➤ use a calculator to find the determinant and inverse of a 3 × 3 matrix

➤ know that the determinant of a 3 × 3 matrix represents the volume scale factor of the corresponding transformation

➤ understand the significance of a zero determinant in terms of transformations

➤ use the product rule for inverse matrices

➤ use matrices to solve a pair of linear simultaneous equations in two unknowns

➤ use matrices to solve three linear simultaneous equations in three unknowns.

KEY POINTS

1 If $\mathbf{M} = \begin{pmatrix} a & b \\ c & d \end{pmatrix}$ then the determinant of $\mathbf{M}$, written $\det \mathbf{M}$ or $|\mathbf{M}|$ is given

   by $\det \mathbf{M} = ad - bc$

2 The determinant of a 2 × 2 matrix represents the area scale factor of the transformation.

   The determinant of a 3 × 3 matrix represents the volume scale factor of the transformation.

3 If $\mathbf{M} = \begin{pmatrix} a & b \\ c & d \end{pmatrix}$ then $\mathbf{M}^{-1} = \dfrac{1}{ad - bc} \begin{pmatrix} d & -b \\ -c & a \end{pmatrix}$

4 $(\mathbf{MN})^{-1} = \mathbf{N}^{-1}\mathbf{M}^{-1}$

5 A matrix is singular if the determinant is zero. If the determinant is non-zero the matrix is said to be non-singular.

6 If the determinant of a matrix is zero, all points are mapped to either a straight line (in two dimensions) or to a plane (three dimensions).

7 If $\mathbf{A}$ is a non-singular matrix, $\mathbf{A}\mathbf{A}^{-1} = \mathbf{A}^{-1}\mathbf{A} = \mathbf{I}$.

8 When solving two simultaneous equations in two unknowns, the equations

   can be written as a matrix equation $\mathbf{M} \begin{pmatrix} x \\ y \end{pmatrix} = \begin{pmatrix} a \\ b \end{pmatrix}$.

   When solving three simultaneous equations in three unknowns, the equations

   can be written as a matrix equation $\mathbf{M} \begin{pmatrix} x \\ y \\ z \end{pmatrix} = \begin{pmatrix} a \\ b \\ c \end{pmatrix}$.

   In both cases, if $\det \mathbf{M} \neq 0$ there is a unique solution to the equations which can be found by pre-multiplying both sides of the equation by the inverse matrix $\mathbf{M}^{-1}$.

   If $\det \mathbf{M} = 0$ there is no unique solution to the equations. In this case there is either no solution or an infinite number of solutions.

7 Vectors and 3D space

Why is there space rather than no space? Why is space three-dimensional? Why is space big? We have a lot of room to move around in. How come it's not tiny? We have no consensus about these things. We're still exploring them.

Leonard Susskind

1 Finding the angle between two vectors

In this section you will learn how to find the angle between two vectors in two dimensions or three dimensions.

Discussion point

→ Are there any right angles in the building shown above?

Prior knowledge

From MEI A Level Mathematics Year 1 (AS) Chapter 12, you need to be able to use the language of vectors, including the terms magnitude, direction and position vector. You should also be able to find the distance between two points represented by position vectors and be able to add and subtract vectors and multiply a vector by a scalar.

Example 7.1

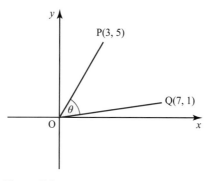

Figure 7.1

Find the angle POQ.

> Remember that $\overrightarrow{OP}$ denotes the vector from O to P, and $\left|\overrightarrow{OP}\right|$ is the **magnitude** (length) of $\overrightarrow{OP}$.

Solution

Using the cosine rule: $\cos\theta = \dfrac{\left|\overrightarrow{OP}\right|^2 + \left|\overrightarrow{OQ}\right|^2 - \left|\overrightarrow{PQ}\right|^2}{2 \times \left|\overrightarrow{OP}\right| \times \left|\overrightarrow{OQ}\right|}$

$\overrightarrow{OP} = \begin{pmatrix} 3 \\ 5 \end{pmatrix}$ so $\left|\overrightarrow{OP}\right| = \sqrt{3^2 + 5^2} = \sqrt{34}$

$\overrightarrow{OQ} = \begin{pmatrix} 7 \\ 1 \end{pmatrix}$ so $\left|\overrightarrow{OQ}\right| = \sqrt{7^2 + 1^2} = \sqrt{50}$

> Using Pythagoras' theorem.

$\overrightarrow{PQ} = \overrightarrow{OQ} - \overrightarrow{OP} = \begin{pmatrix} 7 \\ 1 \end{pmatrix} - \begin{pmatrix} 3 \\ 5 \end{pmatrix} = \begin{pmatrix} 4 \\ -4 \end{pmatrix}$ so $\left|\overrightarrow{PQ}\right| = \sqrt{4^2 + 4^2} = \sqrt{32}$

so $\cos\theta = \dfrac{34 + 50 - 32}{2 \times \sqrt{34} \times \sqrt{50}}$

$\theta = 50.9°$

More generally, to find the angle between $\overrightarrow{OA} = \mathbf{a} = \begin{pmatrix} a_1 \\ a_2 \end{pmatrix}$ and $\overrightarrow{OB} = \mathbf{b} = \begin{pmatrix} b_1 \\ b_2 \end{pmatrix}$ start by applying the cosine rule to the triangle OAB in Figure 7.2.

Discussion point

➜ How else could you find the angle θ?

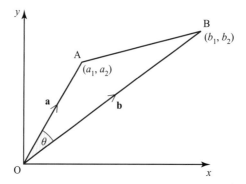

Figure 7.2

$$\cos\theta = \frac{\left|\overrightarrow{OA}\right|^2 + \left|\overrightarrow{OB}\right|^2 - \left|\overrightarrow{AB}\right|^2}{2 \times \left|\overrightarrow{OA}\right| \times \left|\overrightarrow{OB}\right|} \quad ①$$

$\left|\overrightarrow{OA}\right|, \left|\overrightarrow{OB}\right|$ and $\left|\overrightarrow{AB}\right|$ are the lengths of the vectors $\overrightarrow{OA}, \overrightarrow{OB}$ and $\overrightarrow{AB}$.

Also from the diagram:

$$\left|\overrightarrow{OA}\right| = \left|\mathbf{a}\right| = \sqrt{a_1^2 + a_2^2} \text{ and } \left|\overrightarrow{OB}\right| = \left|\mathbf{b}\right| = \sqrt{b_1^2 + b_2^2} \quad ②$$

and

$$\overrightarrow{AB} = \mathbf{b} - \mathbf{a} = \begin{pmatrix} b_1 \\ b_2 \end{pmatrix} - \begin{pmatrix} a_1 \\ a_2 \end{pmatrix} = \begin{pmatrix} b_1 - a_1 \\ b_2 - a_2 \end{pmatrix}$$

so $\left|\overrightarrow{AB}\right| = \sqrt{\left(b_1 - a_1\right)^2 + \left(b_2 - a_2\right)^2} \quad ③$

ACTIVITY 7.1

By substituting ② and ③ into ① show that $\cos\theta = \dfrac{a_1 b_1 + a_2 b_2}{|a||b|}$ where $|a| = \sqrt{a_1^2 + a_2^2}$ and $|b| = \sqrt{b_1^2 + b_2^2}$.

The activity above showed that for Figure 7.2

$$\cos\theta = \frac{a_1 b_1 + a_2 b_2}{|\mathbf{a}||\mathbf{b}|}.$$

The expression on the numerator, $a_1 b_1 + a_2 b_2$, is called the scalar product of the vectors $\mathbf{a}$ and $\mathbf{b}$, which is written $\mathbf{a.b}$.

This is sometimes called the dot product.

So $\cos\theta = \dfrac{\mathbf{a.b}}{|\mathbf{a}||\mathbf{b}|}.$

This result is sometimes written $\mathbf{a.b} = |\mathbf{a}||\mathbf{b}|\cos\theta$.

Using the column format, the scalar product can be written as

$$\mathbf{a.b} = \begin{pmatrix} a_1 \\ a_2 \end{pmatrix} . \begin{pmatrix} b_1 \\ b_2 \end{pmatrix} = a_1 b_1 + a_2 b_2.$$

Note

1 The scalar product, unlike a vector, has size but no direction.

2 The scalar product of two vectors is *commutative*. This is because multiplication of numbers is commutative. For example:

$$\begin{pmatrix} 3 \\ -4 \end{pmatrix} . \begin{pmatrix} 1 \\ 5 \end{pmatrix} = (3 \times 1) + (-4 \times 5) = (1 \times 3) + (5 \times -4) = \begin{pmatrix} 1 \\ 5 \end{pmatrix} . \begin{pmatrix} 3 \\ -4 \end{pmatrix}$$

The scalar product is found in a similar way for vectors in three dimensions:

$$\begin{pmatrix} a_1 \\ a_2 \\ a_3 \end{pmatrix} \cdot \begin{pmatrix} b_1 \\ b_2 \\ b_3 \end{pmatrix} = a_1 b_1 + a_2 b_2 + a_3 b_3$$

This is used in Example 7.2 to find the angle between two vectors in three dimensions.

Example 7.2

The position vectors of three points A, B and C are given by

$$\mathbf{a} = \begin{pmatrix} 2 \\ 5 \\ -1 \end{pmatrix}, \mathbf{b} = \begin{pmatrix} 0 \\ 7 \\ 3 \end{pmatrix} \text{ and } \mathbf{c} = \begin{pmatrix} 8 \\ 0 \\ 3 \end{pmatrix}. \text{ Find the vectors } \overrightarrow{AB} \text{ and } \overrightarrow{CB}$$

and hence calculate the angle ABC.

Solution

Figure 7.3

$$\overrightarrow{AB} = \mathbf{b} - \mathbf{a} = \begin{pmatrix} 0 \\ 7 \\ 3 \end{pmatrix} - \begin{pmatrix} 2 \\ 5 \\ -1 \end{pmatrix} = \begin{pmatrix} -2 \\ 2 \\ 4 \end{pmatrix}$$

$$\overrightarrow{CB} = \mathbf{b} - \mathbf{c} = \begin{pmatrix} 0 \\ 7 \\ 3 \end{pmatrix} - \begin{pmatrix} 8 \\ 0 \\ 3 \end{pmatrix} = \begin{pmatrix} -8 \\ 7 \\ 0 \end{pmatrix}$$

The angle ABC is found using the scalar product of the vectors $\overrightarrow{AB}$ and $\overrightarrow{CB}$.

$$\overrightarrow{AB} \cdot \overrightarrow{CB} = \begin{pmatrix} -2 \\ 2 \\ 4 \end{pmatrix} \cdot \begin{pmatrix} -8 \\ 7 \\ 0 \end{pmatrix} = 16 + 14 + 0 = 30$$

$$\left| \overrightarrow{AB} \right| = \sqrt{(-2)^2 + 2^2 + 4^2} = \sqrt{24} \text{ and } \left| \overrightarrow{CB} \right| = \sqrt{(-8)^2 + 7^2 + 0^2} = \sqrt{113}$$

$$\overrightarrow{AB} \cdot \overrightarrow{CB} = \left| \overrightarrow{AB} \right| \left| \overrightarrow{CB} \right| \cos\theta$$

$$\Rightarrow 30 = \sqrt{24}\sqrt{113} \cos\theta$$

$$\Rightarrow \cos\theta = \frac{30}{\sqrt{24}\sqrt{113}}$$

$$\Rightarrow \theta = 54.8°$$

Discussion point

➜ For the points A, B and C in Example 7.2, find the scalar product of the vectors $\overrightarrow{BA}$ and $\overrightarrow{BC}$, and comment on your answer.

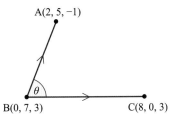

Figure 7.4

Notice that $\overrightarrow{AB}$ and $\overrightarrow{CB}$ are both directed towards the point B, and $\overrightarrow{BA}$ and $\overrightarrow{BC}$ are both directed away from the point B (as in Figure 7.4). Using either pair of vectors gives the angle ABC. This angle could be acute or obtuse.

However, if you use vectors $\overrightarrow{AB}$ (directed towards B) and $\overrightarrow{BC}$ (directed away from B), then you will obtain the angle $180° - \theta$ instead.

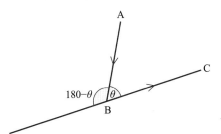

Figure 7.5

Perpendicular vectors

If two vectors are perpendicular, then the angle between them is 90°.

Since $\cos 90° = 0$, it follows that if vectors **a** and **b** are perpendicular then $\mathbf{a}.\mathbf{b} = 0$.

Conversely, if the scalar product of two non-zero vectors is zero, they are perpendicular.

Example 7.3

Two points, P and Q, have coordinates (1, 3, –2) and (4, 2, 5).
Show that angle POQ = 90°
(i)   using column vectors
(ii) using **i**, **j**, **k** notation.

Solution

(i) $\mathbf{p} = \begin{pmatrix} 1 \\ 3 \\ -2 \end{pmatrix}$, $\mathbf{q} = \begin{pmatrix} 4 \\ 2 \\ 5 \end{pmatrix}$

$\mathbf{p}.\mathbf{q} = \begin{pmatrix} 1 \\ 3 \\ -2 \end{pmatrix} . \begin{pmatrix} 4 \\ 2 \\ 5 \end{pmatrix}$

$= (1 \times 4) + (3 \times 2) + (-2 \times 5)$

$= 4 + 6 - 10$

$= 0$

So the angle POQ = 90°.

(ii) **p** = **i** + 3**j** − 2**k**, **q** = 4**i** + 2**j** + 5**k**

> Multiply out the brackets.

p.q = (**i** + 3**j** − 2**k**).(4**i** + 2**j** + 5**k**)

= 4**i.i** + 14**i.j** − 3**i.k** + 6**j.j** + 11**j.k** − 10**k.k**

> Since **i**, **j** and **k** are unit vectors, **i.i** = **j.j** = **k.k** = 1.

= 4 + 6 − 10

= 0

> Since **i**, **j** and **k** are all perpendicular, **i.j** = **i.k** = **j.k** = 0.

So the angle POQ = 90°.

Exercise 7.1

① Find:

(i) $\begin{pmatrix} 2 \\ 3 \end{pmatrix} \cdot \begin{pmatrix} 1 \\ -2 \end{pmatrix}$ (ii) $\begin{pmatrix} 2 \\ 3 \end{pmatrix} \cdot \begin{pmatrix} -1 \\ 2 \end{pmatrix}$

(iii) $\begin{pmatrix} 1 \\ 2 \\ 3 \end{pmatrix} \cdot \begin{pmatrix} 4 \\ 0 \\ -1 \end{pmatrix}$ (iv) $\begin{pmatrix} 1 \\ 2 \\ 3 \end{pmatrix} \cdot \begin{pmatrix} -1 \\ 4 \\ 0 \end{pmatrix}$

② Find the angle between the vectors **p** and **q** shown in Figure 7.6.

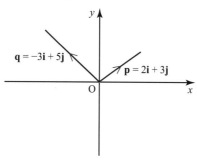

Figure 7.6

③ Find the angle between the vectors:

(i) **a** = 3**i** + 2**j** − 4**k** and **b** = −2**i** + **j** − 3**k**

(ii) **a** = −3**i** − 2**j** + 4**k** and **b** = −2**i** + **j** − 3**k**

(iii) **a** = 3**i** + 2**j** − 4**k** and **b** = 2**i** − **j** + 3**k**

④ Find the angle between the following pairs of vectors and comment on your answers.

(i) $\begin{pmatrix} 3 \\ -2 \\ 5 \end{pmatrix}$ and $\begin{pmatrix} 6 \\ -4 \\ 10 \end{pmatrix}$ (ii) $\begin{pmatrix} 3 \\ -2 \\ 5 \end{pmatrix}$ and $\begin{pmatrix} -9 \\ 6 \\ -15 \end{pmatrix}$

⑤ Find the value of α for which the vectors $\begin{pmatrix} 2 \\ 5 \\ -1 \end{pmatrix}$ and $\begin{pmatrix} 4 \\ -5 \\ \alpha \end{pmatrix}$ are perpendicular.

⑥ Given the vectors $\mathbf{c} = \begin{pmatrix} \alpha \\ 5 \\ 3 \end{pmatrix}$ and $\mathbf{d} = \begin{pmatrix} \alpha \\ \alpha \\ 2 \end{pmatrix}$ are perpendicular, find the possible values of α.

⑦ A triangle has vertices at the points A(2, 1, −3), B(4, 0, 6) and C(−1, 2, 1). Using the scalar product, find the three angles of the triangle ABC and check that they add up to 180°.

⑧ The point A has position vector $\mathbf{a} = \begin{pmatrix} 5 \\ 2 \\ 3 \end{pmatrix}$.

Find the angle that the vector $\mathbf{a}$ makes with each of the coordinate axes.

⑨ The room illustrated in Figure 7.7 has rectangular walls, floor and ceiling. A string has been stretched in a straight line between the corners A and G.

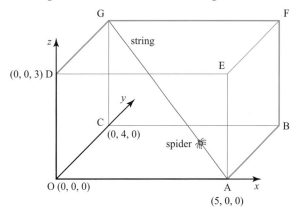

Figure 7.7

The corner O is taken as the origin. A is (5, 0, 0), C is (0, 4, 0) and D is (0, 0, 3), where the lengths are in metres.

A spider walks up the string, starting from A.

(i) Write down the coordinates of G.

(ii) Find the vector $\overrightarrow{AG}$ and the distance the spider walks along the string from A to G.

(iii) Find the angle of elevation of the spider's journey along the string.

⑩ Figure 7.8 shows the design for a barn. Its base and walls are rectangular.

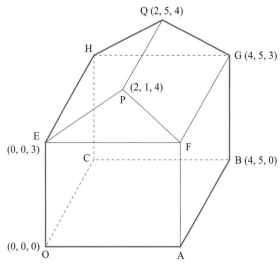

Figure 7.8

(i) Write down the coordinates of the other vertices of the barn.

(ii) Determine whether the section EPF is vertical and hence state the type of quadrilateral formed by the roof sections PFGQ and PQHE.

(iii) Find the cosine of angle FPE and hence find the exact area of the triangle FPE.

The engineer plans to increase the strength of the barn by installing supporting metal bars along OG and AH.

(iv) Calculate the acute angle between the metal bars.

⑪ If $(\mathbf{a} + 2\mathbf{b}).\mathbf{c} - (3\mathbf{a} + \mathbf{c}).\mathbf{b} = 5\mathbf{a}.\mathbf{b} - 3\mathbf{a}.\mathbf{c}$ show that $\mathbf{b}.\mathbf{c} = 4\mathbf{a}.(2\mathbf{b} - \mathbf{c})$.

⑫ Three vectors $\mathbf{a}$, $\mathbf{b}$ and $\mathbf{c}$ have magnitudes 5, 2 and 3 respectively.

Using this information, and the properties of the scalar product, simplify $(\mathbf{a} + \mathbf{b} + \mathbf{c}).\mathbf{a} - (\mathbf{b} + \mathbf{c}).\mathbf{c} - \mathbf{a}.\mathbf{b}$.

⑬ Two vectors are given by $\mathbf{a} = a_1\mathbf{i} + b_1\mathbf{j} + c_1\mathbf{k}$ and $\mathbf{b} = a_2\mathbf{i} + b_2\mathbf{j} + c_2\mathbf{k}$.

Using the fact that $\mathbf{i}.\mathbf{j} = \mathbf{j}.\mathbf{k} = \mathbf{k}.\mathbf{i} = 0$, show algebraically that $\mathbf{a}.\mathbf{b} = a_1a_2 + b_1b_2 + c_1c_2$.

2 The equation of a plane

You can write the equation of a plane in either vector or cartesian form. The cartesian form is used more often but to see where it comes from it is helpful to start with the vector form.

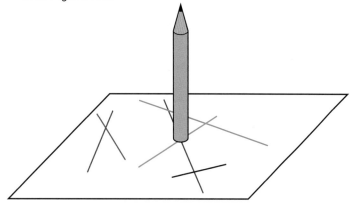

Figure 7.9

The discussion above shows you that there is a direction (that of the pencil) which is at right angles to every straight line in the plane. A line in that direction is said to be perpendicular to the plane and is referred to as a **normal** to the plane.

It is often denoted by $\mathbf{n} = \begin{pmatrix} n_1 \\ n_2 \\ n_3 \end{pmatrix}$.

In Figure 7.10 the point A is on the plane and the vector $\mathbf{n}$ is perpendicular to the plane. This information allows you to find an expression for the position vector $\mathbf{r}$ of a general point R on the plane.

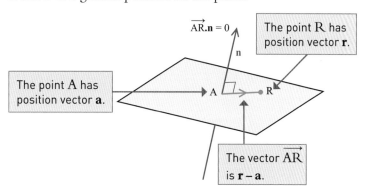

Figure 7.10

The vector $\overrightarrow{AR}$ is a line in the plane, and so it follows that $\overrightarrow{AR}$ is at right angles to the direction $\mathbf{n}$.

$$\overrightarrow{AR}.\mathbf{n} = 0$$

The vector $\overrightarrow{AR}$ is given by $\overrightarrow{AR} = \mathbf{r} - \mathbf{a}$ and so

$$(\mathbf{r} - \mathbf{a}).\mathbf{n} = 0.$$

This is the vector equation of the plane.

Expanding the brackets lets you write this in an alternative form as

$$\mathbf{r.n} - \mathbf{a.n} = 0 \cdot \longleftarrow \boxed{\text{This can also be written as } \mathbf{r.n} = \mathbf{a.n}}$$

Although the vector equation of a plane is very compact, it is more common to use the cartesian form. This is derived from the vector form as follows.

Write the normal vector $\mathbf{n}$ as $\begin{pmatrix} n_1 \\ n_2 \\ n_3 \end{pmatrix}$ and the position vector of A as

$\mathbf{a} = \begin{pmatrix} a_1 \\ a_2 \\ a_3 \end{pmatrix}$. The position vector of the general point R is $\mathbf{r} = \begin{pmatrix} x \\ y \\ z \end{pmatrix}$.

So the equation $\mathbf{r.n} - \mathbf{a.n} = 0$

can be written as $\begin{pmatrix} x \\ y \\ z \end{pmatrix} \cdot \begin{pmatrix} n_1 \\ n_2 \\ n_3 \end{pmatrix} - \begin{pmatrix} a_1 \\ a_2 \\ a_3 \end{pmatrix} \cdot \begin{pmatrix} n_1 \\ n_2 \\ n_3 \end{pmatrix} = 0 \cdot$

> Notice that d is a constant and is a scalar.

This is the same as $n_1 x + n_2 y + n_3 z + d = 0$ where $d = -(a_1 n_1 + a_2 n_2 + a_3 n_3)$.

The following example shows you how to use this.

> **TECHNOLOGY**
>
> If you have access to 3D graphing software, experiment with planes in the form
> $ax + by + cz + d = 0$,
> varying the values of a, b, c and d.

Example 7.4

The point A $(2, 3, -5)$ lies on a plane. The vector $\mathbf{n} = \begin{pmatrix} -4 \\ 2 \\ 1 \end{pmatrix}$ is perpendicular to the plane.

(i) Find the cartesian equation of the plane.

(ii) Investigate whether the points P$(5, 3, -2)$ and Q $(3, 5, -5)$ lie in the plane.

Solution

(i) The cartesian equation of the plane is
$n_1 x + n_2 y + n_3 z + d = 0$.

$\mathbf{n} = \begin{pmatrix} -4 \\ 2 \\ 1 \end{pmatrix}$ so $n_1 = -4$, $n_2 = 2$ and $n_3 = 1$

The equation of the plane is $-4x + 2y + z + d = 0$.

It remains to find d. There are two ways of doing this.

Either:
The point A is $(2, 3, -5)$.
Substituting for x, y and z in
$-4x + 2y + z + d = 0$ gives

$-4 \times 2 + 2 \times 3 - 5 + d = 0$

so $d = 8 - 6 + 5 = 7$.

Or:
$d = -\mathbf{a.n}$
where $\mathbf{a}$ is the position vector of
A, $(2, 3, -5)$.

So $\mathbf{a} = \begin{pmatrix} 2 \\ 3 \\ -5 \end{pmatrix}$ and $\mathbf{n} = \begin{pmatrix} -4 \\ 2 \\ 1 \end{pmatrix}$

$$d = -\begin{pmatrix} 2 \\ 3 \\ -5 \end{pmatrix} \cdot \begin{pmatrix} -4 \\ 2 \\ 1 \end{pmatrix}$$

$$= -[(2 \times -4) + (3 \times 2) + (-5 \times 1)]$$
$$= -[-8 + 6 - 5] = 7$$

So the equation of the plane is $-4x + 2y + z + 7 = 0$.

(ii) P is $(5, 3, -2)$.

Substituting in the left-hand side of the equation of the plane gives $(-4 \times 5) + (2 \times 3) - 2 + 7 = -9$.

Since this is not equal to 0, P does not lie in the plane.

Q is $(3, 5, -5)$.

Substituting in the left-hand side of the equation of the plane gives $(-4 \times 3) + (2 \times 5) - 5 + 7 = 0$.

Since this is equal to 0, Q lies in the plane.

Look carefully at the equation of the plane in this example. You can see at once that the vector $\begin{pmatrix} -4 \\ 2 \\ 1 \end{pmatrix}$, formed from the coefficients of x, y and z, is perpendicular to the plane.

In general the vector $\begin{pmatrix} n_1 \\ n_2 \\ n_3 \end{pmatrix}$ is perpendicular to all planes of the form

$n_1 x + n_2 y + n_3 z + d = 0$, whatever the value of d (see Figure 7.11).

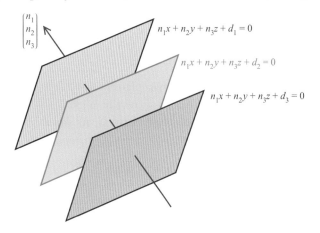

Figure 7.11

Consequently, all planes of that form are parallel; the coefficients of x, y and z determine the direction of the plane, the value of d its location.

Example 7.5

Find the cartesian equation of the plane which is parallel to the plane $3x - y + 2z + 5 = 0$ and contains the point $(1, 0, -2)$.

Discussion point

→ Given the coordinates of three points A, B and C in a plane, how could you find the equation of the plane?

Solution

The normal to the plane $3x - y + 2z + 5 = 0$ is $\begin{pmatrix} 3 \\ -1 \\ 2 \end{pmatrix}$.

Any plane parallel to this plane has the same normal vector, so the required plane has equation of the form $3x - y + 2z + d = 0$.
The plane contains the point $(1, 0, -2)$, so

$(3 \times 1) - 0 + (2 \times -2) + d = 0$

$\Rightarrow d = 1$

The equation of the plane is $3x - y + 2z + 1 = 0$.

Notation

So far the cartesian equation of a plane has been written as
$$n_1 x + n_2 y + n_3 z + d = 0.$$
Another common way of writing it is $ax + by + cz + d = 0$.

In this case the vector $\begin{pmatrix} a \\ b \\ c \end{pmatrix}$ is normal to the plane.

ACTIVITY 7.2

A plane $ax + by + cz + d = 0$ contains the points $(1, 1, 1)$, $(1, -1, 0)$ and $(-1, 0, 2)$.

Use this information to write down three simultaneous equations and use a matrix method to solve these. Hence find the equation of the plane.

The angle between planes

The angle between two planes can be found by using the scalar product. As Figures 7.12 and 7.13 show, the angle between planes π_1 and π_2 is the same as the angle between their normals, $\mathbf{n}_1$ and $\mathbf{n}_2$.

Figure 7.12

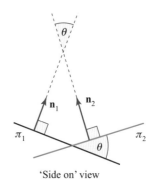

'Side on' view

Figure 7.13

Example 7.6

Find, to 1 decimal place, the acute angle between the planes
$\pi_1 : 2x + 3y + 5z = 8$ and $\pi_2 : 5x + y - 4z = 12$.

Solution

The planes have normals $\mathbf{n}_1 = \begin{pmatrix} 2 \\ 3 \\ 5 \end{pmatrix}$ and $\mathbf{n}_2 = \begin{pmatrix} 5 \\ 1 \\ -4 \end{pmatrix}$ so the angle

between the planes is given by $\mathbf{n}_1.\mathbf{n}_2 = |\mathbf{n}_1||\mathbf{n}_2|\cos\theta$

$$\Rightarrow \begin{pmatrix} 2 \\ 3 \\ 5 \end{pmatrix} . \begin{pmatrix} 5 \\ 1 \\ -4 \end{pmatrix} = \sqrt{4 + 9 + 25}\sqrt{25 + 1 + 16}\cos\theta$$

$$\Rightarrow 10 + 3 - 20 = \sqrt{38}\sqrt{42}\cos\theta$$

$$\Rightarrow \theta = 100.1°$$

So the acute angle between the planes is $79.9°$.

Exercise 7.2

① A plane has equation $5x - 3y + 2z + 1 = 0$.

   (i) Write down the normal vector to this plane.

   (ii) Show that the point $(1, 4, 3)$ lies on the plane.

② Find, in vector form, the equation of the planes which contain the point with position vector $\mathbf{a}$ and are perpendicular to the vector $\mathbf{n}$.

   (i) $\mathbf{a} = 3\mathbf{i} + 5\mathbf{j} - 2\mathbf{k}$ $\qquad$ $\mathbf{n} = \mathbf{i} + \mathbf{j} + \mathbf{k}$

   (ii) $\mathbf{a} = -3\mathbf{i} + 2\mathbf{j} + \mathbf{k}$ $\qquad$ $\mathbf{n} = \mathbf{i} + \mathbf{j} + \mathbf{k}$

   (iii) $\mathbf{a} = 3\mathbf{i} + 5\mathbf{j} - 2\mathbf{k}$ $\qquad$ $\mathbf{n} = -\mathbf{i} - \mathbf{j} - \mathbf{k}$

   (iv) $\mathbf{a} = 2\mathbf{i} + 7\mathbf{j} - \mathbf{k}$ $\qquad$ $\mathbf{n} = 2\mathbf{i} + 2\mathbf{j} + 2\mathbf{k}$

③ Find the cartesian equation of the planes in question 2.

   Comment on your answers.

④ Find, to 1 decimal place, the smaller angle between the planes:

   (i) $\mathbf{r}.\begin{pmatrix} 2 \\ 2 \\ -3 \end{pmatrix} = 4$ and $\mathbf{r}.\begin{pmatrix} 3 \\ -3 \\ -1 \end{pmatrix} = 2$

   (ii) $\mathbf{r}.\begin{pmatrix} 1 \\ 2 \\ -3 \end{pmatrix} = 4$ and $\mathbf{r}.\begin{pmatrix} 3 \\ -3 \\ -1 \end{pmatrix} = 2$

   (iii) $x + y - 4z = 4$ and $5x - 2y + 3z = 13$

⑤ The plane π_1 has equation $-x + 3y - 2z - 13 = 0$.

   Find the cartesian and vector equations of the plane π_2 that is parallel to π_1 and passes through the point $(3, 0, -4)$.

⑥ Find the cartesian equation of the plane which contains the point $(0, 1, -4)$ and is parallel to the plane $(\mathbf{r} - (4\mathbf{i} + 2\mathbf{j} - \mathbf{k})) \cdot (4\mathbf{i} - 5\mathbf{j} + 6\mathbf{k}) = 0$.

⑦ The planes $x - 3y - 2z = 5$ and $k^2x + ky + 2 = 3$ are perpendicular. Find the possible values of k.

⑧ Two sloping roof structures must be constructed at an angle of exactly $60°$. The roof structures can be modelled as planes given by the equations

$$x + 2y + 2z = 5$$

$$ax + y + z = 2$$

where a is a positive constant.

Find the exact value of a.

⑨ Find the equation of the plane π which is perpendicular to the planes

$$3x - y - z + 4 = 0$$

$$x + 2y + z + 3 = 0$$

and which passes through the point P$(4, 3, 5)$.

⑩ The points A, B and C have coordinates $(0, -1, 2)$, $(2, 1, 0)$ and $(5, 1, 1)$.

(i) Write down the vectors $\overrightarrow{AB}$ and $\overrightarrow{AC}$.

(ii) Show that $\overrightarrow{AB} \cdot \begin{pmatrix} 1 \\ -4 \\ -3 \end{pmatrix} = \overrightarrow{AC} \cdot \begin{pmatrix} 1 \\ -4 \\ -3 \end{pmatrix} = 0$.

(iii) Find the equation of the plane containing the points A, B and C.

⑪ (i) Show that the points A$(1, 1, 1)$, B$(3, 0, 0)$ and C$(2, 0, 2)$ all lie in the plane $2x + 3y + z = 6$.

(ii) Show that $\overrightarrow{AB} \cdot \begin{pmatrix} 2 \\ 3 \\ 1 \end{pmatrix} = \overrightarrow{AC} \cdot \begin{pmatrix} 2 \\ 3 \\ 1 \end{pmatrix} = 0$.

(iii) The point D has coordinates $(7, 6, 2)$ and lies on a line perpendicular to the plane through one of the points A, B or C.

Through which of these points does the line pass?

⑫ Three planes have equations

$$\pi_1 : ax + 2y + z = 3$$

$$\pi_2 : x + ay + z = 4$$

$$\pi_3 : x + y + az = 5$$

Given that the angle between planes π_1 and π_2 is equal to the angle between the planes π_2 and π_3, show that a must satisfy the quartic equation:

$$5a^4 + 2a^3 - 2a^2 - 8a - 3 = 0$$

⑬ A plane π has cartesian equation $2x - 3y + 2z + 10 = 0$.

(i) Write down the normal vector $\mathbf{n}$ and the value of $d = -\mathbf{a} \cdot \mathbf{n}$.

(ii) Find a possible position vector $\mathbf{a}$ to represent a point A in the plane.

(iii) Use your answers to parts (i) and (ii) to write down a vector equation for the plane π in the form $(\mathbf{r} - \mathbf{a}) \cdot \mathbf{n} = 0$.

⑭ Four planes are given by the equations

$$\pi_1 : 2x - 3y + 5z + 4 = 0$$
$$\pi_2 : 2x + 3y + z + 4 = 0$$
$$\pi_3 : 4x - 6y + 10z + 4 = 0$$
$$\pi_4 : 2x - 3y + z + 4 = 0$$

Determine whether each *pair* of planes is parallel, perpendicular or neither.

3 Intersection of planes

If you look around you will find objects which can be used to represent planes – walls, floors, ceilings, doors, roofs and so on. You will see that in general the intersection of two planes is a straight line.

> For example, the wall and ceiling of a room meet in a straight line.

In this section you will look at the different possibilities for how *three* planes can be arranged in three-dimensional space.

Geometrical arrangement of three planes

There are five ways in which three distinct planes π_1, π_2 and π_3 can intersect in three-dimensional space.

If two of the planes are parallel, there are two possibilities for the third:

- It can be parallel to the other two (see Figure 7.14).

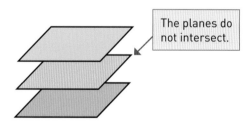

> The planes do not intersect.

Figure 7.14

- It can cut the other two (see Figure 7.15).

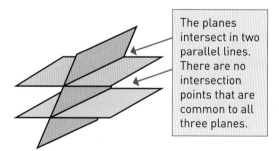

> The planes intersect in two parallel lines. There are no intersection points that are common to all three planes.

Figure 7.15

TECHNOLOGY

If you have access to 3D graphing software, investigate the different ways in which three distinct planes can intersect in three-dimensional space.

If none of the planes are parallel, there are three possibilities.

- The planes intersect in a single point (see Figure 7.16).

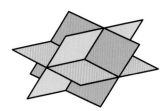

Figure 7.16

- The planes forms a **sheaf** (see Figure 7.17).

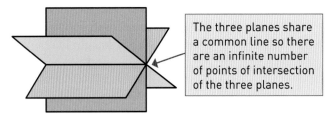

The three planes share a common line so there are an infinite number of points of intersection of the three planes.

Figure 7.17

- The planes form a **triangular prism** (see Figure 7.18).

> **Discussion point**
>
> → Think of an example from everyday life of each of these arrangements of three planes.

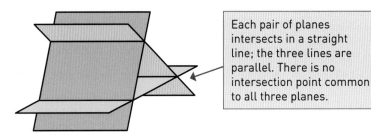

Each pair of planes intersects in a straight line; the three lines are parallel. There is no intersection point common to all three planes.

Figure 7.18

The diagrams above show that three planes intersect either in a unique point, an infinite number of points or do not have a common intersection point.

Finding the unique point of intersection of three planes

You can use 3×3 matrices to find the point of intersection of three planes that intersect in a unique point.

ACTIVITY 7.3

Make sure you remember how to find the inverse of a 3×3 matrix using your calculator.

Check that for the matrix $\mathbf{M} = \begin{pmatrix} 2 & 1 & -2 \\ 1 & 1 & 1 \\ 1 & -1 & -3 \end{pmatrix}$, $\mathbf{M^{-1}M = I}$.

In Chapter 6 you saw how to solve simultaneous equations using matrices. The following example shows how this relates to finding the point of intersection of three planes in three dimensions.

Example 7.7

Find the unique point of intersection of the three planes

$$2x + y - 2z = 5$$
$$x + y + z = 1$$
$$x - y - 3z = -2$$

Solution

$$\begin{pmatrix} 2 & 1 & -2 \\ 1 & 1 & 1 \\ 1 & -1 & -3 \end{pmatrix} \begin{pmatrix} x \\ y \\ z \end{pmatrix} = \begin{pmatrix} 5 \\ 1 \\ -2 \end{pmatrix}$$

> The three planes can be represented by this matrix equation.

> Solving the matrix equation will identify a point that the three planes have in common, i.e. the unique point of intersection of the three planes.

The inverse of the matrix $\mathbf{M} = \begin{pmatrix} 2 & 1 & -2 \\ 1 & 1 & 1 \\ 1 & -1 & -3 \end{pmatrix}$ is

$$\mathbf{M}^{-1} = \begin{pmatrix} -0.5 & 1.25 & 0.75 \\ 1 & -1 & -1 \\ -0.5 & 0.75 & 0.25 \end{pmatrix}.$$

> Using a calculator

> pre-multiplying both sides of the matrix equation by $\mathbf{M}^{-1}$.

$$\begin{pmatrix} -0.5 & 1.25 & 0.75 \\ 1 & -1 & -1 \\ -0.5 & 0.75 & 0.25 \end{pmatrix} \begin{pmatrix} 2 & 1 & -2 \\ 1 & 1 & 1 \\ 1 & -1 & -3 \end{pmatrix} \begin{pmatrix} x \\ y \\ z \end{pmatrix} = \begin{pmatrix} -0.5 & 1.25 & 0.75 \\ 1 & -1 & -1 \\ -0.5 & 0.75 & 0.25 \end{pmatrix} \begin{pmatrix} 5 \\ 1 \\ -2 \end{pmatrix}$$

$$\Rightarrow \begin{pmatrix} 1 & 0 & 0 \\ 0 & 1 & 0 \\ 0 & 0 & 1 \end{pmatrix} \begin{pmatrix} x \\ y \\ z \end{pmatrix} = \begin{pmatrix} -2.75 \\ 6 \\ -2.25 \end{pmatrix}$$

$$\Rightarrow \begin{pmatrix} x \\ y \\ z \end{pmatrix} = \begin{pmatrix} -2.75 \\ 6 \\ -2.25 \end{pmatrix}$$

So the planes intersect in the unique point $(-2.75, 6, -2.25)$.

Determining the other arrangements of three planes

In Example 7.7 you saw that the equations of three distinct planes can be expressed in the form

$$\mathbf{M} \begin{pmatrix} x \\ y \\ z \end{pmatrix} = \begin{pmatrix} d_1 \\ d_2 \\ d_3 \end{pmatrix}.$$

If **M** is non-singular, the planes intersect in a unique point. If **M** is singular, the planes must be arranged in one of the other four possible arrangements:

- three parallel planes
- two parallel planes that are cut by the third to form two parallel lines
- a sheaf of planes that intersect in a common line
- a prism of planes in which each pair of planes meets in a straight line but there are no common points of intersection between the three planes.

One of these cases is covered in the following example.

Example 7.8

Three planes have equations

$$2x - 5y + 3z - 2 = 0$$
$$x - y + z - 3 = 0$$
$$4x - 10y + 6z - 7 = 0$$

(i) Express the equations of the planes in the matrix form

$$\mathbf{M} \begin{pmatrix} x \\ y \\ z \end{pmatrix} = \begin{pmatrix} d_1 \\ d_2 \\ d_3 \end{pmatrix}.$$

(ii) Using your calculator, find det **M** and comment on your answer.

(iii) By comparing the rows of the matrix **M**, determine the arrangement of the three planes.

Solution

(i) The planes can be arranged in the matrix form

$$\mathbf{M} \begin{pmatrix} x \\ y \\ z \end{pmatrix} = \begin{pmatrix} 2 \\ 3 \\ 7 \end{pmatrix}$$

Notice that the constant terms have been moved to the right hand side of each equation.

where $\mathbf{M} = \begin{pmatrix} 2 & -5 & 3 \\ 1 & -1 & 1 \\ 4 & -10 & 6 \end{pmatrix}$.

(ii) det **M** = 0

(iii) The third row is a multiple of the first row, therefore the first and third planes are parallel. The second plane is not parallel and so must cut the other two to form two parallel straight lines.

TECHNOLOGY

Use 3D graphing software to draw the three planes in Example 7.8.

In Example 7.8, you could see quite easily that two of the planes are parallel, but the third is not, by comparing the coefficients of x, y and z. In the same way, you would be able to identify three parallel planes.

If none of the planes are parallel, and the determinant of the matrix is zero, then the planes form either a sheaf of planes or a triangular prism. If they form a sheaf of planes, then equations are **consistent**: there are an infinite number of solutions. If they form a triangular prism, then the equations are **inconsistent**: there are no points which satisfy all three equations.

Sometimes you may have additional information which will help you to decide which arrangement you have. Otherwise, you can try to solve the equations simultaneously to find out whether the equations are consistent or inconsistent. The example below shows how this can be done.

Example 7.9

Three planes have equations

$$3x + 2y - z = 1 \quad ①$$
$$x + 2y + z = 3 \quad ②$$
$$x + y = 2 \quad\quad\quad ③$$

(i) Show that the three planes do not have a unique point of intersection.
(ii) Describe the geometrical arrangement of the three planes.

Solution

(i) $$\begin{pmatrix} 3 & 2 & -1 \\ 1 & 2 & 1 \\ 1 & 1 & 0 \end{pmatrix} \begin{pmatrix} x \\ y \\ z \end{pmatrix} = \begin{pmatrix} 1 \\ 3 \\ 2 \end{pmatrix}$$

Using a calculator, $\det \begin{pmatrix} 3 & 2 & -1 \\ 1 & 2 & 1 \\ 1 & 1 & 0 \end{pmatrix} = 0$ so there is no unique point of intersection.

(ii) First check if any of the planes are parallel.

The normal vectors to the three planes are all different, so none of the planes are parallel. This rules out these two cases:

3 parallel planes

Figure 7.19

and 2 parallel planes with one crossing them.

Figure 7.20

That leaves the two cases of

a sheaf of planes where they all meet in the same line

Figure 7.21

or a triangular prism.

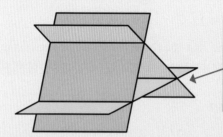

Each pair of planes intersects in a straight line; the three lines are parallel. There is no intersection point common to all three planes.

Figure 7.22

Now see if the planes meet in a single line.

Adding equations ① and ② gives $4x + 4y = 4$

$$\Rightarrow x + y = 1$$

Equation ③ is $x + y = 2$. ◄

The value of $x + y$ cannot be both 1 and 2, so the equations are inconsistent.

So there are no points which satisfy all three equations.

Therefore the planes form a triangular prism and not a sheaf.

TECHNOLOGY

Use 3D graphing software to draw the three planes in Example 7.9 and verify that they form a triangular prism.

Exercise 7.3

① (i) Find the inverse of the matrix $\mathbf{M} = \begin{pmatrix} 2 & 1 & 3 \\ 3 & -1 & -2 \\ 1 & -2 & -1 \end{pmatrix}$.

(ii) Use your answer to part (i) to find the point of intersection of the planes

$$2x + y + 3z = 20$$
$$3x - y - 2z = 10$$
$$x - 2y - z = 30$$

② Using the same method as in question 1, find the unique point of intersection of the three planes

$$4x - 3y - 2z = 2$$
$$x + 2y + 2z = 5$$
$$3x - 3y - 2z = 3$$

③ Determine whether or not the following sets of three planes intersect in a unique point and, where possible, find the point of intersection.

(i) $x - y - 2z - 5 = 0$
$2x + y + 6z + 12 = 0$
$2x + 4y + 6z + 3 = 0$

(ii) $x + y + z - 4 = 0$
$2x + 3y - 4z - 3 = 0$
$5x + 8y - 13z - 8 = 0$

(iii) $x + 2y + 4z = 7$
$3x + 2y + 5z = 21$
$4x + y + 2z = 14$

(iv) $3x + y + z = 4$
$5x - y + 9z = 5$
$x - y + 4z = -1$

④ Three planes are given by the equations
$$-x + y + z = -1$$
$$2x + y + z = 6$$
$$x + y + z = 4$$

(i) Write the equations in the form
$$\mathbf{M}\begin{pmatrix} x \\ y \\ z \end{pmatrix} = \begin{pmatrix} d_1 \\ d_2 \\ d_3 \end{pmatrix}.$$

By comparing the rows of the matrix $\mathbf{M}$ and calculating $\det \mathbf{M}$ determine which arrangements of these planes in three-dimensions are possible.

(ii) The point P $(2, 3, -1)$ is known to lie on at least one of the three planes. By working out on which planes the point P lies, determine the arrangement of the three planes.

(iii) By changing the constant term in one of the plane equations show that a different arrangement of the planes can be obtained.

⑤ Three planes are given by the equations
$$x + 2y - z = 6$$
$$2x + 4y + z = 5$$
$$3x + 6y - 3z = 8$$

Write the equations in the form
$$\mathbf{M}\begin{pmatrix} x \\ y \\ z \end{pmatrix} = \begin{pmatrix} d_1 \\ d_2 \\ d_3 \end{pmatrix}.$$

Determine the arrangement of the planes in three-dimensions.

⑥ The three planes
$$x - y + 2z = k$$
$$3x - y - z = 0$$
$$2x - y + z = m$$

are known to intersect at the point $(-12, -29, -7)$.

Determine the values of k and m.

Intersection of planes

⑦ Three planes are given by the equations

$$3x + 4y + z = 5$$
$$2x - y - z = 4$$
$$5x + 14y + 5z = 7$$

(i) Write the equations in the form

$$\mathbf{M}\begin{pmatrix} x \\ y \\ z \end{pmatrix} = \begin{pmatrix} d_1 \\ d_2 \\ d_3 \end{pmatrix}.$$

By comparing the rows of the matrix $\mathbf{M}$ and calculating $\det \mathbf{M}$ determine which arrangements of the planes in three dimensions are possible.

(ii) The point P$(3, -2, 4)$ is known to lie on at least one of the three planes. By working out on which planes the point P lies, determine the arrangement of the three planes.

⑧ The equations of three planes are

$$kx + my + nz = -6$$
$$2x - y - 2z = -9$$
$$3x + y - z = -2$$

(i) Determine the arrangement of the planes in three dimensions when $k = 1$, $m = -1$, $n = 1$, providing as much detail in your solution as possible.

(ii) State values for k, m and n which would produce an arrangement of two distinct parallel planes cut by the third plane.

(iii) Explain the arrangement of the planes in the case where $k = 9$, $m = 3$ and $n = -3$. State how this case differs from the arrangement in part (ii).

⑨ Two planes in three dimensions are said to be *coincident* if one lies on top of the other, i.e. they are exactly the same plane. Coincident planes are not distinct.

Given *any* three planes, list the ways can they be arranged in three dimensions.

How many different possible arrangements are there in total?

LEARNING OUTCOMES

When you have completed this chapter you should be able to:

➤ find the scalar product of two vectors

➤ use the scalar product to find the angle between two vectors

➤ know that two vectors are perpendicular if and only if their scalar product is zero

➤ identify a vector normal to a plane, given the equation of the plane

➤ find the equation of a plane in vector or Cartesian form

➤ find the angle between two planes

➤ know the different ways in which three distinct planes can be arranged in 3-D space

➤ understand how solving three linear simultaneous equations in three unknowns relates to finding the point of intersection of three planes in three dimensions.

KEY POINTS

1   In two dimensions, the scalar product

$$\mathbf{a.b} = \begin{pmatrix} a_1 \\ a_2 \end{pmatrix} \cdot \begin{pmatrix} b_1 \\ b_2 \end{pmatrix} = a_1b_1 + a_2b_2 = |\mathbf{a}||\mathbf{b}|\cos\theta.$$

2   In three dimensions, $\mathbf{a.b} = \begin{pmatrix} a_1 \\ a_2 \\ a_3 \end{pmatrix} \cdot \begin{pmatrix} b_1 \\ b_2 \\ b_3 \end{pmatrix} = a_1 b_1 + a_2 b_2 + a_3 b_3 = |\mathbf{a}||\mathbf{b}|\cos\theta.$

3   The angle θ between two vectors $\mathbf{a}$ and $\mathbf{b}$ is given by

$$\cos\theta = \frac{\mathbf{a.b}}{|\mathbf{a}||\mathbf{b}|}$$

where $\mathbf{a.b} = a_1b_1 + a_2b_2$ (in two dimensions)

$\mathbf{a.b} = a_1b_1 + a_2b_2 + a_3b_3$ (in three dimensions).

4   The cartesian equation of the plane perpendicular to the vector $\mathbf{n} = \begin{pmatrix} n_1 \\ n_2 \\ n_3 \end{pmatrix}$ and passing through a point with position vector $\mathbf{a}$ is given by $n_1x + n_2y + n_3z + d = 0$ where $d = -\mathbf{a.n}$.

5   The vector equation of the plane through the point with position vector $\mathbf{a}$, and perpendicular to the vector $\mathbf{n} = \begin{pmatrix} n_1 \\ n_2 \\ n_3 \end{pmatrix}$ is given by $(\mathbf{r} - \mathbf{a}).\mathbf{n} = 0$ or $\mathbf{r.n} = \mathbf{a.n}$.

6   The angle between two planes π_1 and π_2 is the same as the angle between their normals, $\mathbf{n}_1$ and $\mathbf{n}_2$. This angle can be found using the scalar product.

7   Three distinct planes in three dimensions will be arranged in one of five ways:
   * meet in a unique point of intersection
   * three parallel planes
   * two parallel planes that are cut by the third to form two parallel lines
   * a sheaf of planes that intersect in a common line
   * a prism of planes in which each pair of planes meets in a straight line but there are no common points of intersection between the three planes.

8   Three distinct planes
$$a_1x + b_1y + c_1z = d_1$$
$$a_2x + b_2y + c_2z = d_2$$
$$a_3x + b_3y + c_3z = d_3$$
can be expressed in the form

$$\mathbf{M}\begin{pmatrix} x \\ y \\ z \end{pmatrix} = \begin{pmatrix} d_1 \\ d_2 \\ d_3 \end{pmatrix}$$

$$\text{where } \mathbf{M} = \begin{pmatrix} a_1 & b_1 & c_1 \\ a_2 & b_2 & c_2 \\ a_3 & b_3 & c_3 \end{pmatrix}.$$

If $\mathbf{M}$ is non-singular, the unique point of intersection is given by $\mathbf{M}^{-1} \begin{pmatrix} d_1 \\ d_2 \\ d_3 \end{pmatrix}.$

Otherwise, the planes meet in one of the other four possible arrangements. In the case of a sheaf of planes, the equations have an infinite number of possible solutions, and in the other three cases the equations have no solutions.

FUTURE USES

■ Work on vectors will be developed further in the A Level Further Mathematics book.

① (i) Describe the transformation represented by the matrix

$$\mathbf{A} = \begin{pmatrix} 1 & 0 \\ 0 & -1 \end{pmatrix}.$$ [1 mark]

(ii) Describe the transformation represented by the matrix

$$\mathbf{B} = \begin{pmatrix} -1 & 0 \\ 0 & 1 \end{pmatrix}.$$ [1 mark]

(iii) Determine **BA** and describe the transformation it represents. [2 marks]

(iv) Determine $(\mathbf{BA})^{-1}$. What do you notice? Explain your answer in terms of the transformation represented by **BA**. [3 marks]

MP ② Let $z_1 = a + b\mathrm{i}$ and $z_2 = c + d\mathrm{i}$.

(i) Find $z_1 z_2$. [2 marks]

(ii) Write down $|z_1|$ and $|z_2|$. [1 mark]

(iii) Prove that $|z_1 z_2| = |z_1||z_2|$. [4 marks]

PS ③

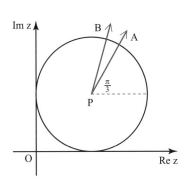

On the Argand diagram above, the point P is at $3 + 3\mathrm{i}$.

(i) The circle centred on P represents a locus of points on the Argand diagram. Write down its equation as a locus in terms of z. [2 marks]

(ii) Write down the equation of the locus of points represented by the half-line from P through A. [2 marks]

(iii) The sector PAB has area $\dfrac{3\pi}{8}$. Find the equation of the locus of points represented by the half line from P through B. [4 marks]

④ A pair of simultaneous equations is represented by $\mathbf{R}\begin{pmatrix} x \\ y \end{pmatrix} = \begin{pmatrix} 12 \\ b \end{pmatrix}$ where

$$\mathbf{R} = \begin{pmatrix} 3 & k \\ 2 & 4 \end{pmatrix}.$$

(i) Write down the pair of equations. [1 mark]

(ii) Prove that $\mathbf{R}^{-1} = \dfrac{1}{12 - 2k}\begin{pmatrix} 4 & -k \\ -2 & 3 \end{pmatrix}$. [2 marks]

(iii) For one particular value of k, $\mathbf{R}^{-1}$ does not exist. What is this value of k? [2 marks]

(iv) For the value of k found in (iii), $\begin{pmatrix} 3 & k \\ 2 & 4 \end{pmatrix}\begin{pmatrix} x \\ y \end{pmatrix} = \begin{pmatrix} 12 \\ b \end{pmatrix}$ has an infinite number of solutions. Find b and describe the relationship between the lines represented by the pair of simultaneous equations. [3 marks]

⑤ The plane p contains the point $(5, 0, 4)$. The vector $\begin{pmatrix} 5 \\ -1 \\ 0 \end{pmatrix}$ is perpendicular to p.

(i) Find the equation of p in the form $ax + by + cz + d = 0$. [2 marks]

(ii) Another plane, q, has equation $4x - 3y + z - 3 = 0$.
Find the angle between p and q. [3 marks]

(iii) Show that the point $(5, 0, -17)$ lies on both planes. [2 marks]

Ⓜ ⑥ A new skyscraper is built in the shape of square-based pyramid, standing on its square base. In a model of the skyscraper, its four triangular faces are parts of four planes and the ground on which is stands is the plane $z = 0$.

The summit of the skyscraper, where its four triangular faces meet, is directly above the centre of its square base and has coordinates $(5, 17, 20)$.

(i) The faces of the skyscraper are modelled by these four planes:

$$20x + z = k$$

$$-20x + z = l$$

$$-20y - z = m$$

$$20y - z = n$$

Find the values of k, l, m and n. [2 marks]

(ii) What angle does each of the skyscraper's sides make to the vertical? [4 marks]

(iii) The triangular sides of another skyscraper built in the form of a square based pyramid are modelled as parts of these four planes.

$$25x + z = 150$$

$$-25x + z = -100$$

$$25y - z = 250$$

$$25y + z = 300$$

What are the coordinates of its summit? [3 marks]

(iv) The length of one unit in this question has not been defined.
Given that this is an extremely tall skyscraper, suggest and justify an actual length for 1 unit. [3 marks]

Ⓣ ⑦ The equations of three planes are:

$$5x - 7y + z = 80$$

$$ax - by - 2z = c$$

$$19x + 17y - 4z = -14$$

(i) State a set of values for a, b and c for which two of the planes are coincident. [3 marks]

(ii) State a set of values for a, b and c for which there are two distinct parallel planes that are cut by a third plane. [2 marks]

(iii) If $a = 1, b = -13$ and $c = -2$ show that the planes must meet at a single point and find the coordinates of that point. [6 marks]

Radians are an alternative way to measure angles. They relate the arc length of a sector to its angle. In Figure 1 the arc AB has been drawn so that it is equal to the length of the radius, r. The angle subtended at the centre of the circle is one radian.

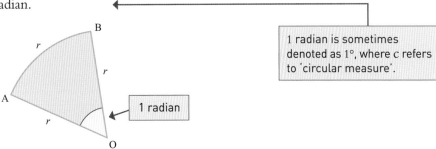

1 radian is sometimes denoted as 1°, where c refers to 'circular measure'.

1 radian

Figure 1

Since an angle of 1 radian at the centre of the circle corresponds to an arc length r it follows that an angle of 2 radians corresponds to an arc length of $2r$ and so on. In general, an angle of θ radians corresponds to an arc length of $r\theta$, as shown in Figure 2.

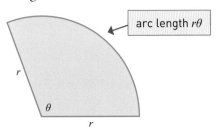

arc length $r\theta$

Figure 2

The circumference of a circle is $2\pi r$, so the angle at the centre of a full circle is $2\pi r$ radians. This is 360°.

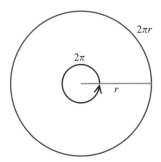

Figure 3

So 360° = 2π radians

$\quad$ 180° = π radians

$\quad\quad$ 90° = $\dfrac{\pi}{2}$ radians

$\quad\quad$ 60° = $\dfrac{\pi}{3}$ radians

$\quad\quad$ 45° = $\dfrac{\pi}{4}$ radians

$\quad\quad$ 30° = $\dfrac{\pi}{6}$ radians

When working in radians, angles are often stated as a fraction or multiple of π.

$360° = 2\pi^c$ and so 1 radian is equivalent to $360 \div 2\pi = 57.3°$ to one decimal place.

The fact that one radian is just under 60° can be a helpful reference point.

When a multiple of π is used the 'c' symbol is usually omitted, as it is implied that the measure is radians.

To convert degrees into radians you multiply by $\dfrac{\pi}{180}$, and to convert radians into degrees you multiply by $\dfrac{180}{\pi}$.

Example

(i) Express in radians, giving your answers as a multiple of π:

(a) 120°   (b) 225°   (c) 390°

(ii) Express in radians, giving your answers to 3 significant figures:

(a) 34°   (b) 450°   (c) 1°

(iii) Express in degrees, giving your answers to 3 significant figures where appropriate:

(a) $\dfrac{5\pi}{12}$ (b) $\dfrac{\pi}{24}$ (c) 3.4^c

Solution

(i) (a) $60° = \dfrac{\pi}{3}$ radians so $120° = \dfrac{2\pi}{3}$ radians

(b) $45° = \dfrac{\pi}{4}$ radians so $225° = 5 \times 45° = \dfrac{5\pi}{4}$

(c) $30° = \dfrac{\pi}{6}$ radians so $390° = 360° + 30° = 2\pi + \dfrac{\pi}{6} = \dfrac{13\pi}{6}$

(ii) (a) $34 \times \dfrac{\pi}{180} = 0.593$ radians

(b) $450 \times \dfrac{\pi}{180} = 7.85$ radians

(c) $1 \times \dfrac{\pi}{180} = 0.0175$ radians

(iii) (a) $\dfrac{5\pi}{12} \times \dfrac{180}{\pi} = 75°$

(b) $\dfrac{\pi}{24} \times \dfrac{180}{\pi} = 7.5°$

(c) $3.4 \times \dfrac{180}{\pi} = 195°$

When working in radians with trigonometric functions on your calculator, ensure it is set in 'RAD' or 'R' mode.

① Express the following angles in radians, leaving your answers in terms of π or to 3 significant figures as appropriate.

(i) 60°   (ii) 45°   (iii) 150°   (iv) 200°

(v) 44.4°   (vi) 405°   (vii) 270°   (viii) 99°

(ix) 300°   (x) 720°   (xi) 15°   (xii) 3°

② Express the following angles in degrees, rounding to 3 significant figures where appropriate.

(i) $\dfrac{\pi}{9}$ (ii) $\dfrac{2\pi}{15}$ (iii) 4^c (iv) $\dfrac{5\pi}{3}$

(v) $\dfrac{\pi}{7}$ (vi) $\dfrac{\pi}{20}$ (vii) 1.8^c (viii) $\dfrac{11\pi}{9}$

(ix) $\dfrac{7\pi}{2}$ (x) 5π (xi) $\dfrac{9\pi}{4}$ (xii) $\dfrac{17\pi}{12}$

An introduction to radians

The identities sin[$\theta \pm \phi$] and cos[$\theta \pm \phi$]

In Chapters 1 and 5 of this book you use the trigonometric identities known as the **addition formulae** or **compound angle formulae**. The proofs of these identities are given in the A Level Mathematics textbook.

These identities are:

$$\sin(\theta + \phi) \equiv \sin\theta\cos\phi + \cos\theta\sin\phi$$

$$\sin(\theta - \phi) \equiv \sin\theta\cos\phi - \cos\theta\sin\phi$$

$$\cos(\theta + \phi) \equiv \cos\theta\cos\phi - \sin\theta\sin\phi$$

$$\cos(\theta - \phi) \equiv \cos\theta\cos\phi + \sin\theta\sin\phi$$

Note the change of sign in the formulae for the cosine of the sum or difference of two angles:

$$\cos(\theta + \phi) \equiv \cos\theta\cos\phi - \sin\theta\sin\phi$$

$$\cos(\theta - \phi) \equiv \cos\theta\cos\phi + \sin\theta\sin\phi$$

Although these results are often referred to as 'formulae', they are in fact identities (as indicated by the identity symbol $\equiv$) and they are true for all values of θ and ϕ. However, it is common for the identity symbol to be replaced by an equals sign when the formulae are being used.

These identities are used:

- in Chapter 1 to look at combinations of two rotations
- in Chapter 5 to look at multiplying two complex numbers in modulus-argument form.

Example

Use the compound angle formulae to find exact values for:

(i)   sin15°

(ii)   cos75°

Solution

(i) $\sin 15° = \sin\left(45° - 30°\right) = \sin 45°\cos 30° - \cos 45°\sin 30°$

$$= \frac{1}{\sqrt{2}} \times \frac{\sqrt{3}}{2} - \frac{1}{\sqrt{2}} \times \frac{1}{2}$$

$$= \frac{\sqrt{3}}{2\sqrt{2}} - \frac{1}{2\sqrt{2}}$$

$$= \frac{\sqrt{3}-1}{2\sqrt{2}} \text{ or } \frac{\sqrt{6}-\sqrt{2}}{4}$$

(ii) $\cos 75° = \cos\left(45° + 30°\right) = \cos 45°\cos 30° - \sin 45°\sin 30°$

$$= \frac{1}{\sqrt{2}} \times \frac{\sqrt{3}}{2} - \frac{1}{\sqrt{2}} \times \frac{1}{2}$$

This is the same as part (i) and so $\cos 75° = \dfrac{\sqrt{6}-\sqrt{2}}{4}$.

The exercise below is designed to familiarise you with these identities.

Exercise

① Use the compound angle formulae to write the following in surd form:

(i) $\cos 15° = \cos(45° - 30°)$

(ii) $\sin 105° = \sin(60° + 45°)$

(iii) $\cos 105° = \cos(60° + 45°)$

(iv) $\sin 165° = \sin(120° + 45°)$

② Simplify each of the following expressions, giving answers in surd form where possible:

(i) $\sin 60° \cos 30° - \cos 60° \sin 30°$

(ii) $\sin 40° \cos 50° + \cos 40° \sin 50°$

(iii) $\cos 3\theta \cos \theta - \sin 3\theta \sin \theta$

(iv) $\cos\left(\dfrac{\pi}{3}\right)\cos\left(\dfrac{\pi}{6}\right) + \sin\left(\dfrac{\pi}{3}\right)\sin\left(\dfrac{\pi}{6}\right)$

(v) $2\sin\left(\dfrac{\pi}{4}\right)\cos\left(\dfrac{\pi}{6}\right) - 2\cos\left(\dfrac{\pi}{4}\right)\sin\left(\dfrac{\pi}{6}\right)$

(vi) $\cos 47° \cos 13° - \sin 13° \sin 47°$

③ Expand and simplify the following expressions:

(i) $\sin(\theta + 45°)$

(ii) $\cos(2\theta - 30°)$

(iii) $\sin\left(\theta - \dfrac{\pi}{6}\right)$

(iv) $\cos\left(3\theta + \dfrac{\pi}{3}\right)$

Answers

Chapter 1

Discussion point (Page 1)

$3, 2, 1, 0$

Discussion point (Page 4)

When subtracting numbers, the order in which the numbers appear is important – changing the order changes the answer, for example: $3 - 6 \neq 6 - 3$. So subtraction of numbers is not commutative.

The grouping of the numbers is also important, for example $(13 - 5) - 2 \neq 13 - (5 - 2)$. Therefore subtraction of numbers is not associative.

Matrices follow the same rules for commutativity and associativity as numbers. Matrix addition is both commutative and associative, but matrix subtraction is not commutative or associative. This is true because addition and subtraction of each of the individual elements will determine whether the matrices are commutative or associative overall.

You can use more formal methods to prove these properties. For example, to show that matrix addition is commutative:

$$\begin{pmatrix} a & b \\ c & d \end{pmatrix} + \begin{pmatrix} e & f \\ g & h \end{pmatrix} = \begin{pmatrix} a+e & b+f \\ c+g & d+h \end{pmatrix} = \begin{pmatrix} e+a & f+b \\ g+c & h+d \end{pmatrix} = \begin{pmatrix} e & f \\ g & h \end{pmatrix} + \begin{pmatrix} a & b \\ c & d \end{pmatrix}$$

Addition of numbers is commutative

Exercise 1.1 (Page 4)

1 (i) 3×2 (ii) 3×3 (iii) 1×2
  (iv) 5×1 (v) 2×4 (vi) 3×2

2 (i) $\begin{pmatrix} 5 & -8 \\ 2 & -3 \end{pmatrix}$ (ii) $\begin{pmatrix} 3 & 1 & -4 \\ 4 & 2 & 12 \end{pmatrix}$

(iii) $\begin{pmatrix} -8 & 5 \\ -3 & 7 \end{pmatrix}$

(iv) Non-conformable   (v) $\begin{pmatrix} -3 & -9 & 14 \\ 0 & 0 & 4 \end{pmatrix}$

(vi) $\begin{pmatrix} 4 \\ 12 \\ 20 \end{pmatrix}$ (vii) $\begin{pmatrix} 9 & 7 & -17 \\ 10 & 5 & 28 \end{pmatrix}$

(viii) Non-conformable

(ix) $\begin{pmatrix} -15 & 8 \\ -4 & 3 \end{pmatrix}$

3 (i) $\begin{pmatrix} 0 & 2 & 1 & 0 \\ 1 & 0 & 2 & 1 \\ 0 & 2 & 0 & 2 \\ 1 & 0 & 1 & 0 \end{pmatrix}$ (ii) $\begin{pmatrix} 0 & 0 & 2 & 2 \\ 1 & 0 & 0 & 0 \\ 2 & 0 & 0 & 1 \\ 0 & 0 & 2 & 0 \end{pmatrix}$

(iii)

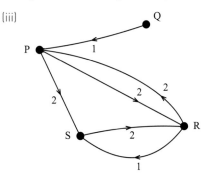

4 $w = 2, x = -6, y = -2, z = 2$

5 $p = -1$ or 6, $q = \pm\sqrt{5}$

6 (i) $\begin{pmatrix} 1 & 0 & 1 & 4 & 4 \\ 0 & 0 & 1 & 0 & 2 \\ 1 & 1 & 0 & 7 & 5 \\ 0 & 1 & 0 & 3 & 3 \end{pmatrix}$

$\begin{pmatrix} 3 & 1 & 1 & 10 & 7 \\ 0 & 0 & 4 & 2 & 10 \\ 3 & 1 & 1 & 11 & 8 \\ 1 & 2 & 1 & 8 & 6 \end{pmatrix}$

(ii) $\begin{pmatrix} 1 & 0 & 0 & 2 & 1 \\ 1 & 1 & 0 & 3 & 2 \\ 0 & 0 & 1 & 1 & 2 \\ 0 & 1 & 1 & 2 & 3 \end{pmatrix}$

City 2 vs United 1
Rangers 2 vs Town 1
Rangers 1 vs United 1

7 (i) $\begin{pmatrix} 15 & 3 & 7 & 15 \\ 5 & 9 & 15 & -3 \\ 19 & 10 & 9 & 3 \end{pmatrix}$

The matrix represents the number of jackets left in stock after all the orders have been dispatched. The negative element indicates there was not enough of that type of jacket in stock to fulfil the order.

(ii) $\begin{pmatrix} 20 & 13 & 17 & 20 \\ 15 & 19 & 20 & 12 \\ 19 & 10 & 14 & 8 \end{pmatrix}$

(iii) $\begin{pmatrix} 12 & 30 & 18 & 0 \\ 6 & 18 & 24 & 36 \\ 30 & 0 & 12 & 18 \end{pmatrix}$

The assumption is probably not very realistic, as a week is quite a short time.

Discussion point (Page 8)

The dimensions of the matrices are $\mathbf{A}$ (3×3), $\mathbf{B}$ (3×2) and $\mathbf{C}$ (2×2). The conformable products are $\mathbf{AB}$ and $\mathbf{BC}$. Both of these products would have dimension (3×2), even though the original matrices are not the same sizes.

Activity 1.1 (Page 9)

$\mathbf{AB} = \begin{pmatrix} 2 & -1 \\ 3 & 4 \end{pmatrix}\begin{pmatrix} -4 & 0 \\ -2 & 1 \end{pmatrix} = \begin{pmatrix} -6 & -1 \\ -20 & 4 \end{pmatrix}$

$\mathbf{BA} = \begin{pmatrix} -4 & 0 \\ -2 & 1 \end{pmatrix}\begin{pmatrix} 2 & -1 \\ 3 & 4 \end{pmatrix} = \begin{pmatrix} -8 & 4 \\ -1 & 6 \end{pmatrix}$

These two matrices are not equal and so matrix multiplication is not usually commutative. There are some exceptions, for example if

$\mathbf{C} = \begin{pmatrix} 2 & 0 \\ 0 & 2 \end{pmatrix}$ and $\mathbf{D} = \begin{pmatrix} 3 & 3 \\ -1 & -1 \end{pmatrix}$ then

$\mathbf{CD} = \mathbf{DC} = \begin{pmatrix} 6 & 6 \\ -2 & -2 \end{pmatrix}$.

Activity 1.2 (Page 10)

(i) $\mathbf{AB} = \begin{pmatrix} -6 & -1 \\ -20 & 4 \end{pmatrix}$

(ii) $\mathbf{BC} = \begin{pmatrix} -4 & -8 \\ 0 & -1 \end{pmatrix}$

(iii) $(\mathbf{AB})\mathbf{C} = \begin{pmatrix} -8 & -15 \\ -12 & -28 \end{pmatrix}$

(iv) $\mathbf{A}(\mathbf{BC}) = \begin{pmatrix} -8 & -15 \\ -12 & -28 \end{pmatrix}$

$(\mathbf{AB})\mathbf{C} = \mathbf{A}(\mathbf{BC})$ so matrix multiplication is associative in this case

To produce a general proof, use general matrices such as

$\mathbf{A} = \begin{pmatrix} a & b \\ c & d \end{pmatrix}$, $\mathbf{B} = \begin{pmatrix} e & f \\ g & h \end{pmatrix}$ and

$\mathbf{C} = \begin{pmatrix} i & j \\ k & l \end{pmatrix}$.

$\mathbf{AB} = \begin{pmatrix} a & b \\ c & d \end{pmatrix}\begin{pmatrix} e & f \\ g & h \end{pmatrix} = \begin{pmatrix} ae + bg & af + bh \\ ce + dg & cf + dh \end{pmatrix}$,

$\mathbf{BC} = \begin{pmatrix} e & f \\ g & h \end{pmatrix}\begin{pmatrix} i & j \\ k & l \end{pmatrix} = \begin{pmatrix} ei + fk & ej + fl \\ gi + hk & gj + hl \end{pmatrix}$

and so

$(\mathbf{AB})\mathbf{C} = \begin{pmatrix} ae + bg & af + bh \\ ce + dg & cf + dh \end{pmatrix}\begin{pmatrix} i & j \\ k & l \end{pmatrix}$

$\begin{pmatrix} aei + bgi + afk + bhk & aej + bgj + afl + bhl \\ cei + cfk + dgi + dhk & cej + cfl + dgj + dhl \end{pmatrix}$

and

$\mathbf{A}(\mathbf{BC}) = \begin{pmatrix} a & b \\ c & d \end{pmatrix}\begin{pmatrix} ei + fk & ej + fl \\ gi + hk & gj + hl \end{pmatrix}$

$= \begin{pmatrix} aei + afk + bgi + bhk & aej + afl + bgj + bhl \\ cei + dgi + cfk + dhk & cej + dgj + cfl + dhl \end{pmatrix}$

Since $(\mathbf{AB})\mathbf{C} = \mathbf{A}(\mathbf{BC})$ matrix multiplication is associative and the product can be written without brackets as $\mathbf{ABC}$.

Exercise 1.2 (Page 10)

1   (i) (a) 3×3 (b) 1×3 (c) 2×3 (d) 2×4
         (e) 2×1 (f) 3×5
    (ii) (a) non-conformable
          (b) 3×5
          (c) non-conformable
          (d) 2×3
          (e) non-conformable

2 (i) $\begin{pmatrix} 21 & 6 \\ 31 & 13 \end{pmatrix}$ (ii) $\begin{pmatrix} -30 & -15 \end{pmatrix}$

(iii) $\begin{pmatrix} -54 \\ -1 \end{pmatrix}$

3 $\mathbf{AB} = \begin{pmatrix} 3 & -56 \\ 20 & -73 \end{pmatrix}$, $\mathbf{BA} = \begin{pmatrix} -25 & 8 \\ 28 & -45 \end{pmatrix}$

$\mathbf{AB} \ne \mathbf{BA}$ so matrix multiplication is non-commutative.

4 (i) $\begin{pmatrix} -7 & 26 \\ 2 & 34 \end{pmatrix}$ (ii) $\begin{pmatrix} 5 & 25 \\ 16 & 22 \end{pmatrix}$

(iii) $\begin{pmatrix} 31 & 0 \\ 65 & 18 \end{pmatrix}$ (iv) $\begin{pmatrix} 26 & 37 & 16 \\ 14 & 21 & 28 \\ -8 & -11 & 2 \end{pmatrix}$

(v) non-conformable (vi) $\begin{pmatrix} 28 & -18 \\ 26 & 2 \\ 16 & 25 \end{pmatrix}$

5 $\begin{pmatrix} -38 & -136 & -135 \\ 133 & 133 & 100 \\ 273 & 404 & 369 \end{pmatrix}$

6 (i) $\begin{pmatrix} 2x^2 + 12 & -9 \\ -4 & 3 \end{pmatrix}$ (ii) $x = 2$ or 3

(iii) $\mathbf{BA} = \begin{pmatrix} 8 & 12 \\ 8 & 15 \end{pmatrix}$ or $\begin{pmatrix} 18 & 18 \\ 12 & 15 \end{pmatrix}$

7 (i) (a) $\begin{pmatrix} 4 & 3 \\ 0 & 1 \end{pmatrix}$ (b) $\begin{pmatrix} 8 & 7 \\ 0 & 1 \end{pmatrix}$

(c) $\begin{pmatrix} 16 & 15 \\ 0 & 1 \end{pmatrix}$ (ii) $\begin{pmatrix} 2^n & 2^n - 1 \\ 0 & 1 \end{pmatrix}$

(iii) $\begin{pmatrix} 1024 & 1023 \\ 0 & 0 \end{pmatrix} = \begin{pmatrix} 2^{10} & 2^{10} - 1 \\ 0 & 1 \end{pmatrix}$

8 (i) $\begin{pmatrix} 1 & 1 & 2 & 0 \\ 1 & 0 & 1 & 0 \\ 1 & 1 & 0 & 2 \\ 0 & 0 & 1 & 0 \end{pmatrix}$

(ii) $\begin{pmatrix} 4 & 3 & 3 & 4 \\ 2 & 2 & 2 & 2 \\ 2 & 1 & 5 & 0 \\ 1 & 1 & 0 & 2 \end{pmatrix}$ $\mathbf{M}^2$ represents the number of two-stage routes between each pair of resorts.

(iii) $\mathbf{M}^3$ would represent the number of three-stage routes between each pair of resorts.

9 (i) $\begin{pmatrix} 8 + 4x & -20 + x^2 \\ -8 + x & -3 - 3x \end{pmatrix}$

(ii) $x = -3$ or 4

(iii) $\begin{pmatrix} -4 & -11 \\ -11 & 6 \end{pmatrix}$ or $\begin{pmatrix} 24 & -4 \\ -4 & -15 \end{pmatrix}$

10 (i) $\mathbf{D} = \begin{pmatrix} 1 & 1 & 1 & 1 \end{pmatrix}$

$\mathbf{DA} = \begin{pmatrix} 299 & 199 & 270 & 175 & 114 \end{pmatrix}$

(ii) $\mathbf{F} = \begin{pmatrix} 1 \\ 1 \\ 1 \\ 1 \\ 1 \end{pmatrix}$, $\mathbf{AF} = \begin{pmatrix} 229 \\ 231 \\ 263 \\ 334 \end{pmatrix}$

(iii) $\mathbf{S} = \begin{pmatrix} 1 \\ 0 \\ 0 \\ 0 \\ 1 \end{pmatrix}$, $\mathbf{DAS} = (413)$,

$\mathbf{C} = \begin{pmatrix} 0 \\ 1 \\ 1 \\ 1 \\ 0 \end{pmatrix}$, $\mathbf{DAC} = (644)$

(iv) $\mathbf{P} = \begin{pmatrix} 0.95 \\ 0.95 \\ 1.05 \\ 1.15 \\ 1.15 \end{pmatrix}$,

$\mathbf{DAP} = (1088.95) = \pounds 1088.95$

11 (i) $\begin{pmatrix} b \\ a \\ c \end{pmatrix}$ (ii) $\begin{pmatrix} 1 & 0 & 0 \\ 0 & 0 & 1 \\ 0 & 1 & 0 \end{pmatrix}$

(iii) $\begin{pmatrix} 0 & 1 & 0 \\ 0 & 0 & 1 \\ 1 & 0 & 0 \end{pmatrix}$, $\begin{pmatrix} b \\ c \\ a \end{pmatrix}$

(iv) $\begin{pmatrix} 0 & 0 & 1 \\ 1 & 0 & 0 \\ 0 & 1 & 0 \end{pmatrix}$, $\begin{pmatrix} c \\ a \\ b \end{pmatrix}$

(v) $\begin{pmatrix} 1 & 0 & 0 \\ 0 & 1 & 0 \\ 0 & 0 & 1 \end{pmatrix}$ The strands are back in the original order at the end of Stage 6.

Discussion point (Page 17)

The image of the unit vector $\begin{pmatrix} 1 \\ 0 \end{pmatrix}$ is $\begin{pmatrix} a \\ c \end{pmatrix}$ and the image of the unit vector $\begin{pmatrix} 0 \\ 1 \end{pmatrix}$ is $\begin{pmatrix} b \\ d \end{pmatrix}$.

The origin maps to itself.

Activity 1.3 (Page 17)

The diagram below shows the unit square with two of its sides along the unit vectors **i** and **j**. It is rotated by 45° about the origin.

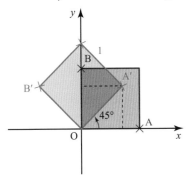

You can use trigonometry to find the images of the unit vectors **i** and **j**.

For A', the x-coordinate satisfies $\cos 45 = \frac{x}{1}$ so $x = \cos 45 = \frac{1}{\sqrt{2}}$.

In a similar way, the y-coordinate of A' is $\frac{1}{\sqrt{2}}$.

For B', the symmetry of the diagram shows that the x-coordinate is $-\frac{1}{\sqrt{2}}$ and the y-coordinate is $\frac{1}{\sqrt{2}}$.

Hence, the image of $\begin{pmatrix} 1 \\ 0 \end{pmatrix}$ is $\begin{pmatrix} \frac{1}{\sqrt{2}} \\ \frac{1}{\sqrt{2}} \end{pmatrix}$ and the image of $\begin{pmatrix} 0 \\ 1 \end{pmatrix}$ is

$\begin{pmatrix} -\frac{1}{\sqrt{2}} \\ \frac{1}{\sqrt{2}} \end{pmatrix}$ and so the matrix representing an

anticlockwise rotation of 45° about the origin is $\begin{pmatrix} \frac{1}{\sqrt{2}} & -\frac{1}{\sqrt{2}} \\ \frac{1}{\sqrt{2}} & \frac{1}{\sqrt{2}} \end{pmatrix}$.

Rotations of 45° clockwise about the origin and 135° anticlockwise about the origin are also represented by matrices involving $\pm\frac{1}{\sqrt{2}}$.

This is due to the symmetry about the origin.

(i) The diagram for a 45° clockwise rotation about the origin is shown below.

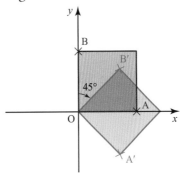

The image of $\begin{pmatrix} 1 \\ 0 \end{pmatrix}$ is $\begin{pmatrix} \frac{1}{\sqrt{2}} \\ -\frac{1}{\sqrt{2}} \end{pmatrix}$ and the image

of $\begin{pmatrix} 0 \\ 1 \end{pmatrix}$ is $\begin{pmatrix} \frac{1}{\sqrt{2}} \\ \frac{1}{\sqrt{2}} \end{pmatrix}$ and so the matrix

representing an anticlockwise rotation of

45° about the origin is $\begin{pmatrix} \frac{1}{\sqrt{2}} & \frac{1}{\sqrt{2}} \\ -\frac{1}{\sqrt{2}} & \frac{1}{\sqrt{2}} \end{pmatrix}$.

(ii) The diagram for a 135° anticlockwise rotation about the origin is shown below.

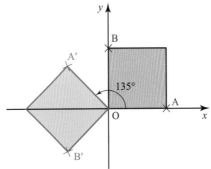

The image of $\begin{pmatrix} 1 \\ 0 \end{pmatrix}$ is $\begin{pmatrix} -\frac{1}{\sqrt{2}} \\ \frac{1}{\sqrt{2}} \end{pmatrix}$ and the image of

$\begin{pmatrix} 0 \\ 1 \end{pmatrix}$ is $\begin{pmatrix} -\frac{1}{\sqrt{2}} \\ -\frac{1}{\sqrt{2}} \end{pmatrix}$ and so the matrix representing

an anticlockwise rotation of 45° about the origin is

$\begin{pmatrix} -\frac{1}{\sqrt{2}} & -\frac{1}{\sqrt{2}} \\ \frac{1}{\sqrt{2}} & -\frac{1}{\sqrt{2}} \end{pmatrix}$.

Discussion point (Page 18)

The matrix for a rotation of $\theta°$ clockwise about the

origin is $\begin{pmatrix} \cos\theta & \sin\theta \\ -\sin\theta & \cos\theta \end{pmatrix}$

Activity 1.4 (Page 19)

(i) The diagram below shows the effect of the matrix

$\begin{pmatrix} 2 & 0 \\ 0 & 1 \end{pmatrix}$ on the unit vectors $\mathbf{i}$ and $\mathbf{j}$.

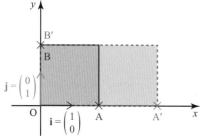

You can see that the vector $\mathbf{i}$ has image $\begin{pmatrix} 2 \\ 0 \end{pmatrix}$ and

the vector $\mathbf{j}$ is unchanged. Therefore this matrix represents a stretch of scale factor 2 parallel to the x-axis.

(ii) The diagram below shows the effect of the matrix

$\begin{pmatrix} 1 & 0 \\ 0 & 5 \end{pmatrix}$ on the unit vectors $\mathbf{i}$ and $\mathbf{j}$.

You can see that the vector $\mathbf{i}$ is unchanged and

the vector $\mathbf{j}$ has image $\begin{pmatrix} 0 \\ 5 \end{pmatrix}$. Therefore this

matrix represents a stretch of scale factor 5 parallel to the y-axis.

The matrix $\begin{pmatrix} m & 0 \\ 0 & 1 \end{pmatrix}$ represents a stretch of scale factor m

parallel to the x-axis.

The matrix $\begin{pmatrix} 1 & 0 \\ 0 & n \end{pmatrix}$ represents a stretch of scale factor n

parallel to the y-axis.

Activity 1.5 (Page 20)

Point A: $6 \div 2 = 3$

Point B: $6 \div 2 = 3$

Point C: $3 \div 1 = 3$

Point D: $3 \div 1 = 3$

The ratio is equal to 3 for each point.

Exercise 1.3 (Page 24)

1 (i) (a)

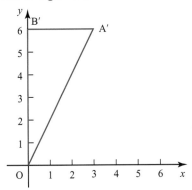

(b) A′ = (3, 6), B′ = (0, 6)

(c) $x' = 3x$, $y' = 3y$

(d) $\begin{pmatrix} 3 & 0 \\ 0 & 3 \end{pmatrix}$

(ii) (a)

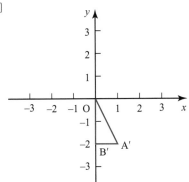

(b) A′ = (1, –2), B′ = (0, –2)

(c) $x' = x$, $y' = -y$

(d) $\begin{pmatrix} 1 & 0 \\ 0 & -1 \end{pmatrix}$

(iii) (a)

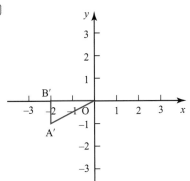

(b) A′ = (–2, –1), B′ = (–2, 0)

(c) $x' - y$ $y' = -x$

(d) $\begin{pmatrix} 0 & -1 \\ -1 & 0 \end{pmatrix}$

(iv) (a)

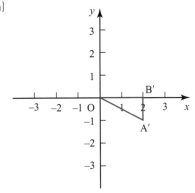

(b) A′ = (2, –1), B′ = (2, 0)

(c) $x' = y$, $y' = -x$

(d) $\begin{pmatrix} 0 & 1 \\ -1 & 0 \end{pmatrix}$

(v) (a)

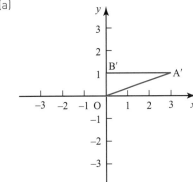

(b) A′ = (3, 1), B′ = (0, 1)

(c) $x' = 3x$, $y' = \frac{1}{2}y$

(d) $\begin{pmatrix} 3 & 0 \\ 0 & \frac{1}{2} \end{pmatrix}$

2 (i) Reflection in the *x*-axis

(ii) Reflection in the line $y = -x$

(iii) Stretch of factor 2 parallel to the *x*-axis and stretch factor 3 parallel to the *y*-axis

(iv) Enlargement, scale factor 4, centre the origin

(v) Rotation of 90° clockwise (or 270° anticlockwise) about the origin

3 (i) Rotation of 60° anticlockwise about the origin

(ii) Rotation of 55° anticlockwise about the origin

(iii) Rotation of 135° clockwise about the origin

(iv) Rotation of 150° anticlockwise about the origin

4 (i)

$$\begin{pmatrix} 1 & 4 \\ 0 & 1 \end{pmatrix}\begin{pmatrix} 1 & 1 & -1 & -1 \\ 1 & -1 & -1 & 1 \end{pmatrix} = \begin{pmatrix} 5 & -3 & -5 & 3 \\ 1 & -1 & -1 & 1 \end{pmatrix}$$

so the transformed square would look like this:

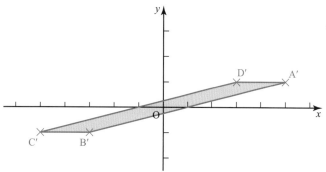

(ii) The transformation is a shear with the x-axis fixed and the point A(1, 1) has image A′(5, 1).

5 (i) (a) The image of the unit square has vertices (0, 0), (1, 5), (0, 1), (1, 6) as shown in the diagram below.

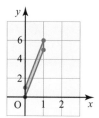

(b) The image of the unit square has vertices (0, 0), (1, 0), (0.5, 1), (1.5, 1) as shown in the diagram below.

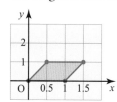

(ii) Matrix **A** represents a shear with the y-axis fixed; the point (1, 1) has image (1, 6). **A** has shear factor 5.
Matrix **B** represents a shear with the x-axis fixed; the point (1, 1) has image (1.5, 1). **B** has shear factor 0.5.

6 (i) $\begin{pmatrix} 0 & -1 & 0 \\ 1 & 0 & 0 \\ 0 & 0 & 1 \end{pmatrix}$ (ii) $\begin{pmatrix} 1 & 0 & 0 \\ 0 & -1 & 0 \\ 0 & 0 & 1 \end{pmatrix}$

(iii) $\begin{pmatrix} 1 & 0 & 0 \\ 0 & -1 & 0 \\ 0 & 0 & -1 \end{pmatrix}$ (iv) $\begin{pmatrix} 0 & 0 & -1 \\ 0 & 1 & 0 \\ 1 & 0 & 0 \end{pmatrix}$

7 (i) A′$(2\sqrt{3} - 1,\ 2)$ (ii) $\begin{pmatrix} 1 & \sqrt{3} \\ 0 & 1 \end{pmatrix}$

8 A′(4, 5), B′(7, 9), C′(3, 4). The original square and the image both have an area of one square unit.

9 (i)

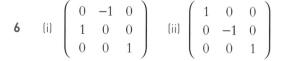

(ii) The gradient of A′C′ is $\frac{1}{2}$, which is the reciprocal of the top right-hand entry of the matrix **M**.

10 (i) Rotation of 90° clockwise about the x-axis
(ii) Enlargement scale factor 3, centre (0, 0)
(iii) Reflection in the plane $z = 0$
(iv) Three-way stretch of factor 2 in the x-direction, factor 3 in the y-direction and factor 0.5 in the z-direction

11 (i) $\begin{pmatrix} -1 & 0 & 0 \\ 0 & 1 & 0 \\ 0 & 0 & 1 \end{pmatrix}$ (ii) $\begin{pmatrix} -1 & 0 & 0 \\ 0 & 1 & 0 \\ 0 & 0 & 1 \end{pmatrix}$

12 $(x, y) \rightarrow (x, x)$
The matrix for the transformation is $\begin{pmatrix} 1 & 0 \\ 1 & 0 \end{pmatrix}$.

13 (i) Any matrix of the form $\begin{pmatrix} 5 & 0 \\ 0 & k \end{pmatrix}$ or $\begin{pmatrix} k & 0 \\ 0 & 5 \end{pmatrix}$.

If $k = 5$ the rectangle would be a square.

(ii) $\begin{pmatrix} \sqrt{2} & 1 \\ 0 & 1 \end{pmatrix}$, $\begin{pmatrix} 1 & 0 \\ 1 & \sqrt{2} \end{pmatrix}$,

$\begin{pmatrix} 1 & \sqrt{2} \\ 1 & 0 \end{pmatrix}$ or $\begin{pmatrix} 0 & 1 \\ \sqrt{2} & 1 \end{pmatrix}$

(iii) $\begin{pmatrix} 7 & \frac{3\sqrt{3}}{2} \\ 0 & \frac{3}{2} \end{pmatrix}$, $\begin{pmatrix} 0 & \frac{3}{2} \\ 7 & \frac{3\sqrt{3}}{2} \end{pmatrix}$,

$$\begin{pmatrix} \dfrac{3\sqrt{3}}{2} & 7 \\ \dfrac{3}{2} & 0 \end{pmatrix} \text{ or } \begin{pmatrix} 0 & \dfrac{3}{2} \\ 7 & \dfrac{3\sqrt{3}}{2} \end{pmatrix}$$

Discussion point (Page 27)

(i) **BA** represents a reflection in the line $y = x$

(ii) The transformation A is represented by the matrix

$$\mathbf{A} = \begin{pmatrix} 1 & 0 \\ 0 & -1 \end{pmatrix}$$ and the transformation

B is represented by the matrix

$$\mathbf{B} = \begin{pmatrix} 0 & -1 \\ 1 & 0 \end{pmatrix}.$$ The matrix product

$$\mathbf{BA} = \begin{pmatrix} 0 & -1 \\ 1 & 0 \end{pmatrix}\begin{pmatrix} 1 & 0 \\ 0 & -1 \end{pmatrix} = \begin{pmatrix} 0 & 1 \\ 1 & 0 \end{pmatrix}.$$

This is the matrix which represents a reflection in the line $y = x$.

Activity 1.6 (Page 28)

(i) $$\mathbf{P'} = \begin{pmatrix} a & b \\ c & d \end{pmatrix}\begin{pmatrix} x \\ y \end{pmatrix} = \begin{pmatrix} ax + by \\ cx + dy \end{pmatrix}$$

(ii) $$\mathbf{P''} = \begin{pmatrix} p & q \\ r & s \end{pmatrix}\begin{pmatrix} ax + by \\ ax + dy \end{pmatrix}$$

$$= \begin{pmatrix} pax + pby + qcx + qdy \\ rax + rby + scx + sdy \end{pmatrix}$$

(iii)

$$\mathbf{U} = \begin{pmatrix} p & q \\ r & s \end{pmatrix}\begin{pmatrix} a & b \\ c & d \end{pmatrix} = \begin{pmatrix} pa + qc & pb + qd \\ ra + sc & rb + sd \end{pmatrix}$$

and so

$$\mathbf{UP} = \begin{pmatrix} pa + qc & pb + qd \\ ra + sc & rb + sd \end{pmatrix}\begin{pmatrix} x \\ y \end{pmatrix}$$

$$= \begin{pmatrix} pax + qcx + pby + rdy \\ rax + scx + rby + sdy \end{pmatrix}.$$ Therefore $\mathbf{UP=P''}$

Discussion point (Page 28)

AB represents 'carry out transformation B followed by transformation A.

(AB)C represents 'carry out transformation C followed by transformation AB, i.e. 'carry out C followed by B followed by A'.

BC represents 'carry out transformation **C** followed by transformation **B**'.

A(BC) represents 'carry out transformation **BC** followed by transformation **A**, i.e. carry out **C** followed by **B** followed by **A**'.

Activity 1.7 (Page 29)

(i) $$\mathbf{A} = \begin{pmatrix} \cos\theta & -\sin\theta \\ \sin\theta & \cos\theta \end{pmatrix},$$

$$\mathbf{B} = \begin{pmatrix} \cos\phi & -\sin\phi \\ \sin\phi & \cos\phi \end{pmatrix}$$

(ii) $$\mathbf{BA} = \begin{pmatrix} \cos\theta\cos\phi - \sin\theta\sin\phi & -\sin\theta\cos\phi - \cos\theta\sin\phi \\ \sin\theta\cos\phi + \cos\theta\sin\phi & -\sin\theta\sin\phi + \cos\theta\cos\phi \end{pmatrix}$$

(iii) $$\mathbf{C} = \begin{pmatrix} \cos(\theta + \phi) & -\sin(\theta + \phi) \\ \sin(\theta + \phi) & \cos(\theta + \phi) \end{pmatrix}$$

(iv) $\sin(\theta + \phi) = \sin\theta\cos\phi + \cos\theta\sin\phi$

$\cos(\theta + \phi) = \cos\theta\cos\phi - \sin\theta\sin\phi$

(v) A rotation through angle θ followed by rotation through angle ϕ has the same effect as a rotation through angle ϕ followed by angle θ.

Exercise 1.4 (Page 30)

1 (i) **A**: enlargement centre (0,0), scale factor 3
   B: rotation 90° anticlockwise about (0,0)
   C: reflection in the x-axis
   D: reflection in the line $y = x$

(ii) $\mathbf{BC} = \begin{pmatrix} 0 & 1 \\ 1 & 0 \end{pmatrix}$, reflection in the line $y = x$

$\mathbf{CB} = \begin{pmatrix} 0 & -1 \\ -1 & 0 \end{pmatrix}$, reflection in the line $y = -x$

$\mathbf{DC} = \begin{pmatrix} 0 & -1 \\ 1 & 0 \end{pmatrix}$, rotation 90° anticlockwise about $(0, 0)$

$\mathbf{A}^2 = \begin{pmatrix} 9 & 0 \\ 0 & 9 \end{pmatrix}$, enlargement centre $(0, 0)$, scale factor 9

$\mathbf{BCB} = \begin{pmatrix} 1 & 0 \\ 0 & -1 \end{pmatrix}$, reflection in the x-axis

$DC^2D = \begin{pmatrix} 1 & 0 \\ 0 & 1 \end{pmatrix}$ returns the object to

its original position

(iii) For example, $\mathbf{B}^4$, $\mathbf{C}^2$ or $\mathbf{D}^2$

2 (i) $\mathbf{X} = \begin{pmatrix} 1 & 0 \\ 0 & -1 \end{pmatrix}$ $\mathbf{Y} = \begin{pmatrix} -1 & 0 \\ 0 & 1 \end{pmatrix}$

(ii) $\mathbf{XY} = \begin{pmatrix} -1 & 0 \\ 0 & -1 \end{pmatrix}$, rotation of 180°

about the origin

(iii) $\mathbf{YX} = \begin{pmatrix} -1 & 0 \\ 0 & -1 \end{pmatrix}$

(iv) When considering the effect on the unit vectors $\mathbf{i}$ and $\mathbf{j}$, as each transformation only affects one of the unit vectors the order of the transformations is not important in this case.

3 (i) $\mathbf{P} = \begin{pmatrix} -1 & 0 \\ 0 & -1 \end{pmatrix}$ $\mathbf{Q} = \begin{pmatrix} 0 & 1 \\ 1 & 0 \end{pmatrix}$

(ii) $\mathbf{PQ} = \begin{pmatrix} 0 & -1 \\ -1 & 0 \end{pmatrix}$, reflection in the line

$y = -x$

(iii) $\mathbf{QP} = \begin{pmatrix} 0 & -1 \\ -1 & 0 \end{pmatrix}$

(iv) The matrix $\mathbf{P}$ has the effect of making the coordinates of any point the negative of their original values,

i.e. $(x, y) \rightarrow (-x, -y)$

The matrix $\mathbf{Q}$ interchanges the coordinates,

i.e. $(x, y) \rightarrow (y, x)$

It does not matter what order these two transformations occur as the result will be the same

4 (i) $\mathbf{J} = \begin{pmatrix} 1 & 0 & 0 \\ 0 & 1 & 0 \\ 0 & 0 & -1 \end{pmatrix}$ $\mathbf{K} = \begin{pmatrix} 1 & 0 & 0 \\ 0 & 0 & -1 \\ 0 & 1 & 0 \end{pmatrix}$

$\mathbf{L} = \begin{pmatrix} -1 & 0 & 0 \\ 0 & 1 & 0 \\ 0 & 0 & 1 \end{pmatrix}$ $\mathbf{M} = \begin{pmatrix} 0 & 0 & 1 \\ 0 & 1 & 0 \\ -1 & 0 & 0 \end{pmatrix}$

(ii) (a) $\mathbf{LJ}$ (b) $\mathbf{MJ}$
    (c) $\mathbf{K}^2$ (d) $\mathbf{JLK}$

5 (i) $\begin{pmatrix} 8 & -4 \\ -3 & 12 \end{pmatrix}$ (ii) $(32, -33)$

6 Possible transformations are $\mathbf{B} = \begin{pmatrix} 0 & 1 \\ -1 & 0 \end{pmatrix}$,

which is a rotation of 90° clockwise about the origin, followed by

$\mathbf{A} = \begin{pmatrix} 3 & 0 \\ 0 & 1 \end{pmatrix}$, which is a stretch of scale factor

3 parallel to the x-axis. The order of these is important as performing $\mathbf{A}$ followed by $\mathbf{B}$ leads

to the matrix $\begin{pmatrix} 0 & 1 \\ -3 & 0 \end{pmatrix}$. Could also have

$\mathbf{B} = \begin{pmatrix} 1 & 0 \\ 0 & 3 \end{pmatrix}$. which represents a stretch of

factor 3 parallel to the y-axis, followed by

$\mathbf{A} = \begin{pmatrix} 0 & 1 \\ -1 & 0 \end{pmatrix}$, which represents a rotation

of 90° clockwise about the origin; again the order is important.

7 (i) $\mathbf{PQ} = \begin{pmatrix} 1 & 0 \\ -3 & -1 \end{pmatrix}$

(ii) $\mathbf{P} = \begin{pmatrix} 1 & 0 \\ 0 & -1 \end{pmatrix}$ represents a reflection in

the x-axis.

$\mathbf{Q} = \begin{pmatrix} 1 & 0 \\ 3 & 1 \end{pmatrix}$ represents a shear with the

y-axis fixed; point B(1,1) has image (1,–4).

8 $\mathbf{X} = \begin{pmatrix} \frac{1}{\sqrt{2}} & \frac{1}{\sqrt{2}} \\ \frac{1}{\sqrt{2}} & -\frac{1}{\sqrt{2}} \end{pmatrix}$

A matrix representing a rotation about the

origin has the form $\begin{pmatrix} \cos\theta & -\sin\theta \\ \sin\theta & \cos\theta \end{pmatrix}$ and so

the entries on the leading diagonal would be equal. That is not true for matrix $\mathbf{X}$ and so this cannot represent a rotation.

9 $\mathbf{Y} = \begin{pmatrix} 0 & 1 & 0 \\ 1 & 0 & 0 \\ 0 & 0 & 1 \end{pmatrix}$

10 (i) $\begin{pmatrix} 1 & 0 \\ 0 & 2 \end{pmatrix}$

(ii) A reflection in the x-axis and a stretch of scale factor 5 parallel to the x-axis

(iii) $\begin{pmatrix} 5 & 0 \\ 0 & -2 \end{pmatrix}$

Reflection in the x-axis; stretch of scale factor 5 parallel to the x-axis; stretch of scale factor 2 parallel to the y-axis. The outcome of these three transformations would be the same regardless of the order in which they are applied. There are six different possible orders.

(iv) $\begin{pmatrix} \frac{1}{5} & 0 \\ 0 & -\frac{1}{2} \end{pmatrix}$

11 (i) $\begin{pmatrix} 1 & -R_1 \\ 0 & 1 \end{pmatrix}$

(ii) $\begin{pmatrix} 1 & 0 \\ -\frac{1}{R_2} & 1 \end{pmatrix}$

(iii) $\begin{pmatrix} 1 & -R_1 \\ -\frac{1}{R_2} & \frac{R_1}{R_2} + 1 \end{pmatrix}$

(iv) $\begin{pmatrix} 1 + \frac{R_1}{R_2} & -R_1 \\ -\frac{1}{R_2} & 1 \end{pmatrix}$

The effect of Type B followed by Type A is different to that of Type A followed by Type B.

12 $a = \sqrt{\dfrac{\sqrt{2}+2}{4}}$ and $b = \sqrt{\dfrac{1}{2\left(\sqrt{2}+2\right)}}$

D represents an anticlockwise rotation of 22.5° about the origin.

By comparison to the matrix
$\begin{pmatrix} \cos\theta & -\sin\theta \\ \sin\theta & \cos\theta \end{pmatrix}$ for an anticlockwise

rotation of θ about the origin, a and b are the exact values of $\cos 22.5°$ and $\sin 22.5°$ respectively.

13 (i) $\mathbf{P} = \begin{pmatrix} \frac{1}{2} & \frac{\sqrt{3}}{2} \\ \frac{\sqrt{3}}{2} & -\frac{1}{2} \end{pmatrix}$ $\mathbf{Q} = \begin{pmatrix} -\frac{1}{2} & \frac{\sqrt{3}}{2} \\ \frac{\sqrt{3}}{2} & \frac{1}{2} \end{pmatrix}$

(ii) $\mathbf{QP} = \begin{pmatrix} \frac{1}{2} & -\frac{\sqrt{3}}{2} \\ \frac{\sqrt{3}}{2} & \frac{1}{2} \end{pmatrix}$, which represents

a rotation of 60° anticlockwise about the origin.

(iii) $\mathbf{PQ} = \begin{pmatrix} \frac{1}{2} & \frac{\sqrt{3}}{2} \\ -\frac{\sqrt{3}}{2} & \frac{1}{2} \end{pmatrix}$, which represents a

rotation of 60° clockwise about the origin.

14 A reflection in a line followed by a second reflection in the same line returns a point to its original position.

Discussion point (Page 33)

In a reflection, all points on the mirror line map to themselves.

In a rotation, only the centre of rotation maps to itself.

Exercise 1.5 (Page 35)

1 (i) Points of the form $\left(\lambda, -2\lambda\right)$

(ii) $(0, 0)$

(iii) Points of the form $\left(\lambda, -3\lambda\right)$

(iv) Points of the form $\left(2\lambda, 3\lambda\right)$

2 (i) x-axis, y-axis, lines of the form $y = mx$

(ii) x-axis, y-axis, lines of the form $y = mx$

(iii) no invariant lines

(iv) $y = x$, lines of the form $y = -x + c$

(v) $y = -x$, lines of the form $y = x + c$

(vi) x-axis, lines of the form $y = c$

3 (i) Any points on the line $y = \frac{1}{2}x$, for example $(0, 0)$, $(2, 1)$ and $(3, 1.5)$

(ii) $y = \frac{1}{2}x$

(iii) Any line of the form $y = -2x + c$

(iv) Using the method of Example 1.12 leads to the equations

$2m^2 + 3m - 2 = 0 \Rightarrow m = 0.5$ or -2

$(4 + 2m)c = 0 \Rightarrow m = -2$ or $c = 0$

If $m = 0.5$ then $c = 0$ so $y = \frac{1}{2}x$ is invariant.

If $m = -2$ then c can take any value and so $y = -2x + c$ is an invariant line.

4   (i) Solving $\begin{pmatrix} 4 & 11 \\ 11 & 4 \end{pmatrix} \begin{pmatrix} x \\ y \end{pmatrix} = \begin{pmatrix} x \\ y \end{pmatrix}$ leads

to the equations $y = -\frac{3x}{11}$ and $y = -\frac{11x}{3}$.

The only point that satisfies both of these is $(0, 0)$.

(ii) $y = x$ and $y = -x$

5   (i) $y = x$, $y = -\frac{9}{4}x$

(ii)

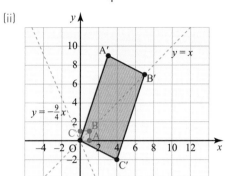

6   (i) $y = x$ (ii) $y = x$

(iii)

9   (i) $x' = x + a$, $y' = y + b$

(iii) (c) $a = -2b$

Chapter 2

Discussion point (Page 39)

$\mathbb{R}$ Real numbers – any number which is not complex

$\mathbb{Q}$ Rational numbers – numbers which can be expressed exactly as a fraction

$\mathbb{Z}$ Integers – positive or negative whole numbers, including zero

$\mathbb{N}$ Natural numbers – non-negative whole numbers (although there is some debate amongst mathematicians as to whether zero should be included!)

Discussion point (Page 40)

Any real number is either rational or irrational. This means that all real numbers will either lie inside the set of rational numbers, or inside the set of real numbers but outside the set of rational numbers. Therefore no separate set is needed for irrational numbers.

The symbol $\overline{\mathbb{Q}}$ is used for irrational numbers – numbers which cannot be expressed exactly as a fraction, such as π.

Activity 2.1 (Page 40)

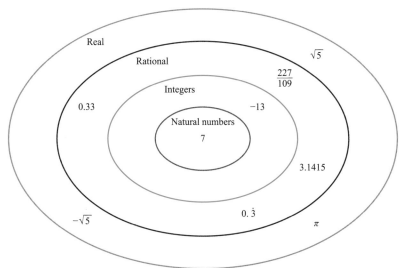

Activity 2.2 (Page 40)

(i) $x = 2$ Natural number (or integer)

(ii) $x = \dfrac{9}{7}$ Rational number

(iii) $x = \pm 3$ Integers

(iv) $x = -1$ Integer

(v) $x = 0,\ -7$ Integers

Discussion point (Page 42)

You know $i^2 = -1$

$i^3 = i^2 \times i = -1 \times i = -i$

$i^4 = i^2 \times i^2 = -1 \times -1 = 1$

$i^5 = i^4 \times i = 1 \times i = i$

$i^6 = i^5 \times i = i \times i = -1$

$i^7 = i^6 \times i = -1 \times i = -i$

The powers of i form a cycle:

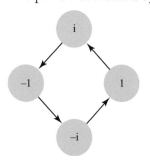

All numbers of the form i^{4n} are equal to 1.

All numbers of the form i^{4n+1} are equal to i.

All numbers of the form i^{4n+2} are equal to -1.

All numbers of the form i^{4n+3} are equal to $-i$.

Discussion point (Page 42)

$$\left(5 + \sqrt{-15}\right)\left(5 - \sqrt{-15}\right)$$
$$= 25 - 5\sqrt{-15} + 5\sqrt{-15} - (-15)$$
$$= 25 + 15$$
$$= 40$$

Discussion point (Page 42)

If the numerators and denominators of two fractions are equal then the fractions must also be equal.

However, it is possible for two fractions to be equal if the numerators and denominators are not equal, for example $\frac{3}{4} = \frac{6}{8}$.

Exercise 2.1 (Page 43)

1   (i)   i   (ii) -1

    (iii) $-i$ (iv)   1

2   (i) $9 - i$ (ii) $-9 + 9i$

    (iii) $3 + 9i$ (iv) $-3 - i$

3   (i) $24 + 2i$ (ii) $-2 + 24i$

    (iii) $20 + 48i$ (iv) $38 - 18i$

4   (i)   (a) 52   (b) 34   (c) 1768

    (ii) The answers are wholly real.

5   (i) $92 - 60i$ (ii) $-414 + 154i$

6   (i) $-1 \pm i$ (ii) $1 \pm 2i$ (iii) $2 \pm 3i$

    (iv) $-3 \pm 5i$ (v) $\frac{1}{2} \pm 2i$ (vi) $-2 \pm \sqrt{2}i$

7   $a = 1$ or $4, b = -1$ or 3

    The possible complex numbers are
    $1 + 9i$, $1 + i$, $16 + 9i$, $16 + i$

8   $a = 3$, $b = 5$ or $a = -3$, $b = -5$

9   $3 + 7i$ and $-3 - 7i$

10 (i)

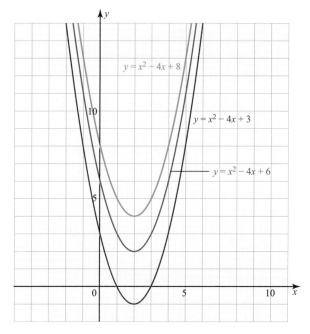

    (ii) (a) $x = 1$, $x = 3$
          (b) $x = 2 \pm \sqrt{2}i$
          (c) $2 \pm 2i$

    (iii) The roots all occur in pairs that are of the
           form $x = 2 \pm k$ where k is either a real
           number or a real multiple of i

11 $a = -7$, $b = 11$

    The second root is $5 - 2i$. The coefficients of
    the equation are not real.

Activity 2.3 (Page 45)

$z + z^{\star} = (x + yi) + (x - yi) = 2x$ which is real

$zz^{\star} = (x + yi)(x - yi) = x^2 - xyi + yxi - y^2i^2 = x^2 + y^2$
which is real

Discussion point (Page 46)

$$\frac{1}{i} = \frac{1}{i} \times \frac{i}{i} = \frac{i}{-1} = -i$$

$$\frac{1}{i^2} = \frac{1}{i^2} \times \frac{i^2}{i^2} = \frac{-1}{1} = -1$$

$$\frac{1}{i^3} = \frac{1}{i^3} \times \frac{i^3}{i^3} = \frac{-i}{-1} = i$$

$$\frac{1}{i^4} = \frac{1}{i^4} \times \frac{i^4}{i^4} = \frac{1}{1} = 1$$

All numbers of the form $\frac{1}{i^{4n}}$ are equal to 1.

All numbers for the form $\frac{1}{i^{4n+1}}$ are equal to $-i$.

All numbers of the form $\frac{1}{i^{4n+2}}$ are equal to -1.

All numbers of the form $\frac{1}{i^{4n+3}}$ are equal to i.

Exercise 2.2 (Page 46)

1 (i) $\frac{21}{50} + \frac{3}{50}i$ (ii) $\frac{21}{50} - \frac{3}{50}i$

 (iii) $-\frac{3}{50} + \frac{21}{50}i$ (iv) $\frac{3}{50} + \frac{21}{50}i$

2 (i) $-\frac{9}{13} + \frac{19}{13}i$ (ii) $-\frac{9}{34} - \frac{19}{34}i$

 (iii) $-\frac{9}{13} - \frac{19}{13}i$ (iv) $-\frac{9}{34} + \frac{19}{34}i$

3 (i) $\frac{94}{25} + \frac{158}{25}i$ (ii) $\frac{204}{625} + \frac{253}{625}i$

4 (i) 6 (ii) 85

 (iii) 12 (iv) 45

 (v) -4 (vi) 45

5 (i) 2 (ii) 3

 (iii) $2 - 3i$ (iv) $6 + 4i$

 (v) $8 + i$ (vi) $-4 - 7i$

6 (i) 0 (ii) 0

 (iii) -39 (iv) $-46 - 9i$

 (v) $-46 - 9i$ (vi) $52i$

7 (i) $\frac{348}{61} + \frac{290}{61}i$ (ii) $\frac{322}{29} - \frac{65}{29}i$

 (iii) $-\frac{600}{3721} + \frac{110}{3721}i$

8 (i) $2 - i$ (ii) 1

 (iii) $3 + i$ (iv) $-\frac{35}{34} + \frac{149}{34}i$

9 $a = -\frac{23}{13}$ $b = -\frac{15}{13}$

10 $a = 9, \ b = 11$

11 (i) $\frac{10}{89}$ (ii) $\frac{10}{89}$

12 $\frac{2x}{x^2 + y^2}$

14 $a = 2, \ b = 2$

15 $z = 0, \ z = 2, \ z = -1 \pm \sqrt{3}i$

16 $z = 8 - 6i, \ w = 6 - 5i$

Discussion point (Page 47)

A complex number has a real component and an imaginary component. It is not possible to illustrate two components using a single number line.

Activity 2.4 (Page 48)

(i)

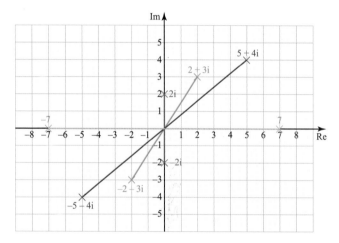

The points representing z and $-z$ have half turn rotational symmetry about the origin.

(ii)

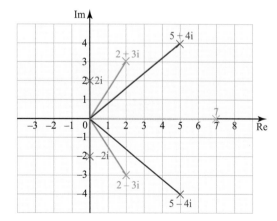

The points representing z and z^* are reflections of each other in the real axis.

Exercise 2.3 (Page 50)

1

2

3

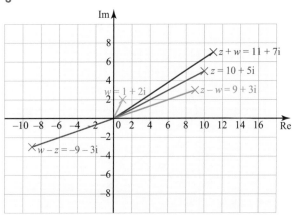

4   (i) $x^2 - 4x + 3 = 0$

(ii) $x^2 - 4x + 5 = 0$

(iii) $x^2 - 4x + 13 = 0$

(iv) All of the form $x^2 - 4x + k = 0$ where $k \in \mathbb{R}$

5

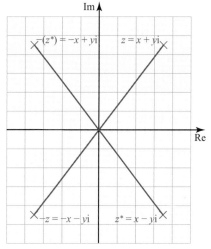

6   (i)

n	-1	0	1	2	3	4	5
z^n	$\frac{1}{2} - \frac{1}{2}i$	1	$1 + i$	$2i$	$-2 + 2i$	-4	$-4 - 4i$

(ii)

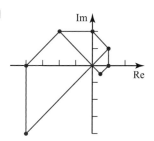

(iii)

n	-1	0	1	2	3	4	5
z^n	$\frac{1}{2} - \frac{1}{2}i$	1	$1 + i$	$2i$	$-2 + 2i$	-4	$-4 - 4i$
Distance from origin	$\frac{1}{\sqrt{2}}$	1	$\sqrt{2}$	2	$2\sqrt{2}$	4	$4\sqrt{2}$

(iv) The half squares formed are enlarged by a factor of $\sqrt{2}$ and rotated through $45°$ each time.

7   (i) $r = \sqrt{a^2 + b^2}$

$zz^* = (a + bi)(a - bi) = a^2 + b^2 = r^2$

(ii) $s = \sqrt{c^2 + d^2}$

(iii) $zw = (a + bi)(c + di) = (ac - bd) + (bc + ad)i$

Distance from origin of zw is

$$\sqrt{(ac - bd)^2 + (bc + ad)^2} = \sqrt{a^2c^2 + b^2d^2 + b^2c^2 + a^2d^2}$$

$$= \sqrt{(a^2 + b^2)(c^2 + d^2)}$$

$$= \sqrt{a^2 + b^2}\sqrt{c^2 + d^2} = rs$$

Chapter 3

Discussion point (Page 53)

$4x^3 + x^2 - 4x - 1 = 0$

Looking at the graph you may suspect that $x = 1$ is a root. Setting $x = 1$ verifies this. The factor theorem tells you that $(x - 1)$ must be a factor, so factorise the cubic $(x - 1)(4x^2 + 5x + 1) = 0$. Now factorise the remaining quadratic factor: $(x - 1)(4x + 1)(x + 1) = 0$, so the roots are $x = 1, -\frac{1}{4}, -1$.

$4x^3 + x^2 + 4x + 1 = 0$

This does not have such an obvious starting point, but the graph suggests only one real root.

Comparing with previous example, you may spot that $x = -\frac{1}{4}$ might work, so you can factorise giving $(4x + 1)(x^2 + 1) = 0$. From this you can see that the other roots must be complex. $x^2 = -1$, so the three roots are $x = -\frac{1}{4}, \pm i$.

Activity 3.1 (Page 54)

Equation	Two roots	Sum of roots	Product of roots
(i) $z^2 - 3z + 2 = 0$	1, 2	3	2
(ii) $z^2 + z - 6 = 0$	2, –3	–1	–6
(iii) $z^2 - 6z + 8 = 0$	2, 4	6	8
(iv) $z^2 - 3z - 10 = 0$	–2, 5	3	–10
(v) $2z^2 - 3z + 1 = 0$	$\frac{1}{2}, 1$	$\frac{3}{2}$	$\frac{1}{2}$
(vi) $z^2 - 4z + 5 = 0$	$2 \pm i$	4	5

Discussion point (Page 54)

If the equation is $ax^2 + bx + c = 0$, the sum appears to be $-\frac{b}{a}$ and the product appears to be $\frac{c}{a}$.

Discussion point (Page 55)

You get back to the original quadratic equation.

Activity 3.3 (Page 57)

(i) $\dfrac{-3 \pm i\sqrt{31}}{4}, \dfrac{-3 \pm i\sqrt{31}}{2}$

(ii) $\dfrac{2 \pm \sqrt{7}}{3}, \dfrac{5 \pm \sqrt{7}}{3}$

Exercise 3.1 (Page 57)

1   (i) $\alpha + \beta = -\frac{7}{2}, \quad \alpha\beta = 3$

(ii) $\alpha + \beta = \frac{1}{5}, \quad \alpha\beta = -\frac{1}{5}$

(iii) $\alpha + \beta = 0, \quad \alpha\beta = \frac{2}{7}$

(iv) $\alpha + \beta = -\frac{24}{5}, \quad \alpha\beta = 0$

(v) $\alpha + \beta = -11, \quad \alpha\beta = -4$

(vi) $\alpha + \beta = -\frac{8}{3}, \quad \alpha\beta = -2$

2   (i) $z^2 - 10z + 21 = 0$

(ii) $z^2 - 3z - 4 = 0$

(iii) $2z^2 + 19z + 45 = 0$

(iv) $z^2 - 5z = 0$

(v) $z^2 - 6z + 9 = 0$

(vi) $z^2 - 6z + 13 = 0$

3   (i) $2z^2 + 15z - 81 = 0$

(ii) $2z^2 - 5z - 9 = 0$

(iii) $2z^2 + 13z + 9 = 0$

(iv) $z^2 - 7z - 12 = 0$

4   (i) Roots are real, distinct and negative (since $\alpha\beta > 0 \Rightarrow$ same signs and $\alpha + \beta < 0 \Rightarrow$ both <0)

(ii) $\alpha = -\beta$

(iii) One of the roots is zero and the other is $-\frac{b}{a}$.

(iv) The roots are real and of opposite signs.

5   Let $az^2 + bz + c = 0$ have roots α and 2α.

Sum of roots $\alpha + 2\alpha = 3\alpha = -\dfrac{b}{a}$ so $\alpha = -\dfrac{b}{3a}$

Product of roots $\alpha \times 2\alpha = 2\alpha^2 = \dfrac{c}{a}$ so

$2 \times \left(-\dfrac{b}{3a}\right)^2 = \dfrac{c}{a}$

Then $2b^2 = 9ac$ as required.

6   (i) $az^2 + bkz + ck^2 = 0$

(ii) $az^2 + (b - 2ka)z + (k^2a - kb + c) = 0$

7   (ii) $z^2 - (5 + 2i)z + (9 + 7i) = 0$

Exercise 3.2 (Page 61)

1   (i) $-\dfrac{3}{2}$

(ii) $-\dfrac{1}{2}$

(iii) $-\dfrac{7}{2}$

2 (i) $z^3 - 7z^2 + 14z - 8 = 0$

   (ii) $z^3 - 3z^2 - 4z + 12 = 0$

   (iii) $2z^3 + 7z^2 + 6z = 0$

   (iv) $2z^3 - 13z^2 + 28z - 20 = 0$

   (v) $z^3 - 19z - 30 = 0$

   (vi) $z^3 - 5z^2 + 9z - 5 = 0$

3 (i) $z = 2, 5, 8$

   (ii) $z = -\dfrac{2}{3}, \dfrac{2}{3}, 2$

   (iii) $z = 2 - 2\sqrt{3}, 2, 2 + 2\sqrt{3}$

   (iv) $z = \dfrac{2}{3}, \dfrac{7}{6}, \dfrac{5}{3}$

4 (i) $z = w - 3$

   (ii) $(w - 3)^3 + (w - 3)^2 + 2(w - 3) - 3 = 0$

   (iii) $w^3 - 8w^2 + 23w - 27 = 0$

   (iv) $\alpha + 3, \beta + 3, \gamma + 3$

5 $w^3 - 4w^2 + 4w - 24 = 0$

6 (i) $2w^3 - 16w^2 + 37w - 27 = 0$

   (ii) $2w^3 + 24w^2 + 45w + 37 = 0$

7 The roots are $\dfrac{3}{2}, 2, \dfrac{5}{2}$ $k = \dfrac{47}{2}$

8 $z = \dfrac{1}{4}, \dfrac{1}{2}, -\dfrac{3}{4}$

9 $\alpha = -1, p = 7, q = 8$ or $\alpha = p = q = 0$

10 Roots are $-p$ and $\pm\sqrt{-q}$ (note $\pm\sqrt{-q}$ is not necessarily imaginary, since q is not necessarily >0)

11 (i) $p = -8\left(\alpha + \dfrac{1}{2\alpha} + \beta\right)$

       $q = 8\left(\dfrac{1}{2} + \alpha\beta + \dfrac{\beta}{2\alpha}\right)$

       $r = -4\beta$

   (iii) $r = 9; x = 1, \dfrac{1}{2}, -\dfrac{9}{4}$

        $r = -6; x = -2, -\dfrac{1}{4}, \dfrac{3}{2}$

12 $z = \dfrac{3}{7}, \dfrac{7}{3}, -2$

13 $ac^3 = b^3d$

    $z = \dfrac{1}{2}, \dfrac{3}{2}, \dfrac{9}{2}$

Exercise 3.3 (Page 64)

1 (i) $-\dfrac{3}{2}$

   (ii) 3

   (iii) $\dfrac{5}{2}$

   (iv) 2

2 (i) $z^4 - 6z^3 + 7z^2 + 6z - 8 = 0$

   (ii) $4z^4 + 20z^3 + z^2 - 60z = 0$

   (iii) $4z^4 + 12z^3 - 27z^2 - 54z + 81 = 0$

   (iv) $z^4 - 5z^2 + 10z - 6 = 0$

3 (i) $z^4 + 4z^3 - 6z^2 - 4z + 48 = 0$

   (ii) $2z^4 + 12z^3 + 21z^2 + 13z + 8 = 0$

4 (i) Let $w = x + 1$ then $x = w - 1$

      new quartic: $x^4 - 6x^2 + 9 = 0$

   (ii) Solutions to new quartic are $x = \pm\sqrt{3}$ (each one repeated), solutions to original quartic are therefore: $\alpha = \beta = \sqrt{3} - 1$ and $\gamma = \delta = -\sqrt{3} - 1$.

5 (i) $\alpha = -1, \ \beta = \sqrt{3}$

   (ii) $p = 4$ and $q = -9$

   (iii) Use substitution $y = x - 3\alpha$ (i.e. $y = x + 3$ then $x = y - 3$) and $y^3 - 8y^2 + 18y - 12 = 0$

6 (i) $\alpha + \beta + \gamma + \delta + \varepsilon = -\dfrac{b}{a}$

      $\alpha\beta + \alpha\gamma + \alpha\delta + \alpha\varepsilon + \beta\gamma + \beta\delta + \beta\varepsilon + \gamma\delta + \gamma\varepsilon + \delta\varepsilon = \dfrac{c}{a}$

      $\alpha\beta\gamma + \alpha\beta\delta + \alpha\beta\varepsilon + \alpha\gamma\delta + \alpha\gamma\varepsilon + \alpha\delta\varepsilon + \beta\gamma\delta + \beta\gamma\varepsilon + \beta\delta\varepsilon + \gamma\delta\varepsilon = -\dfrac{d}{a}$

      $\alpha\beta\gamma\delta + \beta\gamma\delta\varepsilon + \gamma\delta\varepsilon\alpha + \delta\varepsilon\alpha\beta + \varepsilon\alpha\beta\gamma = \dfrac{e}{a}$

      $\alpha\beta\gamma\delta\varepsilon = -\dfrac{f}{a}$

      $\sum\alpha = -\dfrac{b}{a}$

      $\sum\alpha\beta = \dfrac{c}{a}$

      $\sum\alpha\beta\gamma = -\dfrac{d}{a}$

      $\sum\alpha\beta\gamma\delta = \dfrac{e}{a}$

      $\sum\alpha\beta\gamma\delta\varepsilon = -\dfrac{f}{a}$

Exercise 3.4 (Page 67)

1 $4 + 5i$ is the other root.

   The equation is $z^2 - 8z + 41 = 0$.

2 $2 - i, -3$

3 $7, 4 \pm 2i$

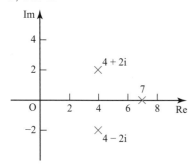

4 (i) $z = -3$

   (ii) $z = -3, \dfrac{5}{2} \pm \dfrac{\sqrt{11}}{2} i$

5 $k = 36$, other roots are $-\dfrac{3}{2} \pm \dfrac{3\sqrt{3}}{2} i$

6 $p = 4, q = -10$, other roots are $1 + i$ and -6

7 $z^3 - z - 6 = 0$

8 $z = 3 \pm 2i, 2 \pm i$

9 (i) $w^2 = -2i, w^3 = -2 - 2i, w^4 = -4$

   (ii) $p = -4, q = 2$

   (iii) $z = -4, -1, 1 \pm i$

10 (i) $z = \pm 3, \pm 3i$

    (ii)

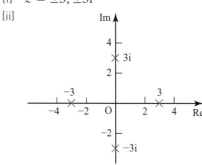

11 (i) $\alpha^2 = -3 - 4i, \alpha^3 = 11 - 2i$

(ii) $z = -1 - 2i, -5$

(iii)

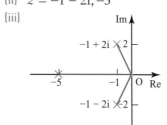

12 A false, B true, C true, D true

13 $a = 2, b = 2, z = -2 \pm i, 1 \pm 2i$

14 $z = \pm 3i, 4 \pm \sqrt{5}$

15 (i) $\alpha^2 = -8 - 6i, \alpha^3 = 26 - 18i$

    (ii) $\mu = 20$

    (iii) $z = -1 \pm 3i, -\dfrac{2}{3}$

    (iv)

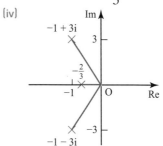

16 $b = -9, c = 44, d = -174, e = 448, f = -480$

Chapter 4

Discussion point (Page 72)

Start at 2 and add 3 each time.

Exercise 4.1 (Page 75)

1 (i) $6, 11, 16, 21, 26$

       Increasing by 5 for each term

   (ii) $-3, -9, -15, -21, -27$

        Decreasing by 6 for each term

   (iii) $8, 16, 32, 64, 128$

         Doubling for each term

   (iv) $8, 12, 8, 12, 8$

        Oscillating

   (v) $2, 5, 11, 23, 47$

       Increasing

   (vi) $5, \dfrac{5}{2}, \dfrac{5}{3}, \dfrac{5}{4}, 1$

        Decreasing, converging to zero

2 (i) $21, 25, 29, 33$

(ii) $u_1 = 1, \; u_{r+1} = u_r + 4$

(iii) $u_r = 4r - 3$

3 (i) (a) $0, -2, -4, -6$

(b) $u_1 = 10, \; u_{r+1} = u_r - 2$

(c) $u_r = 12 - 2r$

(d) -28

(ii) (a) $32, 64, 128, 256$

(b) $u_1 = 1, \; u_{r+1} = 2u_r$

(c) $u_r = 2^{r-1}$

(d) $524\,288$

(iii) (a) $31\,250, 156\,250, 781\,250, 3\,906\,250$

(b) $u_1 = 50, \; u_{r+1} = 5u_r$

(c) $u_r = 10 \times 5^r$

(d) 9.54×10^{14}

4 (i) 25 (ii) -150

(iii) 363 (iv) -7.5

5 (i) $\displaystyle\sum_{r=1}^{7}(56 - 6r)$ (ii) 224

6 2500

7 (i) $-5, 5, -5, 5, -5, 5$
Oscillating

(ii) (a) 0 (b) -5

(iii) $-\dfrac{5}{2} + \dfrac{5}{2}(-1)^n$

8 (i) $0, 100, 2, 102, 4, 104$
Even terms start from 100 and increase by 2, odd terms start from 0 and increase by 2.

(ii) 201

(iii) 102

9 $749\,\text{cm}$

10 $\dfrac{1}{2}n(n^3 + 1)$

11 $10, 5, 16, 8, 4$ (This will reach 1 at c_7 and then repeat the cycle $4, 2, 1$)

Exercise 4.2 (Page 78)

1 (i) $1, 3, 5$ (ii) n^2

2 (i) $4, 14, 30$ (ii) $n(n + 1)^2$

3 (i) $2, 12, 36$ (ii) $\dfrac{1}{12}n(n + 1)(3n^2 + 7n + 2)$

4 n^4

5 $\dfrac{1}{3}n(n + 1)(n + 2)$

6 $\dfrac{1}{4}n(n + 1)(n + 2)(n + 3)$

7 $\dfrac{1}{2}n(3n + 1)$

8 $n^2(4n + 1)(5n + 2)$

9 (ii) 7 layers, 125 left over

10 (i) £227.50

(ii) $\dfrac{1}{24}n(35(n + 1) + 30I)$

Discussion point (Page 81)

As n becomes very large, the top and bottom of $\dfrac{n}{n+1}$ are very close, so the sum becomes very close to 1 (it converges to 1).

Discussion point (Page 84)

As n becomes very large, the expression $\dfrac{n(3n + 7)}{2(n + 1)(n + 2)}$ becomes close to $\dfrac{3n^2}{2n^2}$ (since terms in n^2 are much bigger than terms in n). So the sum becomes very close to $\dfrac{3}{2}$ $\left(\text{it converges to } \dfrac{3}{2}\right)$.

Exercise 4.3 (Page 84)

1 (ii) $(1 - 0) + (4 - 1) + (9 - 4) + \; \ldots \; +$
$[(n - 2)^2 - (n - 3)^2] +$
$[(n - 1)^2 - (n - 2)^2] + [n^2 - (n - 1)^2]$

(iii) n^2

2 (i) First term: $r = 1$, last term: $r = 10$

(iii) $\dfrac{20}{21}$

3 (ii) $n(n^2 + 4n + 5)$ (iv) 99

4 (ii) $\dfrac{n(n + 2)}{(n + 1)^2}$

5 (ii) $\dfrac{n(3n + 5)}{4(n + 1)(n + 2)}$

(iii) $0.7401, 0.7490, 0.7499.$ The sum looks as if it is approaching 0.75 as n becomes large.

6 (ii) $\dfrac{13}{120}$

7 (ii) $\dfrac{n(n+3)}{4(n+1)(n+2)}$

(iii) $0.249\,95\ldots, 0.249\,9995\ldots$ The sum looks as if it is approaching 0.25 as n becomes large.

8 (ii) $8n^3 + 12n^2 + 6n$

9 (ii) $16n^4 + 32n^3 + 24n^2 + 8n$

10 (ii) $A = \dfrac{1}{2}, B = -\dfrac{1}{2}$

(iii) $\dfrac{(3n+2)(n-1)}{4n(n+1)}$

(iv) As $n \to \infty$, the sum $\to \dfrac{3}{4}$

Discussion point (Page 85)

If she was 121 last year then it would be fine, but we don't know if this is true. If she were able to provide any evidence of her age at a particular point then we could work from there, but we need a starting point.

Activity 4.1 (Page 86)

$\dfrac{1}{1 \times 2} = \dfrac{1}{2}$

$\dfrac{1}{1 \times 2} + \dfrac{1}{2 \times 3} = \dfrac{2}{3}$

$\dfrac{1}{1 \times 2} + \dfrac{1}{2 \times 3} + \dfrac{1}{3 \times 4} = \dfrac{3}{4}$

$\dfrac{1}{1 \times 2} + \dfrac{1}{2 \times 3} + \dfrac{1}{3 \times 4} + \dfrac{1}{4 \times 5} = \dfrac{4}{5}$

Activity 4.2 (Page 89)

(i) Assume true for $n = k$, so

$2 + 4 + 6 + \ldots + 2k = \left(k + \dfrac{1}{2}\right)^2.$

For $n = k + 1$,

$2 + 4 + 6 + \ldots +$

$2k + 2(k+1) = \left(k + \dfrac{1}{2}\right)^2 + 2(k+1)$

$= k^2 + k + \dfrac{1}{4} + 2k + 2$

$= k^2 + 3k + \dfrac{9}{4}$

$= \left(k + \dfrac{3}{2}\right)^2$

$= \left(k + 1 + \dfrac{1}{2}\right)^2$

It is not true for $n = 1$.

(ii) It breaks down at the inductive step.

Exercise 4.5 (Page 92)

5 (ii) **M** is a shear, x-axis fixed, $(0, 1)$ maps to $(1, 1)$.
   $\mathbf{M}^n$ is a shear, x-axis fixed, $(0, 1)$ maps to $(n, 1)$.

6 (i) $u_2 = \dfrac{1}{2}, u_3 = \dfrac{1}{3}, u_4 = \dfrac{1}{4}$

(ii) $u_n = \dfrac{1}{n}$

7 (i) $\mathbf{A}^2 = \begin{pmatrix} -3 & -8 \\ 2 & 5 \end{pmatrix}, \mathbf{A}^3 = \begin{pmatrix} -5 & -12 \\ 3 & 7 \end{pmatrix}$

8 (i) $\mathbf{M}^2 = \begin{pmatrix} 7 & 0 \\ 0 & 7 \end{pmatrix},$

$\mathbf{M}^3 = \begin{pmatrix} -7 & 14 \\ 21 & 7 \end{pmatrix}, \mathbf{M}^4 = \begin{pmatrix} 49 & 0 \\ 0 & 49 \end{pmatrix}$

(ii) $\mathbf{M}^{2m} = 7^m \begin{pmatrix} 1 & 0 \\ 0 & 1 \end{pmatrix}, \mathbf{M}^{2m+1} = 7^m \begin{pmatrix} -1 & 2 \\ 3 & 1 \end{pmatrix}$

9 (i) $3, 5, 17, 257, 65\,537$

Practice Questions Further Mathematics 1 (Page 95)

1 (i) Points plotted at $1 + 2i, -3 + 4i, 4i, \dfrac{2}{5}$

   [1], [1], [1], [2]

(ii) $w^2, w - w.$ [1]

2 Either
   Cubic has real coefficients   [1]
   so $3 - i$ a root   [1]
   Sum of $3 + i$ and $3 - i$ is 6; sum of all
   3 roots is 9   [1]
   so real root is 3   [1]
   Or
   $z = 3$ a root by trying factors of 30   [1]
   Factor theorem $(z - 3)$ a factor of cubic   [1]
   $z^3 - 9z^2 + 28z - 30 = (z - 3)(z^2 - 6z + 10)$ [1]
   Roots of quadratic are $3 + i, 3 - i$ [1]

3 (i) $= \dfrac{-6 \pm \sqrt{36 - 20}}{2(2 + i)}$ [1]

$= \dfrac{-5}{2 + i}$ or $\dfrac{-1}{2 + i}$ [1]

$= \dfrac{-5(2 - i)}{(2 + i)(2 - i)}$ or $\dfrac{-(2 - i)}{(2 + i)(2 - i)}$ [1]

$= -(2 - i)$ or $= -\dfrac{1}{5}(2 - i)$: both solutions

193

are in the form $\lambda(2-i)$ with $\lambda = -1$ and
$$\lambda = -\frac{1}{5}$$ [1]

(ii) By substituting the roots into the equation. [1]

4 (i) $\alpha + 1, \beta + 1, \gamma + 1$ satisfy
$$(y-1)^3 + 3(y-1)^2 - 6(y-1) - 8 = 0$$ [1]

$$y^3 - 3y^2 + 3y - 1 + 3y^2 - 6y$$
$$+6 - 8 = 0$$ [1], [1]

$$y^3 - 9y = 0$$ [1]

(ii) $y(y^2 - 9) = 0$ [1]

$y(y-3)(y+3) = 0$ [1]

$y = 0, 3, -3$ [1]

(iii) $x = -1, 2, -4$ [2]

5 (i) Diagram or calculation showing image of shape/points
Rotation 90°... [1]
... about $(0, 0)$, anticlockwise [1]

(ii) Rotation 45° anticlockwise about $(0, 0)$, when repeated, gives transformation corresponding to B. [1]

Diagram showing, for example, unit square or unit vectors rotated by 45°. [1]

$$\begin{pmatrix} \dfrac{1}{\sqrt{2}} & -\dfrac{1}{\sqrt{2}} \\ \dfrac{1}{\sqrt{2}} & \dfrac{1}{\sqrt{2}} \end{pmatrix}$$ [1]

6 $\delta + (\delta + 1) = -\dfrac{b}{a} \Rightarrow b^2 = a^2\left(\delta + (\delta + 1)\right)^2$

$$= a^2\left(\delta^2 + 2\delta(\delta+1) + (\delta+1)^2\right)$$

$$= a^2\left(4\delta^2 + 4\delta + 1\right)$$ [1]

$\delta(\delta+1) = \dfrac{c}{a} \Rightarrow ac$

$$= a^2\left(\delta(\delta+1)\right)$$

$$= a^2\left(\delta^2 + \delta\right)$$ [1]

LHS $= b^2 - 4ac$

$$= a^2\left(4\delta^2 + 4\delta + 1 - 4\left(\delta^2 + \delta\right)\right)$$

$$= a^2(1)$$ [1]

$$= a^2$$ [1]

$$= \text{RHS [complete argument, well set out]}$$

7 (i) $3, 6, 11, 20, 37$ [1]

(ii) To prove $u_n = 2^n + n$
When

$n = 1$, LHS = 3, RHS = $2^1 + 1$
$$= 2 + 1 = 3$$ [1]

So it is true for $n = 1$

Assume it is true for $n = k$, so

$$u_k = 2^k + k$$ [1]

Want to show that $u_{k+1} = 2^{k+1} + k + 1$.

$u_{k+1} = 2u_k - k + 1$

$$= 2(2^k + k) - k + 1$$ [1]

$$= 2^{k+1} + 2k - k + 1$$

$$= 2^{k+1} + k + 1 \text{ as required}$$ [1]

So, if the result is true for $n = k$ then it is true for $n = k + 1$ [1]

Since it is true for $n = 1$, by induction it is true for all positive integers n. [1]

8 (i) Calculations or image correct for three points [1]
Totally correct plot of $(0, 0)$ $(-0.6, 0.8)$ $(0.2, 1.4)$ $(0.8, 0.6)$ [1]

(ii) $$\begin{pmatrix} -\dfrac{3}{5} & \dfrac{4}{5} \\ \dfrac{4}{5} & \dfrac{3}{5} \end{pmatrix}\begin{pmatrix} x \\ y \end{pmatrix} = \begin{pmatrix} x \\ y \end{pmatrix}$$

$$-\frac{3}{5}x + \frac{4}{5}y = x$$ [1]

$$\frac{4}{5}x + \frac{3}{5}y = y$$

$\left.\begin{array}{l} y = 2x \\ y = 2x \end{array}\right\}$ from both equations [1]

$y = 2x$ is equation of line of invariant points. [1]

(iii) Perpendicular line to this, through origin, is
$$y = -\frac{1}{2}x$$

$$\begin{pmatrix} -\dfrac{3}{5} & \dfrac{4}{5} \\ \dfrac{4}{5} & \dfrac{3}{5} \end{pmatrix}\begin{pmatrix} x \\ -\dfrac{1}{2}x \end{pmatrix} = \begin{pmatrix} -\dfrac{3}{5}x - \dfrac{2}{5}x \\ \dfrac{4}{5}x - \dfrac{3}{10}x \end{pmatrix}$$

$$= \begin{pmatrix} -x \\ \frac{1}{2}x \end{pmatrix} = -\begin{pmatrix} x \\ -\frac{1}{2}x \end{pmatrix}$$ [1]

So $y = -\frac{1}{2}x$ is an invariant line, and is perpendicular to line of invariant points, and both go through the origin. [1]

(iv) Two points marked, where image of unit square intersects unit square, at $(0, 0)$ and $(0.5, 1)$. [1],[1]

9 (i)

LHS

$$= \frac{1}{6}(r + 3)(r + 4)(r + 5) - \frac{1}{6}(r + 2)(r + 3)(r + 4)$$

$$= \frac{1}{6}(r + 3)(r + 4)(r + 5 - r - 2)$$ [1]

$$= \frac{1}{6}(r + 3)(r + 4)(3)$$

$$= \frac{1}{2}(r + 3)(r + 4)$$

$$= \text{RHS}$$ [1]

(ii) $\displaystyle\sum_{r=1}^{n} \frac{1}{2}(r + 3)(r + 4) = \sum_{r=1}^{n} \left\{ \frac{1}{6}(r + 3)(r + 4) \right.$

$$\left. (r + 5) - \frac{1}{6}(r + 2)(r + 3)(r + 4) \right\}$$

$$= \frac{1}{6}.4.5.6 - \frac{1}{6}3.4.5$$

$$+ \frac{1}{6}.5.6.7 - \frac{1}{6}4.5.6$$ [1]

$$+ \frac{1}{6}.6.7.8 - \frac{1}{6}.5.6.7$$

$$+ ...$$

$$+ \frac{1}{6}(n + 2)(n + 3)(n + 4) - \frac{1}{6}(n + 1)(n + 2)(n + 3)$$

$$+ \frac{1}{6}(n + 3)(n + 4)(n + 5) - \frac{1}{6}(n + 2)(n + 3)(n + 4)$$ [1]

$$= \frac{1}{6}(n + 3)(n + 4)(n + 5) - \frac{1}{6}.3.4.5$$

(Some indication of telescoping) [1]

$$= \frac{1}{6}(n + 3)(n + 4)(n + 5) - 10$$ [1]

(iii) $4 \times 5 + 5 \times 6 + 6 \times 7 + ...$ to 20 terms

$$= 2 \sum_{r=1}^{20} \frac{1}{2}(r + 3)(r + 4)$$ [1]

$$= 2 \times \left\{ \frac{1}{6}(23)(24)(25) - 10 \right\}$$

$$= 4580$$ [1]

Chapter 5

Discussion point (Page 99)

It is not true that $\arg z$ is given by $\arctan\left(\frac{y}{x}\right)$. For example the complex number $-1 + i$ has argument $\frac{3\pi}{4}$ but $\arctan\left(\frac{1}{-1}\right) = -\frac{\pi}{4}$. A diagram is needed to ensure the correct angle is calculated.

Activity 5.1 (Page 102)

	$\frac{\pi}{6}$	$\frac{\pi}{4}$	$\frac{\pi}{3}$
sin	$\frac{1}{2}$	$\frac{1}{\sqrt{2}}$	$\frac{\sqrt{3}}{2}$
cos	$\frac{\sqrt{3}}{2}$	$\frac{1}{\sqrt{2}}$	$\frac{1}{2}$
tan	$\frac{1}{\sqrt{3}}$	1	$\sqrt{3}$

Exercise 5.1 (Page 104)

1 $z_1 = 4$ or $4(\cos 0 + i \sin 0)$

    $z_2 = -2 + 4i$ or $2\sqrt{5}(\cos 2.03 + i \sin 2.03)$

    $z_3 = 1 - 3i$ or

    $\sqrt{10}\left(\cos(-1.25) + i \sin(-1.25)\right)$

2   (i) $|z| = \sqrt{13}$ $\arg z = 0.588$

    (ii) $|z| = \sqrt{29}$ $\arg z = 2.76$

    (iii) $|z| = \sqrt{13}$ $\arg z = -2.55$

    (iv) $|z| = \sqrt{29}$ $\arg z = -1.19$

3 $|z_1| = \sqrt{13}$ $\arg z_1 = 0.588$

    $|z_2| = \sqrt{13}$ $\arg z_2 = -0.588$

    $|z_3| = \sqrt{13}$ $\arg z_3 = -2.16$

    $|z_4| = \sqrt{13}$ $\arg z_4 = 2.16$

$z_1 \rightarrow z_2$ Reflection in real axis

$z_1 \rightarrow z_3$ Reflection in the line $y = -x$

$z_1 \rightarrow z_4$ Rotation of 90° anticlockwise about the origin

4 (i) $-4i$

   (ii) $-\dfrac{7}{\sqrt{2}} + \dfrac{7}{\sqrt{2}}i$

   (iii) $-\dfrac{3\sqrt{3}}{2} + \dfrac{3}{2}i$

   (iv) $\dfrac{5\sqrt{3}}{2} - \dfrac{5}{2}i$

5 (i) $1(\cos 0 + i \sin 0)$

   (ii) $2(\cos \pi + i \sin \pi)$

   (iii) $3\left(\cos\left(\dfrac{\pi}{2}\right) + i \sin\left(\dfrac{\pi}{2}\right)\right)$

   (iv) $4\left(\cos\left(-\dfrac{\pi}{2}\right) + i \sin\left(-\dfrac{\pi}{2}\right)\right)$

6 (i) $\sqrt{2}\left(\cos\dfrac{\pi}{4} + i \sin\dfrac{\pi}{4}\right)$

   (ii) $\sqrt{2}\left(\cos\dfrac{3\pi}{4} + i \sin\dfrac{3\pi}{4}\right)$

   (iii) $\sqrt{2}\left(\cos\left(\dfrac{-3\pi}{4}\right) + i \sin\left(\dfrac{-3\pi}{4}\right)\right)$

   (iv) $\sqrt{2}\left(\cos\left(\dfrac{-\pi}{4}\right) + i \sin\left(\dfrac{-\pi}{4}\right)\right)$

7 (i) $12\left(\cos\dfrac{\pi}{6} + i\sin\dfrac{\pi}{6}\right)$

   (ii) $5\big(\cos(-0.927) + i\sin(-0.927)\big)$

   (iii) $13\big(\cos 2.75 + i\sin 2.75\big)$

   (iv) $\sqrt{65}\,(\cos 1.05 + i\sin 1.05)$

   (v) $\sqrt{12013}\big(\cos(-2.13) + i\sin(-2.13)\big)$

8 (i) $\dfrac{1}{5}\sqrt{10}\big(\cos 0.322 + i\sin 0.322\big)$

   (ii) $\dfrac{\sqrt{130}}{10}\big(\cos(-0.266) + i\sin(-0.266)\big)$

   (iii) $\dfrac{\sqrt{290}}{10}\big(\cos(-1.63) + i\sin(-1.63)\big)$

9 (i) $z = 2i$ or $0 + 2i$

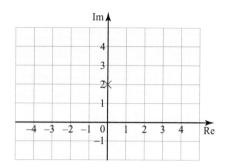

   (ii) $z = \dfrac{3}{2} + \dfrac{3\sqrt{3}}{2}i$

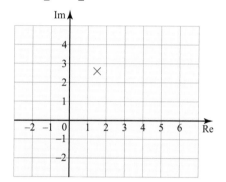

   (iii) $z = -\dfrac{7\sqrt{3}}{2} + \dfrac{7}{2}i$

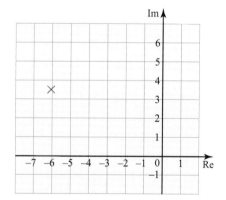

   (iv) $z = \dfrac{1}{\sqrt{2}} - \dfrac{1}{\sqrt{2}}i$

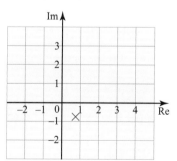

(v) $z = -\dfrac{5}{2} - \dfrac{5\sqrt{3}}{2}i$

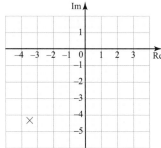

(vi) $z = -2.50 - 5.46i$

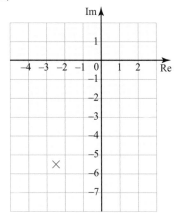

10 (i) $-(\pi - \alpha)$ or $\alpha - \pi$ (ii) $-\alpha$

    (iii) $\pi - \alpha$ (iv) $\dfrac{\pi}{2} - \alpha$

    (v) $\dfrac{\pi}{2} + \alpha$

11 (i) $|z_1| = 5$ $\arg z_1 = 0.927$

        $|z_2| = \sqrt{2}$ $\arg z_2 = \dfrac{3\pi}{4}$

    (ii) (a) $z_1 z_2 = -7 - i$ $\dfrac{z_1}{z_2} = \dfrac{1}{2} - \dfrac{7}{2}i$

       (b) $|z_1 z_2| = 5\sqrt{2}$ $\arg(z_1 z_2) = -3.00$

           $\left|\dfrac{z_1}{z_2}\right| = \dfrac{5\sqrt{2}}{2}$ $\arg\left(\dfrac{z_1}{z_2}\right) = -1.43$

    (iii) $|z_1 z_2| = |z_1||z_2|$ and $\left|\dfrac{z_1}{z_2}\right| = \dfrac{|z_1|}{|z_2|}$

        $\arg z_1 + \arg z_2 = 3.28$ which is greater than π, but is equivalent to -3.00

        i.e. $\arg z_1 + \arg z_2 = \arg z_1 z_2$

        $\arg z_1 - \arg z_2 = \arg\left(\dfrac{z_1}{z_2}\right)$

Activity 5.3 (Page 106)

(i) Rotation of 90° anticlockwise about the origin

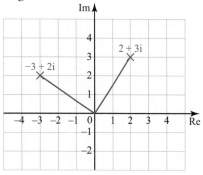

(ii) Rotation of 90° anticlockwise about the origin and enlargement of scale factor 2

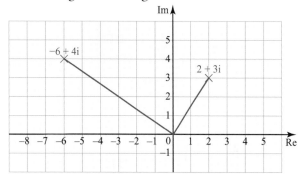

(iii) Rotation of $\dfrac{\pi}{4}$ anticlockwise and enlargement of scale factor $\sqrt{2}$

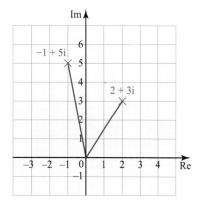

Exercise 5.2 (Page 108)

1 (i) $|w| = \sqrt{2}$ $\arg w = \dfrac{\pi}{4}$

       $|z| = 2$ $\arg z = -\dfrac{\pi}{3}$

    (ii) (a) $|wz| = 2\sqrt{2}$ $\arg(wz) = -\dfrac{\pi}{12}$

       (b) $\left|\dfrac{w}{z}\right| = \dfrac{1}{\sqrt{2}}$ $\arg\left(\dfrac{w}{z}\right) = \dfrac{7\pi}{12}$

(iii)

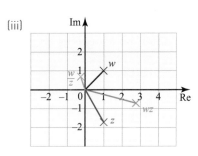

2 (i) $6\left(\cos\dfrac{7\pi}{12} + \mathrm{i}\sin\dfrac{7\pi}{12}\right)$

(ii) $\dfrac{3}{2}\left(\cos\left(\dfrac{\pi}{12}\right) + \mathrm{i}\sin\left(\dfrac{\pi}{12}\right)\right)$

(iii) $\dfrac{2}{3}\left(\cos\left(-\dfrac{\pi}{12}\right) + \mathrm{i}\sin\left(-\dfrac{\pi}{12}\right)\right)$

(iv) $\dfrac{1}{2}\left(\cos\left(-\dfrac{\pi}{4}\right) + \mathrm{i}\sin\left(-\dfrac{\pi}{4}\right)\right)$

3 (i) $\dfrac{2\pi}{3}$ (ii) 6

(iii) $\dfrac{\pi}{2}$ (iv) 108

4 (i) $4\left(\cos\left(-\dfrac{\pi}{2}\right) + \mathrm{i}\sin\left(-\dfrac{\pi}{2}\right)\right)$

(ii) $7776\left(\cos\left(\dfrac{5\pi}{6}\right) + \mathrm{i}\sin\left(\dfrac{5\pi}{6}\right)\right)$

(iii) $10368\left(\cos\left(-\dfrac{\pi}{12}\right) + \mathrm{i}\sin\left(-\dfrac{\pi}{12}\right)\right)$

(iv) $30\left(\cos\left(\dfrac{2\pi}{3}\right) + \mathrm{i}\sin\left(\dfrac{2\pi}{3}\right)\right)$

(v) $2\sqrt{2}\left(\cos 0 + \mathrm{i}\sin 0\right)$

5 (i) Multiplication scale factor $\dfrac{\sqrt{377}}{13}$, angle of rotation -1.36 radians (i.e. 1.36 radians clockwise)

(ii) Multiplication scale factor $\dfrac{3}{\sqrt{17}}$, angle of rotation -1.33 radians (i.e. 1.33 radians clockwise)

6 $\arg\left(\dfrac{w}{z}\right) = \arg w - \arg z \Rightarrow \arg\left(\dfrac{1}{z}\right)$

$= \arg 1 - \arg z = 0 - \arg z = -\arg z$

The exceptions are complex numbers for which both $\mathrm{Im}(z) = 0$ and $\mathrm{Re}(z) \le 0$

since $-180° < \arg z \le 180°$

7 (i) Real part $= \dfrac{-1+\sqrt{3}}{4}$

Imaginary part $= \dfrac{1+\sqrt{3}}{4}$

(ii) $\sqrt{2}\left(\cos\left(\dfrac{3\pi}{4}\right) + \mathrm{i}\sin\left(\dfrac{3\pi}{4}\right)\right)$

$2\left(\cos\left(\dfrac{\pi}{3}\right) + \mathrm{i}\sin\left(\dfrac{\pi}{3}\right)\right)$

(iii)

$\dfrac{-1+\mathrm{i}}{1+\sqrt{3}\mathrm{i}} = \dfrac{\sqrt{2}\left(\cos\left(\dfrac{3\pi}{4}\right) + \mathrm{i}\sin\left(\dfrac{3\pi}{4}\right)\right)}{2\left(\cos\left(\dfrac{\pi}{3}\right) + \mathrm{i}\sin\left(\dfrac{\pi}{3}\right)\right)}$

$= \dfrac{1}{\sqrt{2}}\left(\cos\left(\dfrac{5\pi}{12}\right) + \mathrm{i}\sin\left(\dfrac{5\pi}{12}\right)\right)$

$= \dfrac{-1+\sqrt{3}}{4} + \dfrac{1+\sqrt{3}}{4}\mathrm{i}$

$\Rightarrow \cos\left(\dfrac{5\pi}{12}\right) = \dfrac{\sqrt{3}-1}{2\sqrt{2}} \qquad \sin\left(\dfrac{5\pi}{12}\right) = \dfrac{\sqrt{3}+1}{2\sqrt{2}}$

8 For the complex numbers
$w = r_1\left(\cos\theta_1 + \mathrm{i}\sin\theta_1\right)$ and
$z = r_2\left(\cos\theta_2 + \mathrm{i}\sin\theta_2\right)$ we have proven that
$wz = r_1 r_2\left[\left(\cos\left(\theta_1 + \theta_2\right) + \mathrm{i}\sin\left(\theta_1 + \theta_2\right)\right)\right]$
So,

$wzp = r_1 r_2 [(\cos(\theta_1 + \theta_2) + \mathrm{i}\sin(\theta_1 + \theta_2)] \times r_3\left(\cos\theta_3 + \mathrm{i}\sin\theta_3\right)$
$= r_1 r_2 r_3 [\cos(\theta_1 + \theta_2)\cos\theta_3 + \mathrm{i}\sin(\theta_1 + \theta_2)\sin\theta_3 +$
$\qquad \mathrm{i}\sin(\theta_1 + \theta_2)\cos\theta_3 + \mathrm{i}^2\sin(\theta_1 + \theta_2)\sin\theta_3]$
$= r_1 r_2 r_3 \big\{[\cos(\theta_1 + \theta_2)\cos\theta_3 - \sin(\theta_1 + \theta_2)\sin\theta_3]$
$\qquad +\mathrm{i}[\cos(\theta_1 + \theta_2)\sin\theta_3 + \sin(\theta_1 + \theta_2)\cos\theta_3]\big\}$
$= r_1 r_2 r_3 \big\{\cos\left[(\theta_1 + \theta_2) + \theta_3\right] + \mathrm{i}\sin\left[(\theta_1 + \theta_2) + \theta_3\right]\big\}$

Therefore, $|wzp| = |w|\,|z|\,|p|$ and
$\arg(wzp) = \arg z + \arg w + \arg p$.

Activity 5.4 (Page 113)

(i)

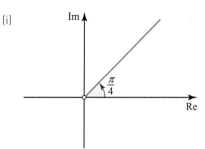

$\arg z = \dfrac{\pi}{4}$ represents a half line. The locus is a half line of points, with the origin as the starting point.

$-2 - 2i$ has argument $-\frac{3\pi}{4}$ and so it is not on this half line.

(ii) Calculating $z - 2$ for each point and finding the argument of $(z - 2)$ gives:

(a) $z = 4 \qquad z - 2 = 2 \qquad \arg(z - 2) = 0$

(b) $z = 3 + i \quad z - 2 = 1 + i \quad \arg(1 + i) = \frac{\pi}{4}$

(c) $z = 4i \qquad z - 2 = 4i - 2 \quad \arg(-2 + 4i) = 2.03$

(d) $z = 8 + 6i \quad z - 2 = 6 + 6i \quad \arg(6 + 6i) = \frac{\pi}{4}$

(e) $z = 1 - i \quad z - 2 = -1 - i \quad \arg(-1 - i) = -\frac{\pi}{4}$

So $\arg(z - 2) = \frac{\pi}{4}$ is satisfied by $z = 3 + i$ and $z = 8 + 6i$.

(iii) $z - 2$ represents a line between the point z and the point with coordinates $(2, 0)$.

So $\arg(z - 2) = \frac{\pi}{4}$ represents a line of points from $(2, 0)$ with an argument of $\frac{\pi}{4}$. This is a half line of points as shown.

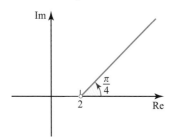

The line is a half line because points on the other half of the line would have an argument of $-\frac{\pi}{4}$ as was the case in part (ii)(e).

Activity 5.5 (Page 115)

The condition can be written as
$\left| z - (3 + 4i) \right| = \left| z - (-1 + 2i) \right|$.
$\left| z - (3 + 4i) \right|$ is the distance of point z from the point $3 + 4i$ (point A) and $\left| z - (-1 + 2i) \right|$ is the distance of point z from the point $-1 + 2i$ (point B).

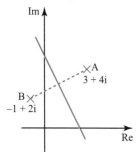

These distances are equal if z is on the perpendicular bisector of AB.

Exercise 5.3 (Page 118)

1 (i)

(ii)

(iii)

(iv)

2 (i)

(ii)

(iii)

(iv)

3   (i)

(ii)

(iii)

(iv)

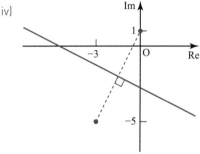

4   (i) $\left|z - (1 + i)\right| = 3$

(ii) $\arg(z + 2i) = \dfrac{3\pi}{4}$

(iii) $\left|z + 1\right| = \left|z - (3 + 2i)\right|$

5   (i) $\left|z - (4 + i)\right| \leq \left|z - (1 + 6i)\right|$

(ii) $-\dfrac{\pi}{4} \leq \arg(z + 2 - i) < 0$

(iii) $\left|z - (-2 + 3i)\right| < 4$

6

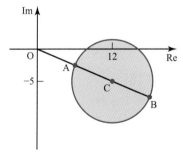

$|z|$ is least at A and greatest at B. Using
Pythagoras' theorem, the distance OC is

$\sqrt{(-5)^2 + 12^2} = 13$. We know AC = 7 and so
OA = 13 − 7 = 6.
So, minimum value of $|z|$ is OA = 6 and
maximum value of $|z|$ is OB = 6 + 14 = 20.

7 (i)

(ii)

(iii)

8 (i)

(ii)

(iii)

(iv)

9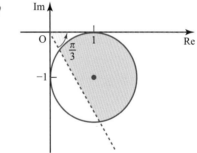

10 (i) (a) $|z + 1 + 2i| = 3$

(b) $|z + 6| = |z + 4i|$

(ii) $|z + 1 + 2i| \leq 3$ and $|z + 6| \geq |z + 4i|$

11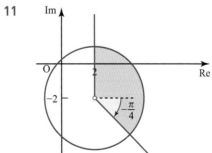

12 (i) $\dfrac{2\pi}{3}$, 2

(ii)

13

14

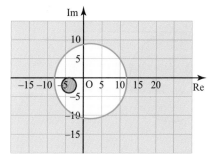

There are no values of z which satisfy both regions simultaneously.

15 The diagram shows $|z - 5 + 4i| = 3$. The minimum value is 7 and the maximum value is 13.

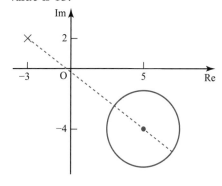

16 (i) Centre is $(3, -12)$, radius 6

(ii)

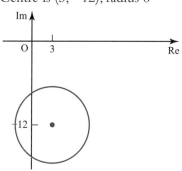

Chapter 6

Discussion point (Page 124)

The triangles are all congruent to each other.
256 yellow triangles make up the purple triangle.

Activity 6.1 (Page 125)

The diagram shows the image of the unit square OIPJ under the transformation with matrix
$\begin{pmatrix} a & b \\ c & d \end{pmatrix}$.

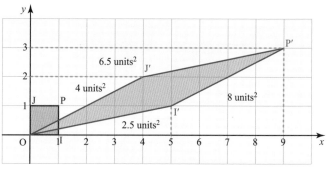

The point A$(1, 0)$ is transformed to the point I′ (a, c); the point C$(0, 1)$ is transformed to the point J′ (b, d). P′ has coordinates $(a + b, c + d)$.

The area of the parallelogram is given by the area of the whole rectangle minus the area of the rectangles and triangles.

Area of rectangle $= b \times c$

Area of first triangle $= \dfrac{1}{2} \times b \times d$

Area of second triangle $= \dfrac{1}{2} \times a \times c$

Area of whole rectangle $= (a + b) \times (c + d)$

Therefore the area of the parallelogram is

$(a + b) \times (c + d) - 2\left(bc + \dfrac{1}{2}bd + \dfrac{1}{2}ac\right) = ad - bc.$

Discussion point (Page 127)

(i) A rotation does not reverse the order of the vertices, e.g. for $\mathbf{A} = \begin{pmatrix} 0 & -1 \\ 1 & 0 \end{pmatrix}$,

$\det \mathbf{A} = 1$ which is positive.

(ii) A reflection reverses the order of the vertices, e.g. for $\mathbf{B} = \begin{pmatrix} 1 & 0 \\ 0 & -1 \end{pmatrix}$,

$\det \mathbf{B} = -1$ which is negative.

(iii) An enlargement does not reverse the order of the vertices, e.g. for $\mathbf{C} = \begin{pmatrix} 2 & 0 \\ 0 & 2 \end{pmatrix}$,

$\det \mathbf{C} = 4$ which is positive

Discussion point (Page 128)

The matrix has determinant 8.

8 represents the volume scale factor of the transformation in three dimensions. If you think about the effect of the transformation represented

by the matrix $\begin{pmatrix} 2 & 0 & 0 \\ 0 & 2 & 0 \\ 0 & 0 & 2 \end{pmatrix}$ on each of the unit

vectors $\mathbf{i} = \begin{pmatrix} 1 \\ 0 \\ 0 \end{pmatrix}$, $\mathbf{j} = \begin{pmatrix} 0 \\ 1 \\ 0 \end{pmatrix}$ and $\mathbf{k} = \begin{pmatrix} 0 \\ 0 \\ 1 \end{pmatrix}$,

the three edges of the unit cube have each increased by a length scale factor of 2. The overall effect would be that the volume would increase by a scale factor of $2 \times 2 \times 2 = 8$.

Discussion point (Page 129)

A 3×3 matrix with zero determinant will produce an image which has no volume, i.e. the points are all mapped to the same plane.

Exercise 6.1 (Page 129)

1 (i) (a)

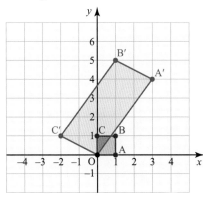

(b) Area of parallelogram = 11
(c) 11

(ii) (a)

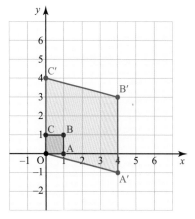

(b) Area of parallelogram = 16
(c) 16

(iii) (a)

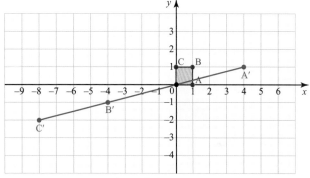

(b) area of parallelogram = 0
(c) 0

(iv) (a)

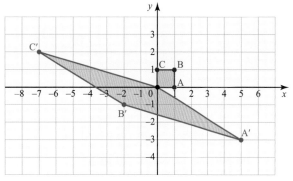

(b) area of parallelogram = 11
(c) −11

2 $x = 2, x = 6$

3 (i) $\mathbf{A} = \begin{pmatrix} 1 & 0 \\ 0 & -1 \end{pmatrix}$ $\mathbf{C} = \begin{pmatrix} 0 & 1 \\ 1 & 0 \end{pmatrix}$

$\mathbf{B} = \begin{pmatrix} -1 & 0 \\ 0 & 1 \end{pmatrix}$ $\mathbf{D} = \begin{pmatrix} 0 & -1 \\ -1 & 0 \end{pmatrix}$

(ii) no solution required

(iii) A

B

C

D

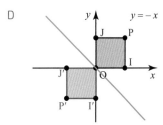

4 66 cm²

5 $ad = 1$

6 (i) $\begin{pmatrix} 1 & 3 \\ 0 & 1 \end{pmatrix}$

(ii) determinant = 1 so area is preserved

7 determinant = 6 so volume of image
$6 \times 5 = 30$ cm³

8 (i) $\det \mathbf{M} = -2,$ $\det \mathbf{N} = 7$

(ii) $\mathbf{MN} = \begin{pmatrix} 9 & 13 \\ 8 & 10 \end{pmatrix},$ $\det(\mathbf{MN}) = -14$
and $-14 = -2 \times 7$

9 (i)

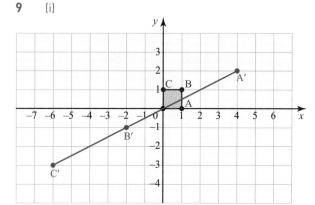

(ii) The image of all points lie on the line. $y = \frac{1}{2}x$
The determinant of the matrix is zero which shows that the image will have zero area.

10 (i) $\begin{pmatrix} 5p - 10q \\ -p + 2q \end{pmatrix}$

(ii) $y = -\frac{1}{5}x$

(iii) $\det \mathbf{N} = 0$ and so the image has zero area

11 (i) $\mathbf{T} = \begin{pmatrix} 1 & 2 \\ 3 & 6 \end{pmatrix},$

$\det \mathbf{T} = (1 \times 6) - (3 \times 2) = 0$

(ii) $\begin{pmatrix} x' \\ y' \end{pmatrix} = \begin{pmatrix} 1 & 2 \\ 3 & 6 \end{pmatrix} \begin{pmatrix} x \\ y \end{pmatrix}$

$\Rightarrow \begin{array}{c} x' = x + 2y \\ y' = 3x + 6y \end{array} \Rightarrow y' = 3x'$

(iii) $(3, 9)$

12 $\begin{pmatrix} x' \\ y' \end{pmatrix} = \begin{pmatrix} a & b \\ c & d \end{pmatrix} \begin{pmatrix} x \\ y \end{pmatrix} \Rightarrow \begin{pmatrix} x' \\ y' \end{pmatrix}$

$= \begin{pmatrix} ax + by \\ cx + dy \end{pmatrix} \Rightarrow \begin{array}{c} x' = ax + by \\ y' = cx + dy \end{array}$

Solving simultaneously and using the fact $ad - bc = 0$ gives the result.

13 (i) $y = 3x - 3s + t$

(ii) $\mathrm{P'}\left(\frac{9}{8}s - \frac{3}{8}t, \ \frac{3}{8}s - \frac{1}{8}t\right)$

(iii) $\begin{pmatrix} \frac{9}{8} & -\frac{3}{8} \\ \frac{3}{8} & -\frac{1}{8} \end{pmatrix}$ which has determinant

$\left(\frac{9}{8} \times -\frac{1}{8}\right) - \left(\frac{3}{8} \times -\frac{3}{8}\right) = 0$

Answers

Activity 6.2 (Page 132)

(i) $\mathbf{P} = \begin{pmatrix} 1 & 0 \\ 0 & -1 \end{pmatrix}$

(ii) $\mathbf{P}^2 = \begin{pmatrix} 1 & 0 \\ 0 & 1 \end{pmatrix}$

(iii) Reflecting an object in the *x*-axis twice takes it back to the starting position and so the final image is the same as the original object. Hence the matrix for the combined transformation is $\mathbf{I}$.

Activity 6.3 (Page 133)

$$\begin{pmatrix} a & b \\ c & d \end{pmatrix} \begin{pmatrix} d & -b \\ -c & a \end{pmatrix} = \begin{pmatrix} ad - bc & 0 \\ 0 & ad - bc \end{pmatrix}$$

To turn this into the identity matrix it would need to be divided by $ad - bc$ which is the value $|\mathbf{M}|$.

Therefore $\mathbf{M}^{-1} = \dfrac{1}{ad - bc} \begin{pmatrix} d & -b \\ -c & a \end{pmatrix}$

Activity 6.4 (Page 134)

(i) $\mathbf{AA}^{-1} = \dfrac{1}{4} \begin{pmatrix} 11 & 3 \\ 6 & 2 \end{pmatrix} \begin{pmatrix} 2 & -3 \\ -6 & 11 \end{pmatrix}$

$= \dfrac{1}{4} \begin{pmatrix} 4 & 0 \\ 0 & 4 \end{pmatrix} = \mathbf{I}$

$\mathbf{A}^{-1}\mathbf{A} = \dfrac{1}{4} \begin{pmatrix} 2 & -3 \\ -6 & 11 \end{pmatrix} \begin{pmatrix} 11 & 3 \\ 6 & 2 \end{pmatrix}$

$= \dfrac{1}{4} \begin{pmatrix} 4 & 0 \\ 0 & 4 \end{pmatrix} = \mathbf{I}$

(ii) $\mathbf{M}^{-1} = \dfrac{1}{ad - bc} \begin{pmatrix} d & -b \\ -c & a \end{pmatrix}$

$\mathbf{MM}^{-1} = \begin{pmatrix} a & b \\ c & d \end{pmatrix} \dfrac{1}{ad - bc} \begin{pmatrix} d & -b \\ -c & a \end{pmatrix}$

$= \dfrac{1}{ad - bc} \begin{pmatrix} a & b \\ c & d \end{pmatrix} \begin{pmatrix} d & -b \\ -c & a \end{pmatrix}$

$= \dfrac{1}{ad - bc} \begin{pmatrix} ad - bc & -ab + ab \\ cd - dc & -cb + ad \end{pmatrix}$

$= \dfrac{1}{ad - bc} \begin{pmatrix} ad - bc & 0 \\ 0 & ad - bc \end{pmatrix} = \begin{pmatrix} 1 & 0 \\ 0 & 1 \end{pmatrix} = \mathbf{I}$

$\mathbf{M}^{-1}\mathbf{M} = \dfrac{1}{ad - bc} \begin{pmatrix} d & -b \\ -c & a \end{pmatrix} \begin{pmatrix} a & b \\ c & d \end{pmatrix}$

$= \dfrac{1}{ad - bc} \begin{pmatrix} da - bc & db - bd \\ -ca + ac & -cb + ad \end{pmatrix}$

$= \dfrac{1}{ad - bc} \begin{pmatrix} ad - bc & 0 \\ 0 & ad - bc \end{pmatrix}$

$= \begin{pmatrix} 1 & 0 \\ 0 & 1 \end{pmatrix} = \mathbf{I}$

Discussion point (Page 134)

First reverse the reflection by using the transformation with the inverse matrix of the reflection. Secondly, reverse the rotation by using the transformation with the inverse matrix of the rotation.

$$(\mathbf{MN})^{-1} = \mathbf{N}^{-1}\mathbf{M}^{-1}$$

Exercise 6.2 (Page 135)

1 (i) $(10, -6)$

(ii) $-\dfrac{1}{2} \begin{pmatrix} 0 & 1 \\ 2 & 5 \end{pmatrix}$

(iii) $(1, 2)$

2 (i) non-singular, $\dfrac{1}{24} \begin{pmatrix} 2 & -3 \\ 4 & 6 \end{pmatrix}$

(ii) singular

(iii) non-singular, $\dfrac{1}{112} \begin{pmatrix} 11 & -3 \\ -3 & 11 \end{pmatrix}$

(iv) singular

(v) singular

(vi) singular

(vii) non-singular, $\dfrac{1}{16(1 - ab)} \begin{pmatrix} -8 & -4a \\ -4b & -2 \end{pmatrix}$

provided $ab \neq 1$

3 (i) non-singular, $\dfrac{1}{140} \begin{pmatrix} 21 & 10 & 27 \\ -7 & -50 & -9 \\ 14 & 20 & -2 \end{pmatrix}$

(ii) singular

(iii) non-singular, $\dfrac{1}{121} \begin{pmatrix} -17 & 15 & 6 \\ -91 & 2 & 25 \\ 46 & -5 & -2 \end{pmatrix}$

4 (i) $\dfrac{1}{3}\begin{pmatrix} 3 & -6 \\ -2 & 5 \end{pmatrix}$ (ii) $\dfrac{1}{2}\begin{pmatrix} -1 & -5 \\ 2 & 8 \end{pmatrix}$

(iii) $\begin{pmatrix} 28 & 19 \\ 10 & 7 \end{pmatrix}$ (iv) $\begin{pmatrix} 50 & 63 \\ -12 & -15 \end{pmatrix}$

(v) $\dfrac{1}{6}\begin{pmatrix} 7 & -19 \\ -10 & 28 \end{pmatrix}$ (vi) $\dfrac{1}{6}\begin{pmatrix} -15 & -63 \\ 12 & 50 \end{pmatrix}$

(vii) $\dfrac{1}{6}\begin{pmatrix} -15 & -63 \\ 12 & 50 \end{pmatrix}$ (viii) $\dfrac{1}{6}\begin{pmatrix} 7 & -19 \\ -10 & 28 \end{pmatrix}$

5 (i) $\dfrac{1}{8}\begin{pmatrix} 2 & 2 \\ -3 & 1 \end{pmatrix}$

(ii) $\mathbf{M}^{-1}\mathbf{M} = \dfrac{1}{8}\begin{pmatrix} 2 & 2 \\ -3 & 1 \end{pmatrix}\begin{pmatrix} 1 & -2 \\ 3 & 2 \end{pmatrix} = \mathbf{I}$

6 $k = 2$ or $k = 3$

7 $\begin{pmatrix} 2 & 1 & 0 & -1 \\ 1 & 0 & -3 & 4 \end{pmatrix}$

8 (i) $(3, 1), (1, 1)$ and $(-6, -2)$

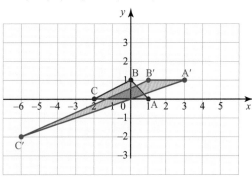

(ii) ratio of area T' to T is 3 : 1.5 or 2 : 1

The determinant of the matrix $\mathbf{M} = 2$ so the area is doubled.

(iii) $\mathbf{M}^{-1} = \dfrac{1}{2}\begin{pmatrix} 1 & -1 \\ -1 & 3 \end{pmatrix}$

9 (ii) $\mathbf{M}^n = (a + d)^{n-1}\mathbf{M}$

10 (iii) $\begin{pmatrix} 0 & \dfrac{1}{5} \\ \dfrac{1}{6} & -\dfrac{11}{10} \end{pmatrix}$ (iv) $\begin{pmatrix} 33 & 6 \\ 5 & 0 \end{pmatrix}$

11 (i) $\begin{pmatrix} 18 & -9 & 4 \\ 1 & -7 & 2 \\ -1 & -4 & 1 \end{pmatrix}$

(ii) $\begin{pmatrix} 1 & a + 7 & b + 7c + 4 \\ 0 & 1 & c + 2 \\ 0 & 0 & 1 \end{pmatrix}$

(iii) $\begin{pmatrix} 1 & -7 & 10 \\ 0 & 1 & -2 \\ 0 & 0 & 1 \end{pmatrix}$

(iv) $\begin{pmatrix} 1 & 0 & 0 \\ -3 & 1 & 0 \\ -11 & 4 & 1 \end{pmatrix}$

(v) $\begin{pmatrix} 1 & -7 & 10 \\ -3 & 22 & -32 \\ -11 & 81 & -117 \end{pmatrix}$

12 $k = 3$

Activity 6.5 (Page 139)

(i) $\begin{pmatrix} 2 & -2 & 3 \\ 5 & 1 & -1 \\ 3 & 4 & -2 \end{pmatrix}\begin{pmatrix} x \\ y \\ z \end{pmatrix} = \begin{pmatrix} 4 \\ -6 \\ 1 \end{pmatrix}$

$\begin{pmatrix} x \\ y \\ z \end{pmatrix} = \dfrac{1}{41}\begin{pmatrix} 2 & 8 & -1 \\ 7 & -13 & 17 \\ 17 & -14 & 12 \end{pmatrix}^{-1}\begin{pmatrix} 4 \\ -6 \\ 1 \end{pmatrix}$

$\Rightarrow x = -1, \ y = 3, \ z = 4$

(ii) $\begin{pmatrix} 2 & -2 & 3 \\ 5 & 1 & -1 \\ 3 & 3 & -4 \end{pmatrix}\begin{pmatrix} x \\ y \\ z \end{pmatrix} = \begin{pmatrix} 4 \\ -6 \\ 1 \end{pmatrix}$

$\begin{pmatrix} x \\ y \\ z \end{pmatrix} = \begin{pmatrix} 2 & -2 & 3 \\ 5 & 1 & -1 \\ 3 & 3 & -4 \end{pmatrix}^{-1}\begin{pmatrix} 4 \\ -6 \\ 1 \end{pmatrix}$

The equations cannot be solved as the determinant of the matrix is zero, so the inverse matrix does not exist. Using an algebraic method results in inconsistent equations, which have no solutions.

Exercise 6.3 (Page 140)

1 (i) $\dfrac{1}{11}\begin{pmatrix} 3 & 1 \\ -2 & 3 \end{pmatrix}$

(ii) $x = 1, \ y = 1$

2 (i) $x = 2$, $y = -1$

    (ii) $x = 4$, $y = 1.5$

3 (i) $\begin{pmatrix} 0.5 & 0 & -0.5 \\ -0.8 & -0.2 & 1.4 \\ 0.3 & 0.2 & 0.1 \end{pmatrix}$

    (ii) $x = -2$, $y = 4.6$, $z = -0.6$

4 $x = 4$, $y = -1$, $z = 1$

5 (i) Single point of intersection at $(8.5, -1.5)$

    (ii) Lines are coincident. There are an infinite number of solutions of the form $(6 - 2\lambda, \lambda)$.

    (iii) Lines are parallel and therefore there are no solutions.

6 $k = 4$, infinite number of solutions

    $k = -4$, no solutions

7 (i) $\begin{pmatrix} k-1 & 0 & 0 \\ 0 & k-1 & 0 \\ 0 & 0 & k-1 \end{pmatrix}$ so

    $\mathbf{A}^{-1} = \dfrac{1}{k-1} \begin{pmatrix} -1 & 3k+8 & 4k+10 \\ -2 & 2k+20 & 3k+25 \\ 1 & -11 & -14 \end{pmatrix}$

    where $k \neq 1$

    (ii) $x = 8$, $y = 6$, $z = 0$

8 $a \neq \pm b$

    $x = \dfrac{3 + b^2}{b^2 - 9}$, $y = \dfrac{4b}{b^2 - 9}$

    $b = -1$ or -3 but since $a \neq \pm b$, $b = -1$

Chapter 7

Discussion point (Page 145)

Could also draw lines perpendicular to the x-axis to the points P and Q as shown.

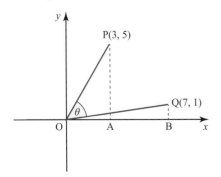

Using trigonometry on the two right-angled triangles, find $\angle POA$ and $\angle QOB$ and calculate the difference between these values, which equals θ.

Activity 7.1 (Page 145)

$$\cos\theta = \frac{\left|\overrightarrow{OA}\right|^2 + \left|\overrightarrow{OB}\right|^2 - \left|\overrightarrow{AB}\right|^2}{2 \times \left|\overrightarrow{OA}\right| \times \left|\overrightarrow{OB}\right|}$$

$$\Rightarrow \cos\theta = \frac{\left(a_1^2 + a_2^2\right) + \left(b_1^2 + b_2^2\right) - \left[(b_1 - a_1)^2 + (b_2 - a_2)^2\right]}{2\sqrt{\left(a_1^2 + a_2^2\right)}\sqrt{\left(b_1^2 + b_2^2\right)}}$$

$$\Rightarrow \cos\theta = \frac{2\left(a_1 b_1 + a_2 b_2\right)}{2\sqrt{\left(a_1^2 + a_2^2\right)}\sqrt{\left(b_1^2 + b_2^2\right)}} = \frac{a_1 b_1 + a_2 b_2}{|\mathbf{a}||\mathbf{b}|}$$

Discussion point (Page 147)

$$\overrightarrow{BA} = \begin{pmatrix} 2 \\ -2 \\ -4 \end{pmatrix} \qquad \overrightarrow{BC} = \begin{pmatrix} 8 \\ -7 \\ 0 \end{pmatrix}$$

$$\begin{pmatrix} 2 \\ -2 \\ -4 \end{pmatrix} \cdot \begin{pmatrix} 8 \\ -7 \\ 0 \end{pmatrix} = 30 \quad \text{which is the same answer as in Example 7.2}$$

Exercise 7.1 (Page 148)

1 (i) -4 (ii) 4

    (iii) 1   (iv) 7

2   64.7°

3 (i) 66.6°   (ii) 113.4°

    (iii) 113.4°

4 (i) 0° The vectors are parallel.

    (ii) 180° The vectors are in opposite directions (one is a negative multiple of the other).

5 -17

6 $-2, -3$

7   52.2°, 33.2°, 94.6°

8   35.8°, 71.1°, 60.9°

9 (i) $(0, 4, 3)$

    (ii) $\begin{pmatrix} -5 \\ 4 \\ 3 \end{pmatrix}$, $5\sqrt{2}$

    (iii) 25.1°

10 (i) $A(4, 0, 0)$ $C(0, 5, 0)$

      $F(4, 0, 3)$ $H(0, 5, 3)$

(ii) EPF not vertical as the points do not have the same y-coordinate. The roof sections form trapezia.

(iii) $\cos\theta = -\dfrac{1}{3}$ Area $= 2\sqrt{2}$

(iv) 68.9°

12   $16 + (\mathbf{a} - \mathbf{b}) \cdot \mathbf{c}$

Discussion point (Page 151)

The pencil is at right angles to any line in the plane. It would not alter.

Discussion point (Page 154)

One method would start by calculating the vectors $\overrightarrow{AB}$ and $\overrightarrow{AC}$. Use the scalar product to find a vector perpendicular to these two vectors, which can be used as the normal $\begin{pmatrix} n_1 \\ n_2 \\ n_3 \end{pmatrix}$ to the plane. Substitute one of the points A, B or C into the equation $n_1 x + n_2 y + n_3 z + d = 0$ to find the value of d.

Alternatively, substitute the three points into the equation $ax + by + cz + d = 0$ to form three simultaneous equations and use a matrix method to solve these equations and hence find the equation of the plane.

Activity 7.2 (Page 154)

$a + b + c = -d$

$a - b = -d$

$-a + 2c = -d$

$\begin{pmatrix} 1 & 1 & 1 \\ 1 & -1 & 0 \\ -1 & 0 & 2 \end{pmatrix} \begin{pmatrix} a \\ b \\ c \end{pmatrix} = \begin{pmatrix} -d \\ -d \\ -d \end{pmatrix} \Rightarrow$

$\begin{pmatrix} a \\ b \\ c \end{pmatrix} = \begin{pmatrix} 0.4 & 0.4 & -0.2 \\ 0.4 & -0.6 & -0.2 \\ 0.2 & 0.2 & 0.4 \end{pmatrix} \begin{pmatrix} -d \\ -d \\ -d \end{pmatrix}$

$= \begin{pmatrix} -0.6d \\ 0.4d \\ -0.8d \end{pmatrix}$

The plane has equation
$-0.6x + 0.4y - 0.8z + 1 = 0$.

Exercise 7.2 (Page 155)

1   (i) $\begin{pmatrix} 5 \\ -3 \\ 2 \end{pmatrix}$

(ii) $(5 \times 1) - (3 \times 4) + (2 \times 3) + 1 = 0$

2   (i) $\mathbf{r} . \begin{pmatrix} 1 \\ 1 \\ 1 \end{pmatrix} = 6$ (ii) $\mathbf{r} . \begin{pmatrix} 1 \\ 1 \\ 1 \end{pmatrix} = 0$

(iii) $\mathbf{r} . \begin{pmatrix} -1 \\ -1 \\ -1 \end{pmatrix} = -6$ (iv) $\mathbf{r} . \begin{pmatrix} 2 \\ 2 \\ 2 \end{pmatrix} = 16$

3   (i) $x + y + z = 6$ (ii) $x + y + z = 0$

(iii) $-x - y - z = -6$

(iv) $2x + 2y + 2z = 16$

The planes are parallel to each other; parts (i) and (iii) represent the same plane.

4   (i) 80.4°   (ii) 90°   (iii) 69.9°

5   $\mathbf{r} . (-\mathbf{i} + 3\mathbf{j} - 2\mathbf{k}) = 5$ $-x + 3y - 2z = 5$

6   $4x - 5y + 6z + 29 = 0$

7   $-1, 4$

8   $\dfrac{16 + 9\sqrt{6}}{5}$

9   $x - 4y + 7z = 27$

10 (i) $\overrightarrow{AB} = \begin{pmatrix} 2 \\ 2 \\ -2 \end{pmatrix}$ $\overrightarrow{AC} = \begin{pmatrix} 5 \\ 2 \\ -1 \end{pmatrix}$

(iii) $x - 4y - 3z = -2$

11 (iii) B

13 (i) $\begin{pmatrix} 2 \\ -3 \\ 2 \end{pmatrix}, 10$

(ii) e.g. $\begin{pmatrix} -1 \\ 2 \\ -1 \end{pmatrix}$

(iii) e.g. $(\mathbf{r} - (-\mathbf{i} + 2\mathbf{j} - \mathbf{k})).(2\mathbf{i} - 3\mathbf{j} + 2\mathbf{k}) = 0$

14 π_1 and π_3 are parallel.

Pairs π_1 and π_2 and π_2 and π_3 are perpendicular.

Discussion point (Page 158)

Some examples are:

- three parallel planes – bookshelves
- intersection at a unique point – three walls meeting in the corner of a room
- sheaf of planes – pages of a book
- triangular prism – the two sloping walls and the floor of a loft located within a roof space, or the sides and base of a triangular-shaped tent.

Exercise 7.3 (Page 162)

1 (i) $\begin{pmatrix} 0.15 & 0.25 & -0.05 \\ -0.05 & 0.25 & -0.65 \\ 0.25 & -0.25 & 0.25 \end{pmatrix}$

   (ii) $(4, -18, 10)$

2 (i) $\begin{pmatrix} 1 & 0 & -1 \\ 4 & -1 & -5 \\ -4.5 & 1.5 & 5.5 \end{pmatrix}$ $(-1, -12, 15)$

3 (i) Intersect at $(1.8, 3, -3.1)$
   (ii) Do not intersect at a unique point
   (iii) Intersect at $(3, -14, 8)$
   (iv) Do not intersect at a unique point

4 (i) $\begin{pmatrix} -1 & 1 & 1 \\ 2 & 1 & 1 \\ 1 & 1 & 1 \end{pmatrix} \begin{pmatrix} x \\ y \\ z \end{pmatrix} = \begin{pmatrix} -1 \\ 6 \\ 4 \end{pmatrix}$

   None of the planes are parallel and $\det \mathbf{M} = 0$ so the planes form either a sheaf or a prism of planes.

   (ii) P lies on the second and third planes but not on the first; the planes form a prism.

   (iii) Changing the first plane to be $-x + y + z = 0$ means P lies on this plane too and so they now form a sheaf.

5 $\begin{pmatrix} 1 & 2 & -1 \\ 2 & 4 & 1 \\ 3 & 6 & -3 \end{pmatrix} \begin{pmatrix} x \\ y \\ z \end{pmatrix} = \begin{pmatrix} 6 \\ 5 \\ 8 \end{pmatrix}$

   The third row of the matrix is a multiple of the first row, but not a multiple of the second row; the first and third planes are parallel and the second plane cuts through them to form two parallel straight lines.

6 $k = 3$, $m = -2$

7 (i) $\begin{pmatrix} 3 & 4 & 1 \\ 2 & -1 & -1 \\ 5 & 14 & 5 \end{pmatrix} \begin{pmatrix} x \\ y \\ z \end{pmatrix} = \begin{pmatrix} 5 \\ 4 \\ 7 \end{pmatrix}$

   $\det \mathbf{M} = 0$ and none of the planes are parallel to each other, so they form a prism or a sheaf.

   (ii) P lies on all three planes, so the planes form a sheaf.

8 (i) The planes intersect in the unique point $\left(-2, 4\frac{1}{3}, \frac{1}{3}\right)$.

   (ii) $k = 2$, $m = -1$, $n = -2$ or any multiple of these would make planes 1 and 2 parallel and cut by the third plane.

   (iii) The first plane is coincident (the same as) the third plane, the second plane cuts through this plane. In part (ii) there were two parallel planes but they would not be coincident unless the values $k = \frac{4}{3}$, $m = -\frac{2}{3}$, $n = -\frac{4}{3}$ were chosen.

9 There are 8 possible arrangements:

- The planes intersect in a unique point.
- Two planes are parallel and are cut by the third plane to form two parallel lines.
- All three planes are parallel.
- The planes form a prism where each pair of planes meets in a straight line.
- The planes form a sheaf with all three intersecting in one straight line.
- Two planes are coincident and the third cuts through them.
- All three planes are coincident.
- Two planes are coincident and the third is parallel to these.

Practice Questions Further Mathematics 2 (Page 167)

1 (i) Reflection in the line $y = 0$. [1]

   (ii) Reflection in the line $x = 0$. [1]

(iii) $\mathbf{BA} = \begin{pmatrix} -1 & 0 \\ 0 & -1 \end{pmatrix}$.　　　　　[1]

It represents rotation of $180°$ about the origin.　　　　　[1]

(iv) $(\mathbf{BA})^{-1} = \begin{pmatrix} -1 & 0 \\ 0 & -1 \end{pmatrix} = \mathbf{BA}$.　　　[1], [1]

A rotation of $180°$ about the origin followed by another rotation of $180°$ about the origin. Is equivalent to one full turn about the origin, which has no effect. This means, the inverse of a rotation of $180°$ about the origin is another rotation of $180°$ about the origin.　　　　　[1]

2　(i)　$z_1z_2 = (a + bi)(c + di)$
$= ac - bd + (ad + bc)i$　　　[1], [1]

(ii)　$|z_1| = \sqrt{a^2 + b^2},\ |z_1| = \sqrt{c^2 + d^2}$　　　[1]

(iii)　$|z_1z_2| = \sqrt{(ac - bd)^2 + (ad + bc)^2}$　　　[1]

$= \sqrt{a^2c^2 - 2abcd + b^2d^2 + a^2d^2 + 2abcd + b^2c^2}$

$= \sqrt{a^2c^2 + b^2d^2 + a^2d^2 + b^2c^2}$　　　[1]

$|z_1||z_2| = \sqrt{a^2 + b^2}\sqrt{c^2 + d^2}$

$= \sqrt{(a^2 + b^2)(c^2 + d^2)}$

$= \sqrt{a^2c^2 + b^2d^2 + a^2d^2 + b^2c^2}$　　　[1]

$\Rightarrow |z_1z_2| = |z_1||z_2|$　　　[1]

3　(i)　$|z - 3 - 3i| = 3$　　　[1], [1]

(ii)　$\arg(z - 3 - 3i) = \dfrac{\pi}{3}$　　　[1], [1]

(iii)　$\dfrac{1}{2}r^2\theta = \dfrac{3\pi}{8}$

$r = 3 \Rightarrow \theta = \dfrac{\pi}{12}$

$\Rightarrow \arg(z - 3 - 3i) = \dfrac{\pi}{3} + \dfrac{\pi}{12} = \dfrac{5\pi}{12}$

So the half-line has equation

$\arg(z - 3 - 3i) = \dfrac{5\pi}{12}$.　　　[1]

4　(i)　$3x + ky = 12$　　　[1]
$2x + 4y = b$

(ii)　$\mathbf{RR}^{-1} = \begin{pmatrix} 3 & k \\ 2 & 4 \end{pmatrix} \dfrac{1}{12 - 2k}\begin{pmatrix} 4 & -k \\ -2 & 3 \end{pmatrix}$

$= \dfrac{1}{12 - 2k}\begin{pmatrix} 3 & k \\ 2 & 4 \end{pmatrix}\begin{pmatrix} 4 & -k \\ -2 & 3 \end{pmatrix}$

$= \dfrac{1}{12 - 2k}\begin{pmatrix} 12 - 2k & 0 \\ 0 & 12 - 2k \end{pmatrix}$

$= \begin{pmatrix} 1 & 0 \\ 0 & 1 \end{pmatrix} = I$　　　[1], [1]

(iii)　$12 - 2k = 0 \Rightarrow k = 6$　　　[1], [1]

(iv)　$3x + 6y = 12$　　　[1]
$2x + 4y = b$
For an infinite number of solutions, $b = 8$
and the two lines are coincident.　　　[1], [1]

5　(i)　$5x - y - 25 = 0$　　　[1], [1]

(ii)　$\begin{pmatrix} 5 \\ -1 \\ 0 \end{pmatrix} \cdot \begin{pmatrix} 4 \\ -3 \\ 1 \end{pmatrix} = \left| \begin{pmatrix} 5 \\ -1 \\ 0 \end{pmatrix} \right| \left| \begin{pmatrix} 4 \\ -3 \\ 1 \end{pmatrix} \right| \cos\theta$　　　[1]

$\Rightarrow 23 = \sqrt{26}\sqrt{26}\cos\theta \Rightarrow \dfrac{23}{26} = \cos\theta$

$\Rightarrow \theta = 27.8°$ [1], [1]

(iii)　$5 \times 5 - 0 - 25 = 0$ and
$4 \times 5 - 3 \times 0 + (-17) - 3 = 0$　　　[1], [1]

6　(i)

$\begin{pmatrix} 20 & 0 & 1 \\ -20 & 0 & 1 \\ 0 & -20 & -1 \\ 0 & 20 & -1 \end{pmatrix}\begin{pmatrix} 5 \\ 17 \\ 20 \end{pmatrix} = \begin{pmatrix} k \\ l \\ m \\ n \end{pmatrix} = \begin{pmatrix} 120 \\ -80 \\ -360 \\ 320 \end{pmatrix}$

$\Rightarrow k = 120,\ l = -80,\ m = -360,\ n = 320$ [1], [1]

There is no need to use matrices, you could simply substitute the coordinates of the vertex, which must be in all four planes, into the equation of each plane to find k, l, m and n.

(i)　Because the summit is directly above the centre of the square base, each face makes the same angle to the vertical.

$\begin{pmatrix} 20 \\ 0 \\ 1 \end{pmatrix} \cdot \begin{pmatrix} 0 \\ 0 \\ 1 \end{pmatrix} = \left| \begin{pmatrix} 20 \\ 0 \\ 1 \end{pmatrix} \right| \left| \begin{pmatrix} 0 \\ 0 \\ 1 \end{pmatrix} \right| \cos\theta$　　　[1]

$$\Rightarrow 1 = \sqrt{401}\cos\theta \Rightarrow \theta = \cos^{-1}\left(\frac{1}{\sqrt{401}}\right) = 87.1°$$
[1], [1]

So each face makes an angle of 2.9° to the vertical. [1]

(iii) The summit of the skyscraper is where any three of the four triangular faces intersect. [1]

$25x + z = 150$
$-25x + z = -100$
Adding gives $z = 25$ [1]

$25y - z = 250$
$25y + z = 300$
Adding gives $y = 11$

$25x + z = 150$
$25y - z = 250$
Substituting in $y = 11$ and adding gives $x = 5$

So the coordinates of the summit are $(5, 11, 25)$ [2]

(iv) A very tall skyscraper might be 300 m high. [1]

The z coordinate of the summit is 25, suggesting each unit might be $\frac{300}{25} = 12$ m. [1], [1]

Other answers, suitably justified, are acceptable.

7 (i) $a = -10$, $b = 14$, $c = -160$, or
$a = -\frac{19}{2}$, $b = -\frac{17}{2}$, $c = 7$ [1], [1], [1]

(ii) $a = -10$, $b = 14$, c is any number other than -160
or $a = -\frac{19}{2}$, $b = -\frac{17}{2}$, c is any number other than 7 [2]

(iii) If the planes meet at a single point, the point (x, y, z) where the three planes meet can be represented by the matrix equation

$$\begin{pmatrix} 5 & -7 & 1 \\ 1 & -13 & -2 \\ 19 & 17 & -4 \end{pmatrix}\begin{pmatrix} x \\ y \\ z \end{pmatrix}$$

$$= \begin{pmatrix} 80 \\ -2 \\ -14 \end{pmatrix} \Rightarrow \begin{pmatrix} x \\ y \\ z \end{pmatrix}$$

$$= \begin{pmatrix} 5 & -7 & 1 \\ 1 & -13 & -2 \\ 19 & 17 & -4 \end{pmatrix}^{-1}\begin{pmatrix} 80 \\ -2 \\ -14 \end{pmatrix}$$ [1], [1]

Using a calculator,

$$\begin{pmatrix} 5 & -7 & 1 \\ 1 & -13 & -2 \\ 19 & 17 & -4 \end{pmatrix}^{-1} = \frac{1}{932}\begin{pmatrix} 86 & -11 & 27 \\ -34 & -39 & 11 \\ 264 & -218 & -58 \end{pmatrix}$$

Since this inverse matrix exists, the planes must meet at a single point. [1]

$$\begin{pmatrix} x \\ y \\ z \end{pmatrix} = \frac{1}{932}\begin{pmatrix} 86 & -11 & 27 \\ -34 & -39 & 11 \\ 264 & -218 & -58 \end{pmatrix}\begin{pmatrix} 80 \\ -2 \\ -14 \end{pmatrix}$$ [1]

$$= \frac{1}{932}\begin{pmatrix} 6524 \\ -2796 \\ 22368 \end{pmatrix} = \begin{pmatrix} 7 \\ -3 \\ 24 \end{pmatrix}$$ [1]

So the planes meet at $(7, -3, 24)$ [1]

An introduction to radians
Exercise (Page 171)

1 (i) $\frac{\pi}{3}$ (ii) $\frac{\pi}{4}$ (iii) $\frac{5\pi}{6}$

(iv) $\frac{10\pi}{9}$ (v) 0.775^C (3 s.f.)π (vi) $\frac{9\pi}{4}$

(vii) $\frac{3\pi}{2}$ (viii) 1.73^C (3 s.f.) or $\frac{11\pi}{20}$

(ix) $\frac{5\pi}{3}$ (x) 4π

(xi) $\frac{\pi}{12}$ (xii) $\frac{\pi}{60}$ or 0.0524^C (3 s.f.)

2 (i) 20°   (ii) 24°

(iii) 229° (3 s.f.)   (iv) 300°

(v) 25.7° (3 s.f.)   (vi) 9°

(vii) 103° (3 s.f.)   (viii) 220°

(ix) 630°   (x) 900°

(xi) 405°   (xii) 255°

The identities $\sin(\theta \pm \phi)$ and $\cos(\theta \pm \phi)$
Exercise (Page 173)

1 (i) $\frac{1 + \sqrt{3}}{2\sqrt{2}}$ (ii) $\frac{1 + \sqrt{3}}{2\sqrt{2}}$

(iii) $-\frac{1 + \sqrt{3}}{2\sqrt{2}}$ (iv) $\frac{\sqrt{3} - 1}{2\sqrt{2}}$

2 (i) $\dfrac{1}{2}$ (ii) 1

(iii) $\cos 4\theta$ (iv) $\dfrac{\sqrt{3}}{2}$

(v) $\dfrac{\sqrt{3}-1}{\sqrt{2}}$ (vi) $\dfrac{1}{2}$

3 (i) $\dfrac{1}{\sqrt{2}}(\sin\theta + \cos\theta)$

(ii) $\dfrac{\sqrt{3}}{2}\cos 2\theta + \dfrac{1}{2}\sin 2\theta$

(iii) $\dfrac{\sqrt{3}}{2}\sin\theta - \dfrac{1}{2}\cos\theta$

(iv) $\dfrac{1}{2}\cos 3\theta - \dfrac{\sqrt{3}}{2}\sin 3\theta$

Index

Index